Clive Hamilton is an Australian author and academic. His influential books include *Silent Invasion*, *Growth Fetish*, *Requiem for a Species: Why we resist the truth about climate change* and *Defiant Earth: The fate of humans in the Anthropocene*. For fourteen years he was the executive director of The Australia Institute, a think tank he founded. A professor at Charles Sturt University in Canberra, he has held visiting academic positions at the University of Oxford, Yale University and Sciences Po. His articles have appeared in *Foreign Affairs*, *The Guardian*, *The New York Times*, *Times Higher Education Supplement*, *Nature* and *Scientific American*.

Mareike Ohlberg is a researcher based in Berlin who focuses on China's digital policies and the global influence of the Chinese Communist Party. From 2016 to 2020 she was a research associate at the Mercator Institute for China Studies. Her work involves briefing European governments and policy-makers on developments in China. She has an MA in East Asian Studies from Columbia University and a PhD in Chinese Studies from the University of Heidelberg. Her doctoral thesis was on Chinese propaganda targeted at foreign audiences, and she was a co-author of the landmark report *Authoritarian Advance: Responding to China's growing political influence in Europe*. Her articles have been published in *The New York Times*, *The Neue Zürcher Zeitung* and various other European media.

CLIVE HAMILTON
MAREIKE OHLBERG

HIDDEN HAND

EXPOSING HOW THE CHINESE COMMUNIST PARTY IS RESHAPING THE WORLD

Hardie Grant
BOOKS

Published in 2020 by Hardie Grant Books,
an imprint of Hardie Grant Publishing

Hardie Grant Books (Melbourne)
Building 1, 658 Church Street
Richmond, Victoria 3121

Hardie Grant Books (London)
5th & 6th Floors
52–54 Southwark Street
London SE1 1UN

hardiegrantbooks.com

A catalogue record for this book is available from the National Library of Australia

Hidden Hand
ISBN 978 1 74379 557 6

10 9 8 7 6 5 4

Typeset in 11.5/15 pt Adobe Garamond Pro by Post Pre-Press Group
Cover image: Watercolour map, Niddle/Shutterstock; Paint in water, Picsfive/Shutterstock; China flag, T. Lesia/Shutterstock
Printed in Australia by Griffin Press, an Accredited
ISO AS/NZS 14001 Environmental Management System printer

FSC www.fsc.org MIX Paper | Supporting responsible forestry FSC® C018684

The paper this book is printed on is certified against the Forest Stewardship Council® Standards. Griffin Press – a member of the Opus Group holds chain of custody certification SCS-COC-001185. FSC® promotes environmentally responsible, socially beneficial and economically viable management of the world's forests.

Contents

Preface

The comforting belief that democratic freedoms have history on their side and will eventually prevail everywhere has always been tinged with wishful thinking. World events of the past two or three decades have shown that we can no longer take these things for granted. Universal human rights, democratic practice and the rule of law have powerful enemies, and China under the Chinese Communist Party is arguably the most formidable. The Party's program of influence and interference is well planned and bold, and backed by enormous economic resources and technological power. The wide-ranging campaign of subverting institutions in Western countries and winning over their elites has advanced much further than Party leaders might have hoped.

Democratic institutions and the global order built after the Second World War have proven to be more fragile than imagined, and are vulnerable to the new weapons of political warfare now deployed against them. The Chinese Communist Party is exploiting the weaknesses of democratic systems in order to undermine them, and while many in the West remain reluctant to acknowledge this, democracies urgently need to become more resilient if they are to survive.

The threat posed by the CCP affects the right of all to live without fear. Many Chinese people living in the West, along with Tibetans, Uyghurs, Falun Gong practitioners and Hong Kong democracy activists, are at the forefront of the CCP's repression and live in a constant state of fear. Governments, academic institutions and business executives are afraid of financial retaliation should they incur Beijing's wrath. This fear is contagious and toxic. It must not be normalised as the price nations have to pay for prosperity.

Every Western democracy is affected. As Beijing is emboldened by the feebleness of resistance, its tactics of coercion and intimidation are being used against an increasingly broad spectrum of people. Even for those who do not feel the heavy hand of the CCP directly, the world is changing, as Beijing's authoritarian norms are exported around the globe.

When publishers, filmmakers and theatre managers decide to censor opinions that might 'hurt the feelings of the Chinese people', free speech is denied. A simple tweet that upsets Beijing can cost someone their job. When university leaders pressure academics to temper their criticisms of the CCP, or ban the Dalai Lama from their campuses, academic freedom is eroded. When Buddhist organisations pledge their loyalty to Xi Jinping, and spies are placed in church congregations, religious freedom is under threat. With Beijing's growing system of surveillance, including cyber intrusions and filming citizens attending lawful protests, personal privacy is violated. Democracy itself is assailed when CCP-linked organisations and Party proxies corrupt political representatives, and when Beijing co-opts powerful business lobbies to do its work.

The what, why and how of the CCP's influence, interference and subversion in North America and Western Europe (hereafter the West) is the subject of this book. The CCP's activities in Australia (detailed in *Silent Invasion*) and New Zealand receive occasional mention. But it's important to keep in mind that the CCP's enterprise is geared towards reordering the entire world, and that while the form varies, the experience of the West is very similar to that of countries around the globe. It's hard to think of any nation that has not been extensively targeted, from Samoa to Ecuador, from the Maldives to Botswana. CCP influence in the global South is in urgent need of detailed study and exposure, but is outside the scope of this book.

The CCP works hard to convince people in China and abroad that it speaks for *all* Chinese people. It yearns to be seen as the arbiter of all things Chinese, and insists that for Chinese people, wherever they are, to love the country means to love the Party, and only those who love the Party truly love the country. It claims that the Party *is* the people, and any criticism of the Party is therefore an attack on the Chinese people.

It is disturbing to find so many people in the West falling for this ruse and labelling critics of CCP policies racist or Sinophobic. In so doing they are not defending Chinese people, but silencing or marginalising the voices of those Chinese opposed to the CCP, and the ethnic minorities who are persecuted by it. At worst, they are agents of influence for the Party. In this book, then, we draw a sharp distinction between the Chinese Communist Party and the Chinese people. When we use the word 'China' we do so as shorthand for the political entity ruled by the CCP, in the same way that one might say, for example, that 'Canada' voted in favour of a resolution at the United Nations.

Conflating the Party, the nation and the people leads to all kinds of misunderstanding, which is just what the CCP wants. One consequence is that overseas Chinese communities have come to be regarded by some as the enemy, when in fact many are the foremost victims of the CCP, as we shall see. They are among the best informed about the Party's activities abroad and some want to be engaged in dealing with the problem.

The distinction between the Party and the people is also vital to understanding that the contest between China and the West is not a 'clash of civilisations', as has been claimed. We face not some Confucian 'other', but an authoritarian regime, a Leninist political party replete with a central committee, a politburo and a general secretary backed by enormous economic, technological and military resources. The real clash is between the CCP's repressive values and practices, and the freedoms enshrined in the UN's Universal Declaration of Human Rights: the freedom of speech, assembly, religion and belief; freedom from persecution; the right to personal privacy; and equal protection under the law. The CCP rejects each of these, in words or in deeds.

People who live in close proximity to China understand this much better than do most in the West. It is this understanding that has fuelled the recent protests in Hong Kong, and led to the re-election in January 2020 of Taiwan's President Tsai Ing-wen. In a landslide vote, the people of Taiwan used the ballot box to say no to the CCP.

Some on the left, despite their history of defending the oppressed, find reasons to blind themselves to the nature of China's government under Xi Jinping. They have forgotten how totalitarianism can overpower human rights. Even so, anxiety about the CCP's activities crosses political boundaries, not least within the US Congress where Democrats and Republicans have formed an alliance to challenge Beijing. The same applies in Europe. Despite their other disagreements, people from the left and the right can agree that China under the CCP is a grave threat not only to human rights, but to national sovereignty.

The reasons why so many people in the West downplay or deny the threat posed by the CCP is a theme of this book. One reason is of course financial interest. As Upton Sinclair put it, 'It is difficult to get a man to understand something when his salary depends on his not understanding it.' Another reason, especially in the case of some on the left, is 'whataboutism'. China may be doing some unpleasant things, goes this argument, but what about the United States? The tactic is more effective with Donald Trump in the White House, but whatever criticisms one might have of the US and its foreign policy, both historically and today—and we are strong critics—they do not in any way diminish or excuse the extreme violation of human rights and suppression of liberties by the CCP regime.

And for all its faults, the United States, like other democracies around the world, continues to have an effective opposition; elections that change the government; courts that are largely independent of the state; a media that is diverse, unconstrained and often highly critical of the government; and a thriving civil society that can organise against injustices. China under the CCP has none of these. The autocratic tendencies of some politicians in Western democracies are indeed worrying, but they are restrained by the system in which they operate. Very little restrains Xi Jinping's autocratic impulses—even less now that he and his allies have dismantled the political accord set up by the Party to prevent the rise of another supreme leader like Mao Zedong. So while there's much that is wrong in the West and democracies in general, the political model offered by the CCP is not the answer.

Ignorance explains some of the difficulty the West is having in coming to grips with the threat of the CCP, as does the fact that it has not previously had to contend with such an adversary. During the Cold War, no Western country had a deep economic relationship with the Soviet Union. Conscious of the economic and strategic importance of China, many nations are trying to get smarter about the country at the very time Beijing is pouring money into helping us 'better understand China'. Receiving information straight from the horse's mouth might seem a sensible route, but, as we will show, this is a bad mistake.

1
An overview of the CCP's ambitions

The Chinese Communist Party is determined to transform the international order, to shape the world in its own image, without a shot being fired. Rather than challenging from the outside, it has been eroding resistance to it from within, by winning supporters, silencing critics and subverting institutions.

Whereas analysts on both sides of the Atlantic continue to agonise over whether to label China an opponent or even an enemy, the CCP decided this matter thirty years ago. In the post-Soviet world, it saw itself surrounded by enemies that it needed to defeat or neutralise. While the CCP and its supporters in the West like to speak of a 'new Cold War' being waged against China, the Party itself has all along been engaged in an ideological struggle against 'hostile forces'. For the CCP, the Cold War never ended.

The reshaping of alliances and the remoulding of the way the world thinks about it are essential to the Party securing continued rule at home, as well as to its reach and eventually making China the number one global power. The Party's plans have been explained at length in speeches and documents. Its implementation strategy is to target elites in the West so that they either welcome China's dominance or accede to its inevitability, rendering resistance futile. In some nations, mobilising the wealth and political influence of the Chinese diaspora, while at the same time silencing critics within it, is central to the strategy.

Backed by its enormous economic clout, China engages in arm-twisting, diplomatic pressure, united front and 'friendship' work, and the manipulation of media, think tanks and universities—all these tactics overlap and reinforce each another. Some people claim that Beijing's influence around the world is no different to that of any other country. While not everything the Party does in this respect is unique, the scope, degree of organisation, and eagerness to use coercion distinguish the CCP's actions from other nations' diplomatic activities.

As the world's largest factory and second-biggest economy, China has been a magnet for Western businesses and many Western politicians. Some industries are heavily dependent on access to China's huge market, and Beijing is willing to use this dependence as a political weapon. In the words of one close observer, 'If you don't do what Beijing's political leaders want they will punish you economically. They put the economic vise on politicians around the world. They have been doing it for years and it works.'[1]

At times, the vice has been tightened in conspicuous ways. After the arrest of Huawei executive Meng Wanzhou in Canada in 2018, for example, imports of Canadian soybeans, canola and pork were blocked. Beijing reacted in a similar way in 2017 when South Korea, in response to aggression from the North, began installing an American antiballistic missile system. Beijing took forty-three retaliatory measures, including banning Chinese tourist groups to South Korea, driving a large Korean conglomerate out of China, barring K-pop stars, and blocking imports of electronics and cosmetics.[2] Beijing was still punishing South Koreans in October 2019 when it demanded that the prestigious Eastman School of Music at the University of Rochester, in New York State, exclude three Korean students from its top orchestra if it wanted a planned tour of China to go ahead.[3] Citing the damage to Eastman's reputation in China if the tour were to be cancelled, the dean agreed to leave the Koreans behind. Only after an outcry by students and alumni did the school decide to cancel the tour.[4]

When Daryl Morey, general manager of the Houston Rockets basketball team, tweeted his support for Hong Kong protesters in late 2019,

Beijing's backlash was instantaneous.[5] (The torrent of criticism on Twitter appears to have come from trolls and fake accounts in China.[6]) The televising of Rockets games to its huge fan base in China was suspended. Sponsors withdrew. Beijing raged that Morey had 'hurt the feelings of the Chinese people'. The state broadcaster, China Central Television, redefined freedom of speech to exclude 'challenging national sovereignty and social stability'.[7] Desperate to protect its growing market in China, the US National Basketball Association issued a fawning apology that read as if written by the CCP's Central Propaganda Department.[8]

While only a few examples of extreme punishment are needed in order to sow fear in everyone, Beijing prefers to keep its threats vague and thus deniable, to keep the targets guessing. As Perry Link puts it, vagueness frightens more people because no-one can rule themselves out, and those in the frame therefore 'curtail a wider range of activity'.[9]

Beijing has become the world's master practitioner of the dark arts of economic statecraft, in part because in recent decades Western nations' commitment to free-market policies makes them reluctant to manipulate trade for political reasons. That's why the world was shocked when Donald Trump launched a trade war against China in 2018. While he is wrong on many other things, Trump is right that Beijing has been systematically violating the principles of international economic engagement and getting away with it.

Beijing's vast program of infrastructure investment abroad, known as the Belt and Road Initiative, is the ultimate instrument of economic statecraft or, more accurately, economic blackmail. It provides an outlet for China's construction industry and enormous capital reserves, while at the same time supplying the investment needs of other countries who are short of capital and excluded from mainstream sources of finance. The offer of low-interest loans is hard to resist, especially when they come without environmental or other conditions.[10]

However, the objectives of the BRI, also known as the New Silk Road (see the list of acronyms on page 277), go well beyond providing an outlet for surplus Chinese capital or helping poorer nations develop; the initiative is Beijing's primary mechanism for reordering the global geopolitical system.[11] Xi Jinping's signature policy is now so closely integrated with almost all Chinese government activity abroad—commercial, technological, academic, cultural—that it cannot be separated from the PRC's overall diplomatic engagement.

Xi Jinping has repeatedly referred to the BRI as essential to his vision of constructing 'a community of common destiny for humankind'.[12] While the idea might sound good to Western ears, its aim is a Sinocentric world; that is, the one envisaged by the hawks elevated by Xi to the top leadership positions. They view a China-led world order as an essential part of the 'great rejuvenation of the Chinese people'.[13]

So the BRI is the most powerful vehicle by which Beijing is changing the postwar international order.[14] In a revealing 2015 speech, defence strategist and retired PLA major-general Qiao Liang described the BRI purely as the vehicle for China to achieve dominance over the United States. It represents, he stated, China's new and irresistible form of globalisation, the success of which will be measured by the renminbi displacing the dollar as the world currency, leaving the United States 'hollowed out'.[15] While Qiao is a pusher of boundaries, the geostrategic rationale of the BRI is also made plain elsewhere, such as the leaked minutes of a 2019 Chinese–Malaysian meeting on a BRI project, which noted that despite the project's 'political nature', the public had to see it as market-driven.[16]

The adjective most frequently attached to the BRI is 'vast', and when China's top diplomat, Yang Jiechi, said in April 2019 that the BRI 'does not play little geopolitical games', he was speaking the truth.[17] The former editor of the *Far Eastern Economic Review*, Nayan Chanda, describes the BRI as 'an overt expression of China's power ambitions in the 21st century'.[18]

Like other so-called parallel institutions created by the Chinese government, such as the Asian Infrastructure Investment Bank, the BRI pretends to pose no challenge to countries' existing institutions, while incrementally realigning their interests and shifting the global balance of power. A key part of the CCP's thinking on global and regional power dynamics is the identification of a 'main contradiction' and a 'main enemy' to unite against. On a global scale, that enemy is the United States, which needs to be split from its allies and isolated.

Brexit, dissension in the European Union and the election of Donald Trump have created a strategic opportunity for Beijing to weaken the transatlantic alliance and further erode European unity. Long seen by the CCP as the largely irrelevant junior partner of the United States, Europe is now viewed as the great prize. By winning over Europe, the CCP hopes to convince the world that China is the 'champion of multilateralism' and a much-needed counterweight to US hegemony and unilateralism.[19] Beijing wants to mobilise European support for its initiatives in the developing world. (Although we won't be covering them in this book, similar strategies of breaking up existing alliances play out in other parts of the world.)

Despite all the news stories about 'debt diplomacy', 'global connectivity' and 'win-win cooperation', it's apparent that the BRI's goal of strategic rebalancing is to be achieved not only by the political influence that goes with infrastructure investment, but also by a subtle and multi-pronged program of global thought management. The BRI is about the projection of power through controlling the terms of the debate. (We develop this argument in chapter six.) It no longer makes sense to confine discussion of the BRI to business and economics, because it sprouts everywhere, from the Silk Road network of think tanks, media agreements, and ties between cultural institutions, to the establishment of sister cities and 'people-to-people exchanges', all of which are incorporated into BRI memoranda of understanding.

Today, the CCP remains deeply anxious about 'ideological infiltration' by hostile forces bent on regime change in China. As a manual published by the Central Propaganda Department in 2006 explained, 'when hostile forces want to bring disarray to a society and overthrow a political regime, they always start by opening a hole to creep through in the ideological field and by confusing people's thought'.[20] This Cold War mentality is vital to an understanding of the CCP's international activities, which are first and foremost the global extension of the Party's desire for regime security.

In the face of this threat of ideological infiltration, the CCP decided that the best form of defence is attack. Thus when its leaders talk of making the international order more 'democratic', 'open' and 'diverse', this is code for an order in which 'authoritarian systems and values have global status equal to liberal democratic ones', as Melanie Hart and Blaine Johnson express it.[21]

In April 2016 the *Global Times*, the Party's pugnacious tabloid, gave its readers a glimpse into the mindset of the CCP when it justified the internet-censoring Great Firewall as a *temporary* defensive tool that 'quelled Western intentions to penetrate China ideologically'.[22] That is to say, once the CCP has reshaped global opinion, once its values, political system and policies have gained worldwide acceptance, the threat to the CCP of Western ideas will be overcome and the Great Firewall may no longer be needed. The Party believes it is now powerful enough to transform the global conversation.[23]

Beijing also seeks to ensure that the world community shuns Chinese dissidents and proponents of an independent Taiwan. It wants international support for the idea that the CCP is the sole party fit to rule China. It also craves recognition that its political and economic system is superior to Western democracy and the liberal-capitalist economic order, and that CCP-ruled China, in contrast to the United States, is a responsible global actor working for the greater good of humankind.

Some have argued that this attempt to export the Party's ideology is bound to fail, but it's an argument that no longer holds, as we shall see. For others, Beijing's claim to be a responsible world power, and its criticism of the United States as an 'irresponsible global rogue', have appeal in the light of evidence from the Snowden leaks, the calamitous invasion of Iraq, and Donald Trump's call for regime change in Venezuela, among other events. The irony of Trump is that he has been pushing back hard against China's economic power while at the same time playing into the CCP's hands by isolating the US from its allies, making them more vulnerable to Party interference. China's rising influence in Europe has been welcomed by those who distrust America, as well as by some Eurosceptics who view China as a counterweight to the European Union or Europe's larger, more powerful countries.

Beyond these camps, others are questioning the effectiveness of democracy and expressing admiration for China's system of authoritarian government. Others still, including squads of Western journalists on all-expenses-paid tours, are awed by China's high-speed growth and technological progress, forgetting that other countries grew just as fast during their economic catch-up phases, and ignoring the fact that it was the CCP itself that prevented China from progressing at all for several decades. While many in the West repeat the CCP's claim to have lifted 700 million people out of poverty, it is more accurate to say that for three decades after the founding of the PRC in 1949 the CCP *kept* hundreds of millions in poverty, and it was only when it granted basic freedoms—to own property, to start a business, to change jobs, to move one's place of residence—that the Chinese people lifted themselves out of poverty.

2
A Leninist party goes out to the world

The CCP's Cold War mentality

One of the Chinese Party-state's favourite rhetorical tools to deflect criticism is to accuse its opponents of 'McCarthyism' or having a 'Cold War mindset'. Hua Chunying, a foreign affairs spokesperson, frequently uses the latter term, along with another favourite, 'zero sum thinking'.[1] In 2019 the nationalistic *Global Times* proclaimed that the nation's telecom equipment giant, Huawei, had become a victim of 'high-tech McCarthyism'.[2] The Chinese ambassador to the United Kingdom, Liu Xiaoming, has described American freedom of navigation exercises in the South China Sea as 'gunboat diplomacy, motivated by a Cold War mentality'.[3] Even condemnations of China's abysmal human rights record are rejected as rooted in the same thinking.[4]

The charge of a Cold War mentality is often echoed in the West. In March 2019, at a global symposium at Peking University, Susan Shirk, deputy assistant secretary of state in the Clinton administration, warned of a looming 'McCarthyite Red Scare' directed against China in the United States.[5] According to Shirk, a 'herding instinct' is driving Americans to see China threats everywhere, with potentially disastrous consequences.[6]

This is not only unfortunate for its casual dismissal of legitimate concerns, but also ironic, because there are few people more beset by a

Cold War mentality than the leadership of the CCP itself, and under Xi Jinping this thinking has reached new heights. In December 2012, as the new general secretary of the Party, Xi gave a speech warning that China, despite its economic growth, should not forget the lessons learned from the fall of the Soviet Union. He identified three particular failures that had doomed the Soviet empire, allowing it to collapse overnight. First, the leaders of the Communist Party of the Soviet Union had failed to control the military. Second, they had failed to control corruption. Third, by abandoning its guiding ideology, especially under Mikhail Gorbachev, the CPSU had removed the barriers to ideological infiltration by 'Western hostile forces'. The CPSU had sealed its own fate.[7]

For astute observers, Xi's speech was the first sign that the hope that he would be a liberal reformer—further opening up China and allowing it to integrate into the international order—would prove unjustified.[8]

In March 2019 the CCP's flagship theory journal *Qiushi* ('Seeking Truth') published an excerpt from another of Xi's speeches, given in January 2013 to the 300 members of the Party's Central Committee. Its theme was 'upholding and developing socialism', and he told cadres that even though the Chinese system would eventually triumph over the capitalist system, they must prepare for 'long term cooperation and struggle between the two systems'. He repeated his warning that a major reason for the Soviet Union's collapse was that 'they had completely negated the history of the Soviet Union and the history of the CPSU; they negated Lenin and negated Stalin; they engaged in "historical nihilism" [i.e., were critical of the Party's own past] and brought chaos to their ideology'.[9]

Xi's words were not mere rhetoric; they were followed up with decisive actions. In April 2013 the Party's Central Committee prepared a communiqué titled 'Notice on the Current State of the Ideological Sphere', better known as Document No. 9. This notorious bulletin, distributed to leading cadres at or above the prefectural level, outlined seven 'false ideological trends' they were no longer permitted to support—Western constitutional democracy, 'universal values', civil society, neoliberalism, Western principles of journalism, historical nihilism, and doubting the socialist nature of socialism with Chinese characteristics.[10] The Party was categorically rejecting democracy and universal human rights, and the circulation of the notice was soon followed by a harsh crackdown on those promoting them in China. Document No. 9 was only the beginning of the CCP's renewed attempt to eradicate ideas it believed would threaten its grip on power.[11] The CCP seemed to be following a dictum attributed to Stalin: 'Ideas are more powerful than guns. We would not let our enemies have guns, why should we let them have ideas?'

In October 2013 an internal documentary, likely produced by the PLA's National Defense University and entitled *Silent Contest*, was leaked.[12] This ninety-minute film repeated the charge that the United States was trying to bring about regime change through 'ideological infiltration' of China. It pointed the finger at foreign NGOs like the Ford Foundation, as well as 'turned' Chinese academics who represented an 'inside threat'. After the leak, the *Global Times* tried to present the documentary as the view of a few nationalistic military academics.[13] Yet aggressive campaigns against 'heterodox thinking' at Chinese universities, the tightening of control over media, and new legislation, such as the foreign NGO law of 2018 that severely curbed the activities of international NGOs, all echoed the warning made in *Silent Contest*, suggesting that the documentary presented the CCP's take on ideological threats to the Party.[14]

However, most Western observers continued to ignore the deeply ideological nature of the Xi regime, and this is only now slowly changing. In August 2017 John Garnaut, a former Beijing correspondent and adviser to the Australian government, who has a deep understanding of the workings of the Party, gave an internal speech to senior Australian officials that laid out Xi's return to the thinking of Stalin and Mao.[15] While Xi Jinping has stressed ideology more than his predecessors, Garnaut pointed out that the real turning point occurred in 1989, when Party leaders were shocked by student protests in Tiananmen Square and used violence to suppress them. And five months later, they were even more deeply disturbed by the fall of the Berlin Wall, which triggered the collapse of the mighty Soviet bloc. They began to focus on 'ideological security' as an indispensable component of regime security.[16] As Anne-Marie Brady has shown, these events prompted the Party to massively expand its propaganda and ideological work.[17] The primary emphasis was on political indoctrination at home, including 'patriotic education' in Chinese schools and the prevention of 'hostile ideas' reaching China.

In 1990 Joseph Nye introduced the concept of soft power.[18] To Party leaders, his ideas were proof that America planned to undermine China ideologically. Excerpts from Nye's book *Bound to Lead* were almost immediately translated into Chinese, and were published by the Military Affairs Translations Press in January 1992. In the preface, the military editors explained that they had 'specially invited' Beijing's professional translators to render it into Chinese quickly to expose America's plans.[19] They informed readers that Nye was proposing to intensify cultural and ideological inflows to China, the former Soviet Union and the Third World in order to make these countries accept the American values system. America was planning to further its world domination not only politically, but also culturally and ideologically, and Chinese people needed to understand that the struggle against the American plot of 'peaceful evolution' would be long-lasting, complex and intense.[20]

The idea that China was facing a life-or-death contest against hostile Western forces who were trying to cause chaos in China became entrenched within the CCP. In 2000 Sha Qiguang, an official from the Office of External Propaganda, which externally goes by the name of State Council Information Office, went so far as to argue that the West had been engaged in a 'smokeless Third World War' against China for the previous ten years.[21] 'Ideological subversion' is not seen as an abstract danger, in other words. The 2014 Sunflower Movement in Taiwan and Hong Kong's Umbrella Movement in the same year were interpreted as Western plots to destabilise China.[22] So, of course, were the Hong Kong protests that began in 2019, despite the vast crowds marching for democratic freedoms.

Neither China's admission to the World Trade Organization in late 2001 nor its growing interdependence with Western economies alleviated anxieties about ideological infiltration. If anything, the period between 2000 and 2004, which saw the first Colour revolutions in Eastern Europe, made the CCP more paranoid. It commissioned a series of studies on the fall of the Soviet Union.[23] In 2004 the Party conceded for the first time that its continued grip on power was not assured. It began to realise that it needed more reliable and permanent sources of legitimacy than economic performance, which could fail, and nationalism, which could backfire if the Party could not deliver on the expectations of hyper-nationalistic citizens.[24]

Party leaders saw that, despite China's economic clout, it lacked the power to shape the international debate—that is, how other nations thought about China, its system and its role in the world. In the international court of public opinion, the Party concluded, 'the West was strong, and China was weak'.[25] That had to change; it needed 'discourse power' (*huayuquan*) and an image to match its status.[26]

'Big external propaganda'

In 1993 a young professor at Shanghai's Fudan University, Wang Huning, who had toured a number of American campuses a few years earlier, picked up on the concept of soft power, and in an article in *Journal of Fudan University* introduced the idea to a broader circle of Chinese scholars of international relations.[27] Initially seen as something to defend against, soft power was later redefined as something China could deploy itself. In 2017 Wang was unexpectedly helicoptered by Xi Jinping into the Party's top leadership body, the seven-member Standing Committee of the Politburo. As one of Xi's most trusted lieutenants, and officially the fifth most powerful man in China, Wang is China's chief ideologue, in charge of propaganda and thought work.[28]

Wang Huning is building on work carried out over decades. In the earlier stages, reframing international support for the CCP and its ideas and policies formed part of the Party's reflection on how it could rise to become a global power without running into resistance from the established powers.[29] In December 2003, in a little publicised speech, then Party general secretary Hu Jintao declared that 'creating a favourable international public opinion environment' is important 'for China's national security and social stability'.[30] The CCP adopted an all-of-society approach to propagating China abroad, known as 'big external propaganda', by involving more departments as well as larger sections of the population in its external propaganda effort.[31]

For the CCP to feel safe, its message needs to become 'the loudest of our times'.[32] The domestic motive behind the work at gaining global legitimacy, reshaping the global order and directing global conversations doesn't make it any less consequential. On the contrary, the fact that it's tied to regime security means the stakes for the Party could not be higher.

If the concepts of ideological infiltration and a new Cold War of ideas have been a consistent theme since the 1990s, the ways in which the Party has tried to neutralise perceived threats have changed substantially, and become much more aggressive. As early as 2005, in an article titled 'On external propaganda and building the ability of the Party to rule', a Party theorist explained how reshaping international public opinion could help avert the undermining of the CCP at home. It described the propaganda China was targeting at foreigners as 'the vanguard of the [struggle] against "peaceful evolution"'; it was helping to discredit the messages of hostile forces before they reached China.[33]

The financial crisis of 2008–09 was viewed by Party leaders and Chinese scholars as an opportunity for China to become a globally influential voice, and to present the Chinese political-economic model as an alternative to the Western order. Party analysts highlighted how the crisis revealed the weaknesses of financial deregulation and lack of oversight. By comparison, they argued, China's more careful reforms could prevent such a meltdown. This led to the first extensive discussion in Chinese academic circles of the 'China model' as a globally exportable alternative to Western models of governance.[34]

Under Xi Jinping, these efforts have taken on a new quality. While previous generations of leaders avoided using the term 'China model', the CCP is now openly promoting what it calls 'the China case' and 'Chinese wisdom' to other countries.[35] During the 2019 National People's Congress, Colin Linneweber, an American working for China's official state news agency, Xinhua, proclaimed that 'it is widely acknowledged that a key to China's success is its system of democracy'.[36] While on a visit to Paris in 2019, Xi Jinping offered 'the China case' and the Belt and Road Initiative as solutions to the erosion of trust and cooperation in the international community.[37]

As the National Endowment for Democracy has argued, authoritarian powers like China do not rely on soft power but on *sharp power*, the exercising of coercive and manipulative influence.[38] Indeed, this shows up in Chinese debates on the subject, which are always more concerned with the power aspect than with the soft.

It would be a mistake to be complacent about the CCP's efforts to promote 'democracy with Chinese characteristics', and the various other concepts with Chinese characteristics (human rights, the legal system and so on), or to believe that these efforts are doomed to fail because that system lacks appeal. For one thing, large parts of the Party's target audience in developing countries and in the West don't know much about China other than its economic achievements. Some believe that Western governments and media 'distort China'. Others, as recent surveys show, are attracted to more authoritarian government, and some of the CCP's talking points may actually resonate well with them, as the Party exploits crises in democracies to illustrate China's strengths. Brexit and the election of Donald Trump in 2016 were both seized on to support the claim that democracy inevitably results in chaos and inefficiency.[39]

The Party rules

In July 2021 the Chinese Communist Party will turn one hundred. It has grown from a little more than a dozen members in 1921 to 90 million, with its own military force of 2 million personnel, and a multitude of organisations trying to control every aspect of Chinese society. It has a state apparatus that allows it to walk the international stage on terms that seem normal to the rest of world. Yet in the debate about China's influence in the world, many in the West write the Party out of the story.

One of the biggest challenges in dealing with China is precisely this political illiteracy of foreign interlocutors, especially when combined with the proliferation of Party-linked influence organisations that mask their ties. The international community has repeatedly failed to understand the comprehensive role the CCP plays in China. To grasp just how much the Party dominates all other institutions, note that the People's Liberation Army is *not* a national army, but the armed wing of the CCP.[40] Executives of state-owned enterprises are appointed by the Organisation Department of the CCP. Chinese media are not state-owned but Party-owned, with the controlling share belonging to the CCP's propaganda apparatus.

Too many Westerners routinely speak of China as if the Party does not exist, but focusing on the Party is indispensable for any understanding of the political entity we are dealing with. China's influence abroad is, as we've seen, an extension of the Party's domestic goals, an adaptation of its domestic strategies and agencies. These actions make sense only when viewed through the lens of the Party's distinctiveness and history.

There have been times since the creation of the People's Republic of China when Chinese institutions and people interacted with foreigners more freely. Xi Jinping has reversed the trend of gradual loosening. At the 19th Party Congress in 2017 he famously used a quotation from Mao to explain the role of the Party in China: 'Government, military, society and schools, north, south, east and west—the party rules everything'. These were not empty words. Half a year later, at its 2018 annual meeting, the National People's Congress announced a series of changes that saw several government organisations dissolved and merged into Party departments.[41] Every delegation permitted to leave China is accompanied by at least one Party official whose explicit job it is to keep an eye on everybody else.[42]

The CCP is a Leninist party founded with the specific purpose of becoming the 'revolutionary vanguard' of the Chinese people. As such it was set up as the central organisation, penetrating all sections of Chinese society and placed above all other institutions, including the military and state agencies. The most important and powerful organisations involved in influence work have always been part of the Party bureaucracy, not the Chinese government, which acts more as an extended arm of the CCP. The Propaganda Department, the International Liaison Department, and the United Front Work Department are all Party organisations.

The task of the United Front Work Department (considered in the next section) is to liaise with all forces outside the CCP, such as recognised religious organisations and other interest groups. It's also tasked with guiding the 50–60 million people of Chinese heritage abroad. The line between its domestic and overseas work is blurred because of the diaspora's family and business links to China.

By comparison, the International Liaison Department (see chapter four) is in charge of liaising with political parties abroad.[43] It serves 'as a kind of "radar" for identifying up-and-coming foreign politicians before they attain national prominence and office'.[44] In May 2018 Xi gave a speech emphasising Party leadership over China's foreign affairs work.[45] As Anne-Marie Brady points out: 'This change reveals how the CCP's revolutionary and transformative foreign policy agenda and methods are now being fused with the Chinese state's more mainstream foreign policy activities such as trade, investment and top-level diplomatic meetings. The last time that these two aspects were joined was in the 1940s before the CCP came to power.'[46]

Of course, state organs continue to be involved in influence work but they are under tight Party control, serving the Party's interests and carrying out its orders. While some previous leaders tried to separate Party and state and gradually reduce the role of the CCP to a few core functions, Xi Jinping has decisively reversed the trend.

The same is true for the economy. Private businesses have long been obliged to establish Party cells, but it is only under Xi that this requirement has been widely enforced again. All large and medium-sized firms, including foreign-owned enterprises, are required to set up Party organisations inside their businesses.[47] While corporations operating internationally, like Huawei, Alibaba and Tencent, have put a great deal of effort into showing their independence from the CCP, the gap between private and state-owned businesses in China is steadily narrowing.

The united front

An understanding of CCP influence activity in the West is impossible without an understanding of the CCP's united front work, the objective of which is to induce, co-opt and coerce those outside the Party to form a 'united front'—or coalition of groups that act in ways that suit the Party's interests—and to undermine those it designates as enemies.[48] (Note that we refer to United Front groups, upper case, if they belong to the United Front Work Department's network of organisations, and united front groups, lower case, if their influence work comes under the wider umbrella of Party and Party-linked organisations.)

The united front strategy was inspired by Leninist theory. Developed in the 1920s and put into practice during the civil war in the 1930s and 1940s, its aim was to win over smaller parties and ethnic minorities. As Anne-Marie Brady puts it, it is about 'forging the broadest possible coalition of interests so as to undermine the "chief enemy"'.[49] Mao Zedong described united front work as one of the three 'magic weapons' of the Chinese Communist Party.[50] After the founding of the PRC, the broad strategy, and the relevant agencies within the Party structure, continued to be used to co-opt and subdue ethnic and religious minorities, and to retain the support of independent and marginalised groups.

The Party sees the united front strategy as a science, one based on Marxist-Leninist fundamentals that is adjusted as it is put into practice.[51] Party theorists have developed a set of united front theories covering such fields as political parties, intellectuals outside the Party, ethnic groups, religious organisations, private companies and overseas Chinese communities. In 2015 the Ministry of Education approved a postgraduate degree program in United Front Studies, and Shandong University produced its first batch of graduates in 2018.[52]

Overseen by the CCP's United Front Work Department, work is carried out by a sprawling infrastructure of Party agencies, and organisations linked to the Party, and forms the core of the Party's overseas influence and interference activity. (More detail, including an organisational chart, is provided in chapter seven.) United front work is not confined to the activities of the UFWD but is the responsibility of every Party member.[53]

United front work intensified when Xi Jinping became Party general secretary in 2012.[54] Speaking in 2014 of work among overseas Chinese (known as *qiaowu*), he declared: 'As long as the overseas Chinese are united, they can play an irreplaceable role in realizing the Chinese Dream of National Rejuvenation as they are patriotic and rich in capital, talent, resources and business connections.'[55] Elevated to 'a new level of ambition', in the words of Brady,[56] united front activity has been shaped into an even more potent 'magic weapon' than Mao imagined, notably in countries where the ethnic Chinese population is relatively large and successful.

In recent years, united front work has increasingly been oriented towards promoting a more favourable view of the PRC in the mainstream of Western nations, and it's these activities that are explored throughout this book. Efforts to shape thinking and attitudes have mostly been directed at elites, countering negative perceptions of CCP rule and highlighting the positives. As we will see, influential Westerners keen to engage with Chinese culture or get to know Chinese businesspeople may find that the organisation they are dealing with is a covert part of the united front structure of the Party and that they are being worked on.

Political leaders are a natural target, the more so if, for electoral reasons, they want to engage with their local Chinese community. United front activity is particularly prevalent in hometown and cultural groups and in the business community, including Chinese chambers of commerce, where influence operations have been supercharged by the rapid growth in trade and investment. Western business executives welcome the opportunities to get to know and work with Chinese-heritage businesspeople. United front operatives in the business community gather information to feed to China's consulates, and cultivate relationships with a view to promoting opinions sympathetic to the PRC. Many leading Western business figures now serve as megaphones for Beijing's message to their governments and the wider public, not least in warning about 'damaging the relationship', and the risks of retaliation when statements are made that may upset Beijing. (A similar story is told about university elites in chapter twelve.)

Espionage may not appear to fall under the rubric of foreign influence operations because in the West, spies steal secrets for military and strategic benefit. But China's espionage activities are closely integrated into Beijing's influence operations. Information on the personal lives, health status, political affiliations and sexual proclivities of Western leaders, businessmen, university chiefs and opinion-makers is used to build personal profiles, and at times to coerce targets. The Party's united front operatives pass information to intelligence agents and vice versa. United front activity as it relates to Beijing's spying is considered in detail in chapter eight.

Double-hatting and double-plating

When foreigners fail to recognise the ubiquitous role of the Party and are mistaken about who they are dealing with, it's not solely their fault; the CCP actively attempts to obfuscate. A leading tactic is the front group. In Western countries, hundreds of organisations for ethnic Chinese people have been formed, each with direct or indirect links to the network operated by the United Front Work Department. They may be expressly political, such as those with 'peaceful reunification' in their names, but more often they are business groups, professional associations, or cultural and community organisations. These are explored in detail in chapter seven, but it's worth stressing that the covert nature of united front work often makes it difficult to identify them, even if one understands the operation of united front work.

In addition, within the official structures of the CCP, it's common for individuals to wear several different hats, and for organisations to use different nameplates depending on the setting. For example, Zheng Bijian, the man who coined the idea of China's 'peaceful rise', is variously introduced as 'a Chinese thinker', as the chair of the China Reform Forum ('a nongovernmental and non-profit academic organization'), and as an 'adviser to China's leaders'.[57] From these positions he has befriended a wide range of global political and intellectual leaders. The titles are all misleading because his other positions describe much more accurately who he really is inside the CCP, and that is a very senior and trusted cadre. From 1992 to 1997 Zheng served as the deputy head of the CCP's Central Propaganda Department, and from 1997 to 2002 he served as executive vice president (in effect, the top leader) of the Central Party School. And he was a leading member of the Chinese People's Political Consultative Conference (CPPCC).[58]

To take another example, Lu Jianzhong is a member of the National People's Congress and chairman of the Silk Road Chamber of International Commerce. But he also introduces himself as chairman of the board of Xi'an Tang West Market Culture Industry Investment Co., vice president of China's International Chamber of Commerce, vice chairman of the China International Studies Foundation, or chairman of the Shaanxi Association for the Promotion of Chinese Culture.[59]

While this double-hatting is intended as a smokescreen for foreigners, it also has an unintended advantage: it allows us to roughly reconstruct where a particular organisation is located in the Chinese bureaucracy. Typically, if a person is concurrently chair of organisation B and vice chair of organisation A, one of the organisations is under the direct leadership of the other. In some cases, A and B are simply different nameplates for the same organisation. For instance, until recently, the head of the China Association for International Friendly Contact concurrently served as the deputy head of the Liaison Department of the General Political Department of the PLA, suggesting an institutional link.[60]

The government's State Council Information Office, under that name, holds government press conferences and generally acts, as far as the outside world can see, as if it were a part of the government rather than the Party. However, internally it is known as the Central Office of External Propaganda of the CCP, and official Chinese sources confirm that it is under the leadership of the Party, specifically the Central Propaganda Department (since the latest major institutional overhaul, in 2018).[61]

These practices of double-hatting and double-plating are normal in China, and at times the CCP relies on the ignorance of foreigners to mask its control. For example, in 1997 a new academy tasked with carrying out cultural united front work overseas was set up within the Central Institute of Socialism, a united front training school directly under the command of the UFWD. Aware that a name with the word 'socialism' in it would be 'inconvenient' internationally, the CCP settled on the Academy of Chinese Culture for use abroad.[62]

China's media and other organisations involved in external propaganda have been instructed to avoid presenting themselves as government organs (let alone Party ones) when dealing with foreigners, and to 'appear with their business face'.[63] The Foreign Language Bureau of the CCP, for instance, interacts with the outside world under its 'commercial nameplate', the China International Publishing Group (CIPG).

As we'll see, the PLA and the Ministry of State Security also use front organisations for intelligence gathering. In some cases, such as the China Association for International Friendly Contact, the link to the PLA or MSS is known. However, the latter uses businesspeople as intermediary contacts with foreigners, and also uses research institutions like the Shanghai Academy of Social Sciences as a front to approach them.[64]

The people and their friends and enemies

Other fronts for engaging with foreigners are the so-called people's organisations. 'The people' and their 'friendship' with foreigners are concepts with special meanings in Chinese politics—meanings that few in the West understand. The Party's cynical, opportunistic concept of friendship was explained in 2017 by Xi Jinping, who told cadres that their friends outside the Party are not their 'own personal resources', but should be made 'friends for the Party' or 'for the public good'. He went on to say, 'Of course, friendships made outside the party will develop into personal friendships. But personal friendships must comply with the work for the public good. Principles, discipline, and rules must be maintained.'[65]

Anne-Marie Brady's 2003 book *Making the Foreign Serve China* is an indispensable guide to understanding the 'external friendship' system developed by the CCP.[66] She writes that political friendship is 'an application of united front principles to divide the enemy by focusing on contradictions and uniting all forces that can be united around a common goal'. In the language of the CCP, 'friendship' does not refer to an intimate personal bond, but to a strategic relationship. The Party's terminology of friendship 'is a means to neutralise opposition psychologically and to reorder reality'. Foreign friends, writes Brady, are those willing and able to promote China's interests.[67]

In China, civic organisations are never independent but always tied into the Party system through united front organisations. Just as in the United Kingdom no community organisation can use the word 'royal' in its title without official permission, in China no community group would include the words 'people' or 'friendship' in its title without Party approval.

Other words that sound benign, such as 'benevolent', 'peace', 'development', 'understanding' and 'unity', when used in nameplates indicate Party-controlled, united front organisations. The Chinese People's Association for Friendship with Foreign Countries, the China Council for the Promotion of Peaceful National Reunification, and the Chinese Association for International Friendly Contact are all examples that will come up throughout this book.

In his 1937 essay 'On contradiction', Mao defined two types—'contradictions among the people' (*renmin neibu maodun*) and 'contradictions between the people and the enemies of the people' (*di wo maodun*).[68] The idea of the people and the enemies of the people shows up in many different forms, on both the domestic and international level. In his speech at the 2013 National Work Conference for Propaganda and Ideology, Xi Jinping identified three zones in the Chinese ideological sphere: red (CCP stronghold), grey (middle ground) and black (negative public opinion, the 'enemy' zone).[69] Xi instructed the Party to hold the red zone, reach out to the grey zone so as to incorporate it into the red zone, and fight the black zone.[70] In its approach to international relations, the CCP divides foreigners into those already sympathetic to the Party; the 'political middle', who are the main target of influence work; and hardliners who cannot be convinced.[71]

In dealing with debate and dissent, the CCP again identifies three categories for contentious issues, each requiring a different approach: academic issues, misunderstandings (defined as 'problems of ideological grasp'), and political issues. Academic issues are those for which the Party has not outlined a clear position.[72] It therefore allows more open discussion and exchange on these, which represent, in Mao's sense, conflicts among the people. Misunderstandings, the second category, are issues on which the CCP has a clear stance on what is correct but for which it assumes no malicious or premeditated intent on the part of a person or group who voices a position diverging from it. In these cases, the CCP tries to convince by patiently explaining the correct position. In Mao's terminology, misunderstandings are a conflict among the people.

The third category, political issues, consists of those for which the CCP has identified a correct position but which 'hostile forces' at home and abroad are trying to undermine by intentionally spreading falsehoods. Once malicious intent and premeditation are assumed, the person or group expressing the incorrect position falls into the 'enemy' camp and needs to be repudiated firmly. Under Xi, Party theorists have moved more and more issues into the political category.[73]

The idea of premeditation is used to classify political actions. When groups assert that a protest was spontaneous, they do so in order to avoid their activity being labelled political, and led by hostile forces, or 'black hands' (*heishou*). And the CCP often labels pro-CCP demonstrations 'spontaneous' in order to pre-empt charges that it orchestrated or implicitly encouraged them. For example, in 2019 the Chinese consulate general in Auckland, New Zealand praised the 'spontaneous patriotism' of students from mainland China who attacked Hong Kong protesters at the University of Auckland.[74] Conversely, the CCP makes sure to label those protests it disapproves of as 'not having occurred spontaneously', and being 'orchestrated' by 'foreign hostile forces'.[75]

Importantly, when confronted by a contradiction between the people and the enemies of the people, there are no limits to what the CCP can do. It will do whatever it can to stop 'enemies of the people', who have no rights. In the ideological cosmos of the CCP, these people impede the progress of human history and therefore need to be dealt with by any means necessary. This distinction between the people and its enemies is used by the Party to justify its extremely brutal treatment of dissidents and other 'troublemakers', such as human rights lawyers and Falun Gong practitioners.[76] Tellingly, the distinction between 'contradictions among the people' and 'contradictions between the people and the enemies' has been formally re-introduced into Party regulations under Xi Jinping.[77]

The 5 per cent rule and quiet diplomacy

So how is the population divided between 'the people' and 'the enemies of the people'? Mao declared that '95 per cent of people are good'; that is, they are on the people's side and therefore on the side of the CCP, the Party being the 'vanguard of the people' after all. China's political system is notorious for setting quotas, and this declaration about the 95 per cent affected domestic campaigns during the Mao period, when quotas for 'bad' people who were to be purged were often set at 5 per cent.[78] The official verdict on the Tiananmen movement remains that 'a tiny handful of people exploited student unrest to launch a planned, organized and premeditated political turmoil'.[79]

This kind of framing is also common in the international setting. Since China is good, and the overwhelming majority of the people are good, it is impossible for a large number of people ever to be against China. Beijing's propaganda generally presents China as being in line with what the majority of the world thinks. Anyone who opposes the CCP must by default be in a tiny minority. For instance, in response to a letter demanding the freeing of Canadians Michael Kovrig and

Michael Spavor, detained by the CCP, a foreign ministry spokesperson wrote in the *China Daily*: 'If every Chinese citizen sent an open letter to Canadian leaders, their voice would be more resounding, and would certainly join with the *mainstream voice* of the international community, which is on the side of justice. … The *handful of people* behind the open letter are intentionally creating an air of panic.'[80] (The emphasis is ours, both here and in the following paragraph.)

When, on the basis of intelligence advice, the Australian government cancelled the permanent residency visa of businessman Huang Xiangmo, he told the *Global Times* that 'the anti-China group [in Australia] is only *a very small handful* of people'.[81] The Chinese embassy in Sweden issued a statement in 2019 in which it lamented that a '*very small handful* of people' posed as China experts to spread their anti-China sentiment.[82] And according to a Chinese government spokesperson, it is 'futile for a *handful of Hong Kong people* collaborating with foreign forces to intervene in Hong Kong affairs'.[83]

The actual number of people who oppose CCP policies, be they at home or abroad, doesn't matter—the CCP will always claim it is small, as this is vital to its claim to legitimacy. However, especially in the international context, where the Party has nothing close to an information monopoly, this kind of framing requires other opponents of CCP policy to remain quiet when not directly attacked. If they were to speak up on behalf of those attacked, it would contradict the Party's narrative. This explains why the CCP has been so forcefully pushing the idea that quiet diplomacy behind the scenes is more effective than vocal diplomacy. Unfortunately, many around the world have fallen for this ploy, allowing themselves to be manipulated.

During the 2016 South China Sea dispute, the official CCP narrative was that elites in the United States (the enemy of the people) manipulated the Philippines (which, as a country in the developing world, is by default part of 'the people') into bringing a claim to the international tribunal in The Hague. The United States was the ringleader while Filipinos were misled or coerced. The same narrative has been used in the battle over Huawei's participation in 5G, where the United States is portrayed by China as the sole instigator of an unjust 'war against Huawei', fought for ulterior motives.

Although small in number, hostile forces can have a large impact if they succeed in misleading or manipulating the people, and the CCP views these forces as a dark version of itself—a small group of people smart enough to manipulate others, but which uses its powers to mislead rather than to lead people in the correct direction, as the CCP claims to.

Linked to the idea that 95 per cent of people are good and therefore on the side of the Party is the political act of declaring one's allegiance with the CCP. As David Shambaugh explains it, to declare allegiance (*biaotai*), by repeating a particular slogan (*kouhao*) or other political phrase, is in China an important 'ritualistic, rhetorical, and significant political act'.[84]

The practice of *biaotai* is also becoming more common among foreigners. The CCP demands, for example, repeated verbal commitments from foreign interlocutors regarding the 'One China Policy', each repetition of which adds to the Party's sense of its legitimacy. Members of the Silk Road Think Tank Network must declare that they commit to 'the common understanding that the Belt and Road Initiative is an important endeavor to promote world economic growth'.[85] Whether they know it or not, these international think tanks and organisations—including Chatham House, the Elcano Royal Institute, and the German Development Institute, among many others—are engaging in acts of *biaotai*. Repeating someone else's wording to express political loyalty is not unknown in other parts of the world, but it is taken to an extreme in China under the CCP; we will give several other examples later.

In 'On contradiction', Mao made another argument that continues to shape the thinking of the CCP. Groups of people can be allies in one situation, defined by time, place or issue, and the main adversary in another. China's biggest global adversary at present is the one standing in the way of 'the irresistible historical trend toward multipolarity', the United States.[86] This conflict is classified as one between the people and an enemy of the people (*di wo maodun*), meaning the US cannot be won over. So why then does the CCP still try to win over the American public and specific American interest groups? Because the US is only the enemy when looking at the power balance in the world as a whole (*zhengti*). Inside American society itself, only a 'small number' are true enemies, regressive forces of world history; the majority are part of 'the people'. Some of the latter may have been misled in their thinking, but as long as the CCP continues to patiently explain the truth to them, they can be won over, as opposed to those who try to hold onto American dominance and thereby stand against the 'irresistible historical trend towards multipolarity', a euphemism for US decline.[87]

CCP operating procedures

As a rule, the CCP tries not to antagonise too many people at the one time, especially when acting in a situation where the majority of people oppose the Party's point of view. If several countries do something the CCP dislikes, it will often single out one or two for criticism, either as a test balloon or as a deterrent to others. In some cases it will even stay silent altogether. This is informed by the idea that the 95 per cent are still potential allies; it also helps ensure that the majority of people don't feel pressured by the CCP.

Another working rule enunciated by Mao for united front work is expressed in the slogan 'round outside, square within' (*wai yuan nei fang*).[88] Alternatively translated as 'firmness of principles, flexibility of strategy', this approach allows certain concessions to be made for strategic purposes, as long as the most important principles are not lost sight of.

A further principle indicative of the CCP's flexibility is the practice of strategically allowing some friendly forces to venture criticism so that they gain credibility. Known as 'big help with a little badmouth' (*xiao ma da bangmang*), the idea derives from the CCP's observation of the newspapers under the Nationalists (Kuomintang) prior to 1949.[89] By criticising the Nationalists on small issues while supporting them on the big questions, the press managed to present itself as objective and balanced, despite being firmly in the Nationalists' camp. Today, the CCP's approach to the *South China Morning Post* (owned since 2016 by the Alibaba Group) should be understood as applying the principle of *xiao ma da bangmang*. The *Post* can go only so far in any criticism of the Party.

The fact that so many businesspeople in the West are making money in their dealings with China, or hope to, gives the CCP powerful lobby groups there. A few hints from Chinese officials about how well a relationship has been going is usually enough to prompt business groups or billionaires to pressure their government to do nothing to upset Beijing; this tactic is known as *yi shang bi zheng* (literally, 'using business to pressure government'). Examples are legion—Taiwanese tourism operators marched in the street because Beijing slashed tourist numbers from China, Australian mining tycoons urged Canberra not to make a statement about the death of dissident writer Liu Xiaobo, and US business organisations have pressured Donald Trump to end the trade war. Often, business groups act pre-emptively, before Beijing makes threats.

Prior to taking power in China in 1949, the CCP was forced to retreat from the cities and establish bases in the countryside. It later incorporated the lessons learned from this in the strategy of 'using the countryside to surround the cities' (*nongcun baowei chengshi*). This slogan should not be understood only in the literal sense; the idea is to go to areas where the CCP's enemies are weak or not well represented, organise the population there and then use them to encircle the enemy's strongholds. In global terms, the CCP has drawn a parallel between 'the countryside' and 'the developing world'. That is to say, the developing world is seen as a region in which it is comparatively easy for the CCP to establish itself. Once enough developing countries are on China's side, it becomes easier for the CCP to chip away at the developed world's grip on power.

A similar idea is expressed in the slogan 'using the local to surround the centre' (*difang baowei zhongyang*), or moving from the periphery to the centre, from the small to the big, from the fringe to the mainstream.[90] This is a tried and tested strategy of CCP influencing abroad, and also of Party-owned media like Xinhua or Chinese companies like Huawei. By winning over smaller or more marginal groups, usually more easily convinced, CCP-affiliated institutions slowly make their way towards the mainstream. This principle, noted throughout this book, helps explain the emphasis Beijing places on local councils and sister-city relationships in the West.

3

Political elites at the centre: North America

Making friends

When considering Beijing's structure of influence in the West, we need to look at the world the way Beijing does: by studying where the centres of power lie in each country, and determining who are the elites in business, politics, academia, think tanks, media and cultural institutions. Information is collected on who they have connections with and who their friends and family members are.[1] Business and personal links in China are especially useful. Front groups associated with the United Front Work Department and the PLA are then tasked with selecting people to get close to.[2]

The elite power map for the United States will be unlike the one for Germany, for example, which in turn will not resemble those for Canada and Britain. But the targets will include past, present and future political leaders at each level of government—national, provincial or municipal. High-level officials who advise and influence political leaders are also of great interest.

The Party allocates foreigners to various categories, according to Richard Baum.[3] The first is 'first-category "friend"', someone who agrees with the Party on everything; they are often quoted in the official media. The second is 'friendly personage', someone who is relied upon but not really trusted, like businesspeople; they are open to manipulation as they have an interest in appearing friendly. The third category, which often includes scholars and journalists, are 'those who really love China but know all the vices of Chinese communism'. These people are beyond influence. The fourth category is made up of 'those people who love China but hate Chinese communism'.[4] They are classed as 'enemies' and are discredited whenever the opportunity arises. The final category is reserved for those who either 'didn't know or didn't care much about China'. These people are potentially useful because they can always be invited to a film or cultural event and will hopefully leave with a positive impression.

Invitations are also made to those targeted as potential friends of China—to a conference, a reception or a cultural occasion, events organised by apparently neutral charities or academic organisations, where warm feelings are cultivated. Gifts may be given, setting up a sense of obligation and reciprocity. A free trip to China might follow, during which the target is worked on intensively in a carefully scripted program of meetings and tours. While the hosting organisations are often front groups allied to the UFWD or the Liaison Department of the Political Work Department of the CMC, state-owned companies can also serve in these roles, and, in the Xi Jinping era, private corporations too.

In his memoir, George H.W. Bush proved just how easy it is for naive Western politicians to walk into the trap of 'friendship': 'When Deng called me a *lao pengyou*, an old friend of China, I felt the phrase was not just the usual flattery, but a recognition that I understood the importance of the US-China relationship and the need to keep it on track.'[5] Deng then gave Bush 'a rare insight into his thoughts' on Sino-Soviet relations.

Those who believe they have been entrusted with the inner thoughts of top leaders often proceed to act as Beijing's messengers, urging others to have 'greater understanding', 'to see it from China's perspective' and 'adopt a more nuanced position'. Former Australian prime minister Paul Keating, appointed along with Henry Kissinger to the international advisory council of the China Development Bank, hinted that he had access to the private thoughts of the top leadership, including meetings with President Xi. Keating is one of the regime's most committed advocates, describing human rights as 'Western values' that do not apply in

China, and praising the CCP government as 'the best government in the world in the last thirty years. Full stop.'[6]

A former senior US State Department official, Susan Thornton, also positions herself as a friend of China. In a widely read attack on the United States' pushback against Beijing in 2019, she argued that the breakdown in relations was the fault of the US and that with good diplomacy China could be coaxed into becoming a responsible global citizen.[7] Beijing, she wrote, was working hard to provide more 'international public goods'. Thornton claims that 'the China Dream is to be more like the United States', and that senior Party officials are more concerned with getting their children into top US universities than seeing their country dominate the United States.

Susan Thornton is one of the principal authors of a July 2019 open letter, signed by roughly one hundred concerned American scholars, foreign policy experts and business representatives, repudiating the tougher position taken by the Trump administration on China.[8] While acknowledging that China's behaviour has in recent times been 'troubling', the signatories called for a continuation of the cooperative and welcoming stance of previous decades. For them, nothing has happened to undo the belief that, as China is drawn into the global economic order, the forces of political liberalisation at home are becoming stronger and must sooner or later prevail. The fact that the very opposite has been taking place, that the authoritarians under Xi have been vastly strengthened by the integration of China into the global economy, has passed these signatories by.

Tellingly, the letter speaks only of 'China', with no mention of the Chinese Communist Party. The signatories believe that 'China' has no interest in replacing the United States as the global leader. For them, 'China' is not a serious 'economic enemy' or a security risk. They believe that the real problem is the United States, with its adversarial posture and exaggerated sense of the threat posed by the PRC. President Trump's aggressive stance, they argue, is weakening those in China who want a 'moderate, pragmatic and genuinely cooperative' relationship with the West.

Naturally, this intervention by US experts arguing for a continuation of the warm and fuzzy approach that the CCP has for years been cultivating was applauded by Party officials. The foreign ministry described the letter as 'rational and objective'.[9] The *Global Times* interviewed one of the five initiators of the letter, Michael Swaine, a senior fellow at the Carnegie Endowment for International Peace (an institution that provided nine of the signatures).[10] Swaine condemned America's 'cold war' response and 'extreme policy' approach to China, saying China does not want to overthrow the international order, only introduce some reforms to it.

In one of the most effective rebuttals, John Pomfret argued that the letter is in the tradition of the United States' 'profoundly paternalistic' view of China, which is based on the belief that the natural superiority of the American system will coax China's leaders into emulating it.[11] As for China's liberal leaders in waiting, in whose lap the letter-writers place their hopes, Xi has converted, purged, imprisoned or otherwise silenced them.

The sad case of John McCallum

Over its history, the CCP has developed sophisticated techniques of psychological manipulation of friends and enemies alike. They have been applied to excellent effect on a wide range of people in Western countries identified for their value to the Party. The aim, once again, is to draw them into alignment with Beijing's political objectives, often by convincing them that they have a special relationship with China. As China scholar James Jiann Hua To writes, this kind of psychological work is 'an effective tool for intensive behavioural control and manipulation' while at the same time appearing 'benign, benevolent and helpful'.[12]

When Huawei's chief financial officer, Meng Wanzhou, was arrested in Canada in December 2018, on an extradition request from the United States, she was accused of bank fraud, among other things. At the height of the angry diplomatic fight that ensued—in which Beijing made dire threats to Ottawa rather than Washington and jailed two Canadian citizens on trumped-up charges—Canada's ambassador to China, John McCallum, gave a press conference to Chinese-language media in Ontario in which he offered advice to Meng as to how she could mount the best legal defence against extradition.[13] McCallum, already well known as a friend of China—he'd recently said that Canada had more in common with China than with the United States—listed what he saw as serious flaws in the extradition case.[14]

Some suggested the ambassador sounded as if he were speaking for the government of China rather than defending Canada's position.[15] In Beijing, the *Global Times* praised McCallum for his 'truth-telling' and reproached Canadians for their lack of 'moral righteousness'.[16] After widespread criticism of McCallum at home, his former chief of staff characterised his speech as a 'verbal miscue' and defended him as 'a fundamentally decent and optimistic man', a longstanding Sinophile who'd travelled often to China over three decades—all of which goes a long way towards explaining how the ambassador could have fallen victim to the CCP's psychological techniques.[17]

A few days later McCallum followed up his advice to Meng on how to fight her extradition by saying it would be good for Canada to release her, thereby privileging the pacification of Beijing over Canada's legal obligation to the United States. Prime Minister Justin Trudeau was forced to sack him, leaving observers to puzzle over how such an experienced politician and diplomat could misfire so badly.

Others like McCallum who are targets of the CCP are wooed not by inducements, but by playing to their vanity and their desire to be agreeable. As one headline writer sardonically put it, 'I think that Chinese official really likes me!'[18]

One who did recognise why McCallum was saying the things he did in support of Meng Wanzhou was former Mexican ambassador to Beijing, Jorge Guajardo. He had been groomed in the same way.[19] Envoys new to Beijing are isolated from senior Chinese officials. After a time, a message is sent that a high-ranking official wishes to meet them. They meet and are told they have a 'unique understanding of the nuance and delicacy of the party's position'. They begin to see themselves as 'special'. They are granted rare access to top leaders and believe they've been entrusted with an unusual insight into the inner workings of Chinese politics. Of course, other envoys are being groomed to believe the same. As special friends of China, the envoys' advice to their masters back home reflects their unique insight, and is exactly the advice Beijing wants them to communicate.[20]

Self-belief coupled with the need to feel important opens people to seduction. The CCP's expert manipulation of vanity was identified by a previous Canadian ambassador to China, David Mulroney: 'You and you alone are sufficiently gifted and experienced to understand the situation and explain it to your government. The fate of the bilateral relationship is in your hands.'[21] Far more so than with any other country, diplomats in China become convinced that 'the most important thing in the world is maintaining good relations'.[22] They are persuaded that China is difficult for foreigners to understand, and instead of explaining their countries' viewpoint to China, ambassadors see their role as explaining China's position to their governments, and so they become a conduit for the CCP's messaging. That was McCallum's mistake.

This situation is unlike the Cold War, in which loyal citizens were 'turned' and began to work consciously for the other side. It's far more effective if those arguing the CCP's case believe in their hearts that they remain loyal but have come to the view that China's position is in the best interests of their own country. (It was therefore inept for one of the most popular newspapers in China to declare in a headline, when McCallum gave his support to Meng, that the Canadian ambassador had 'changed sides'.[23])

The conviction that maintaining good relations with Beijing is paramount is rife in foreign affairs departments across the Western world, and colours the advice they give their ministers on a daily basis. For these officials, calm relations with plenty of bilateral meetings are regarded as successful diplomacy; in truth, they put the CCP in the box seat. When Beijing cancels meetings and puts diplomats in the freezer, Western officials are inclined to panic and advise their governments to relent.

Influence in Washington D.C.

In the targeting of anyone who may have the ear of a political leader, official and unofficial advisers, civil servants, party colleagues, donors, friends, spouses and other family members, business associates and military brass are all fair game. Influence operations become much easier when there is a financial reward for the target, and business dealings therefore facilitate China's influence in the United States in a way the old Soviet Union could only dream of. Think tanks, especially those headed by former political or business leaders, are seduced through donations and research cooperation. (This topic is covered in chapter eleven, with other avenues for influencing Washington's decision-makers considered in earlier chapters. While it's not possible to provide a full account of CCP influence in Washington, we aim to give a strong sense of its dimensions.)

In 2018 the well-connected *Washington Post* columnist Josh Rogin pointed out that China had been building networks of influence in the United States over many years, and that the US government 'is preparing for the possibility that the Chinese government will decide to weaponize' them to get what it wants.[24] (Although Beijing is not known to use Russian-style 'active measures' in the West, deploying them is only a matter of political calculation.) One of the CCP's most audacious penetration operations, Chinagate in 1996, saw a top intelligence operative meeting a naive President Clinton in the White House, along with donations to the Clinton campaign made through people with ties to the Chinese military. (See chapter eight.)

Beijing has been working to gain influence in the US Congress since the 1970s. Through the activities of the CCP's International Liaison Department, and Party-linked bodies like the China Association for International Friendly Contact (considered later), China has made some influential friends.[25] Nevertheless, Congress has for the most part remained sceptical of China, although its voice has been muted at times by the influence of 'pro-China' members.[26] The president, the White House, the bureaucracy, think tanks and business lobby groups have all been targeted by Beijing, to good effect.

Until recently, almost all players in Washington D.C. and beyond were convinced by the 'peaceful rise of China' trope, and the value of 'constructive engagement'. The common belief was that as China developed economically, it would naturally morph into a liberal state. This view was not without foundation, because the more liberal factions within the CCP did struggle with the hardliners, but in the US it reinforced a kind of institutional naivety that was exploited by Beijing. Many of those who stuck to this view even after the evidence pointed firmly to the contrary had a strong personal investment in defending Beijing.

In May 2019 Joe Biden distinguished himself from all of the other candidates for the Democratic Party's presidential nomination by ridiculing the idea that China is a strategic threat to the United States. 'China is going to eat our lunch? Come on, man,' he told a campaign crowd in Iowa City.[27] Biden had for years adopted a soft approach to China. When President Obama's secretary of state, Hillary Clinton, was taking a tougher position towards China's adventurism in Asia, Vice President Biden was urging caution. Biden had formed a warm personal relationship with Xi Jinping when Xi was vice president and president-in-waiting.[28]

In his second term, Obama replaced Clinton as secretary of state with the more accommodating John Kerry. The dynamics help to explain why Obama's 2012 'pivot to Asia' was a damp squib. The United States stood back while China annexed islands and features in the South China Sea and built military bases on them, something Xi had promised Obama he would not do. Breaking the promise has given China an enormous strategic advantage.

Joe Biden cleaves to the belief, now abandoned by many China scholars and most Washington politicians, that engagement with China will entice it into being a responsible stakeholder. The University of Pennsylvania's D.C. think tank—named, for him, the Penn Biden Center for Diplomacy and Global Engagement—aims to address threats to the liberal international order, yet China is absent from the threats identified on its website: Russia, climate change and terrorism.[29] Biden has spoken about China's violation of human rights but still clings to the idea of China's 'peaceful rise'.

So does it matter if Joe Biden has a different view of China? It does, because there is evidence that the CCP has been currying his favour by awarding business deals that have enriched his son, Hunter Biden. One account of this is given by Peter Schweizer in his 2019 book *Secret Empires*.[30] Some of his key claims were subsequently challenged and Schweizer refined them in an op-ed in the *New York Times* (famous for fact-checking).[31] In short, when Vice President Biden travelled to China in December 2013 on an official trip, his son flew with him on Airforce Two. While Biden senior was engaging in soft diplomacy with China's leaders, Hunter was having other kinds of meetings. Then, 'less than two weeks after the trip, Hunter's firm … which he founded with two other businessmen [including John Kerry's stepson] in June 2013, finalized a deal to open a fund, BHR Partners, whose largest shareholder is the government-run Bank of China, even though he had scant background in private equity'.[32]

The Bank of China is owned by the state and controlled by the CCP. Hunter Biden's exact role in the company is disputed, but one expert has said that his share in it would be worth around $20 million.[33]

However, the point here is not the ethics of the Bidens (as the news media have framed it[34]) but the way in which the CCP can influence senior politicians. This 'corruption by proxy', in which top leaders keep their hands clean while their family members exploit their association to make fortunes, has been perfected by the 'red aristocracy' in Beijing. In the crucial years 2014 and 2015, Beijing was aggressively expanding into the South China Sea while Obama, Kerry and Biden were sitting on their hands.

The billionaire businessman and former New York mayor Michael Bloomberg was a late entrant in the contest to become the 2020 Democratic Party candidate for US president. He is the most Beijing-friendly of all aspirants. With extensive investments in China, he opposes the tariff war and often speaks up for the CCP regime. His media company has suppressed stories critical of CCP leaders, and Bloomberg himself claimed in 2019 that 'Xi Jinping is not a dictator' because he has to satisfy his constituency.[35] *The Washington Post*'s Josh Rogin argued that 'his [Bloomberg's] misreading of the Chinese government's character and ambitions could be devastating for U.S. national security and foreign policy. He would be advocating for a naive policy of engagement and wishful thinking that has already been tried and failed.'[36]

Republicans too have seen the influence of money from China. Since 2015, Kentucky Senator Mitch McConnell has been Senate majority leader and the most powerful man in Washington after the president. Once a hardliner, in the 1990s he became a noted China dove (although in 2019, in a likely instance of 'big help with a little badmouth', he voiced support for Hong Kong protesters[37]). In 1993 he married the daughter of one of his donors, Chinese-American businessman James Chao. Elaine Chao went on to serve as secretary of labor under President George W. Bush and in 2017 was sworn in as President Trump's transportation secretary. She wasted no time organising a trip to China that included meetings between members of her family and Chinese government officials, a plan that was spiked only when the State Department raised ethical concerns.[38]

James Chao has excellent *guanxi*—connections—in China, including his classmate Jiang Zemin, the powerful former president of China. Chao became rich through his shipping company, Foremost Group, which flourished due to its close association with the state-owned behemoth the China State Shipbuilding Corporation. McConnell, after his marriage to Chao's daughter, was courted by the highest CCP leaders, and his in-laws were soon doing deals with Chinese government corporations.[39]

In 2008 James Chao made a gift of several million dollars to his daughter and her husband, making Mitch McConnell one of the richest members of Congress. Since the 1990s he has been working to shift the Republicans to a more China-friendly position.[40] In 1999, when Republicans strongly backed a resolution pledging support for Taiwan, McConnell was missing in action. He has opposed measures to punish China for human rights violations and currency manipulation. For her part, Elaine Chao was dismissive of a report in 2000 calling out China's espionage activity, refusing to acknowledge that China could pose any threat to the United States.[41]

The White House

When Donald Trump occupied the Oval Office in February 2017, the US government's attitude towards China began to change, although more slowly than might have been expected given Trump's red-hot rhetoric on the campaign trail. Throughout much of his first year in office, the administration was hedging its bets. One of the new president's first acts was to can the Trans-Pacific Partnership, a trade agreement between twelve Pacific-rim nations that would have served as a counterweight to China's increasing economic dominance. Powerful voices in the White House, people with deep China connections, were urging a conciliatory approach.

Wilbur Ross, the new commerce secretary, had extensive investments in China, and one of his companies was partnered with a state-owned Chinese corporation (under pressure, Ross appears to have divested in 2019).[42] While in China in 2017 he talked up a partnership between Goldman Sachs and the state-owned investment fund China Investment Corp, to provide up to $5 billion to buy into US manufacturers, including sensitive assets.[43] (Readers might consult this book's index to grasp the outsized role Goldman Sachs plays in Beijing's influence operations.)

Trump's director of the National Economic Council, Gary Cohn, had been president of Goldman Sachs, which was heavily involved with Chinese banks, giving Cohn a personal stake in their success. Among his financial interests in China before his appointment was a multimillion-dollar stake in a huge Party-controlled bank, the Industrial and Commercial Bank of China, which he helped to buy assets in the US. The bank is reported to be the largest commercial tenant in Trump Tower.[44] Having worked at furthering US–China trade and investment links, Cohn also has deep connections with Chinese financial and political elites.

Trump's treasury secretary, Steven Mnuchin, had also once worked for Goldman Sachs and held stocks in the company, worth several million dollars, which he divested soon after taking office. Mnuchin quickly became the leading China dove in the White House, working to head off or derail moves to impose tariffs and other sanctions.[45]

Donald Trump's own family had high hopes of enriching themselves in China. When Trump appointed his son-in-law, Jared Kushner, as White House senior adviser, Kushner held substantial investments in Blackstone, an investment company owned by Trump's friend Stephen Schwarzman which was heavily invested in China. In 2018 it was reported that Kushner's real estate company was being investigated over a scheme to lure Chinese investors to buy into apartment towers with the promise of obtaining visas to live in the United States.[46]

Ivanka Trump, the president's daughter, owns valuable trademarks in China, some of which were granted after her father won office. She was executive vice president of Trump Hotels, which planned to build some twenty to thirty hotels in China.

Initially, President Trump referred often to his 'great friend' Xi Jinping,[47] but in 2018 the atmosphere in Washington D.C. turned sour. 'Constructive engagement' was replaced with an adversarial approach. The structures of influence the CCP had built proved impotent, but not for want of trying. In March 2019 the journal *Mother Jones* broke a tawdry story about a Chinese-American Trump donor named Cindy Yang, who operated brothels in Florida. She was reported to be arranging visas for rich Chinese, and working hard to get close to Trump, without much success. She did, however, get the president's sister, Elizabeth Trump-Grau, to participate in an event at the Mar-a-Lago resort. Yang was active in CCP united front organisations, notably the Florida branch of the China Council for the Promotion of Peaceful National Reunification. She also held a position on the National Committee of the Asian American Republican Party. Known as the 'Asian GOP', its aim, according to executive director Cliff Zhonggang Li, was to 'promote Chinese-American political participation', words that signal engagement in the CCP's *huaren canzheng* work (literally, 'ethnic Chinese participation in politics', explained in chapter seven).[48]

There have been more sophisticated and effective programs to influence America's first families. During the 2016 presidential primaries, Jeb Bush looked like a better bet than Donald Trump. One of the stand-out donors to Jeb's campaign was a Singapore-based Chinese couple named Gordon Tang and Huaidan Chen, owners of a property development company in California. They had previously attracted attention for their links to Gary Locke, the former Washington state governor who was appointed US ambassador to China by Obama.[49] In 2013, while Locke was ambassador, Huaidan Chen bought his home in Bethesda, Maryland for $1.68 million.[50] (Ethics experts said it was a clear conflict of interest.[51]) After Locke left office, they began paying him as an adviser to their company.

Although Gordon Tang and Huaidan Chen's $1.3 million donation to Jeb Bush's election campaign did not pay off, they had appointed his brother, Neil Bush, as non-executive chairman of their company SingHaiyi as early as 2013.[52] The Bush family's China friendship began in 1974, when George H.W. Bush served as de facto ambassador in Beijing. He would later say, 'I know how China works,' and was deeply respected in China as 'an old friend', a rarely bestowed honorific reserved for world figures who have rendered great help to China. (Henry Kissinger and former head of the International Olympic Committee, Juan Antonio Samaranch, have received the same honour.[53]) As president in 1989 Bush worked hard to smooth relations after the June massacre in Tiananmen Square, sending a secret delegation to Beijing in early July, just a month after the bloody crackdown.[54]

Today the Bush legacy is carried on by Neil, the former president's third son. He chairs the George H.W. Bush China-U.S. Relations Foundation, which among other activities staged a major conference in Washington D.C. in October 2018 in conjunction with the important united front body, the Chinese People's Association for Friendship with Foreign Countries.[55] The CPAFFC works with the Bush foundation to promote closer ties between the two countries and 'to create a more peaceful and prosperous future'.[56]

The problem is that the CPAFFC, commonly abbreviated in Chinese as *youxie* ('friendship association'), is an official organisation masquerading as an NGO. It is an agency of the Chinese People's Political Consultative Conference, a top-level advisory body that forms an integral part of the CCP's united front work. Its task is to win friends under the banner of people-to-people diplomacy. Friendship, or *youyi*, writes Anne-Marie Brady, 'is a term that has come to be closely associated with foreigners and the CCP's system of structures and strategies for dealing with them'.[57] Winning foreign friends through the activities of organisations like the CPAFFC is integral to the CCP's system of exerting influence abroad. For example, in May 2019 Xinhua reported the signing of a memorandum of understanding between the CPAFFC and a think tank in Ireland, AsiaMatters, to promote people-to-people exchanges and cooperation. At the ceremony, Ireland's foreign minister and deputy prime minister, Simon Coveney, said the deepening relationship would help Ireland reach out to the European Union so as to advance China's interests in the EU.[58]

In June 2019 the *People's Daily* enthusiastically reported Neil Bush opining that the United States was using trade barriers 'as a political weapon to bully' China.[59] While China is becoming more mature, said Bush, US democracy is flawed and politicians are 'brainwashing'

Americans into seeing China as a problem. The role of his organisation, he explained, is to help Americans see the truth about China. In an interview with the state broadcaster CGTN, he gushed about 'the natural kindness and gift giving of the Chinese people', unwittingly revealing the tactics used to groom him.[60]

A month later Neil Bush was in Hong Kong giving the keynote speech at a conference organised by Tung Chee-hwa, former Hong Kong chief executive and top united front operative. Bush blamed 'anti-China' sentiment in the US for the tension between the two powers, telling the audience that the US should not meddle in China's affairs, that CCP leaders are motivated by concern for the people, and that 'US-style democracy' is not suited to China.[61] Bush developed these themes in another sycophantic interview on CGTN in October, where he said that Americans would change their view of China if they could only see 'the rise of the freedom people are enjoying' there.[62] His words so closely echoed those generated by the CCP's Propaganda Department they could have been written by it.

The Department of Enemy Work

In recent years, China has used increasingly bellicose language and military muscle flexing, not least in its annexation and militarisation of islands in the South China Sea. Behind the scenes, a quieter and more powerful process of achieving supremacy has been taking place, a process of 'disintegrating' the enemy. At the heart of it lies the International Liaison Department of the Political Work Department of the Central Military Commission. Previously known as the Department of Enemy Work, the Liaison Department is an integral element of China's intelligence community.[63] However, as China scholar Geoff Wade writes: 'its functions are broader, as it develops links with global elites and aims at influencing the policies and behaviour of countries, institutions and groups beyond China. It engages in a broad range of activities including propaganda, liaison, influence peddling, information gathering and perception management.'[64]

CCP experts Mark Stokes and Russell Hsiao have described its *modus operandi.* Elite individuals and organisations in foreign defence and the military are classified as friend, enemy, or those in the middle who can be won over—this is similar to the CCP's classification of people in China that we saw in chapter two, and to Richard Baum's taxonomy described above. 'Psychological assessments of elite figures,' write Stokes and Hsiao, 'examine leaders, assess an individual's career, level of culture, motivation, values, political orientation and factional affiliation, social status, family, and professional competency.'[65]

Information acquired by cyber hacking of personnel databases, health records, personal email accounts and so on can be especially useful when aiming to create rapport with members of military and political elites, both past and present, along with academics. To conduct this work, the Liaison Department has created or supports a number of front groups and front companies.[66]

A month after Donald Trump's inauguration, a Chinese-American businesswoman, Angela Chen, bought a $15.8 million condo in Trump Park Avenue.[67] Journalists Andy Kroll and Russ Choma, writing in *Mother Jones*, revealed that Chen, whose consulting firm sells access to powerful people, chairs an overseas influence organisation tied to China's military intelligence.[68] This organisation, the China Arts Foundation International, is a non-profit group that sponsors cultural events and hosts galas that bring together the rich and powerful. (We examine its activities in more length in chapter ten.) It is linked to the China Association for International Friendly Contact, a front group of the Liaison Department.[69] (Among the CAIFC's other subsidiaries is the Centre for Peace and Development Studies.) Although its official aim is to 'promote international people-to-people exchanges and cooperation' to enhance world peace and development, its main function, according to Stokes and Hsiao, 'is establishing and maintaining rapport with senior foreign defense and security community elites, including retired military officers and legislators'.[70] More bluntly, according to a manual seen by Australian Beijing correspondent John Garnaut, it specialises in 'carrying out work of disintegrating the enemy and uniting with friendly military elements'.[71] In one instance, uncovered by Garnaut, a group of Australia's most senior businessmen was courted by CAIFC officials, unaware that their solicitous contact, Xing Yunming, was a lieutenant-general in the PLA.[72] Xing was until 2015 the executive vice president of the CAIFC and the head of the PLA's Liaison Department.[73]

He has also hosted Tony Blair and Bill Gates, among other dignitaries. Geoff Wade notes: 'This intense engagement by senior members of the PLA in CAIFC activities clearly shows the degree to which it is a covert arm of the PLA, engaged in intelligence and propaganda work.'[74]

China has drawn many former US officials into its network of influence operations.[75] One of the more important recruits was US Admiral (rtd) Bill Owens, former vice chairman of the Joint Chiefs of Staff.[76] Owens was given extraordinary access to top PLA leaders, including the vice chairman of the Central Military Commission, Xu Qiliang, and according to Garnaut, writing in 2013, he 'has probably spent more time with top Chinese generals in the past six years than have all serving American generals combined'.[77]

After retiring from the US Navy in 1996, Owens used his China connections to build a lucrative career in a Hong Kong investment firm and as an adviser for cross-border technology transfers. He also mixed with Washington D.C. opinion-makers and held board positions at think tanks, including Brookings, Carnegie, Rand and the Council on Foreign Relations.[78] Beginning in 2008 Owens arranged meetings between a stream of high-ranking US military officers and their Chinese counterparts; it was known as the Sanya Initiative. Some US officers came away from these meetings echoing CCP propaganda, such as that China's intentions are peaceful and not a threat. Owens himself wrote opinion articles for the *Financial Times*, one of which, headlined 'America must start treating China as a friend', argued that it's not in America's interests to sell arms to Taiwan.[79] A report of a 2008 Sanya Initiative meeting claimed that 'all four American generals have already begun to discuss writing op-ed pieces to provide a counterpoint to the current writing about China's military'.[80] The CAIFC also attempted to delay the publication of a Pentagon report on PRC military power.[81]

In 2013 Owens founded a consultancy firm named Red Bison, which opens up partnerships with China.[82] He continued his work of introducing senior military officers to their 'Chinese counterparts'. A 2012 paper by the Congressional Research Service raised concerns about the nature of the contact between current and former US military officers and the PLA. It specifically discussed Owens's involvement with the Sanya group and his business interests in China.[83] When it was put to him, Owens declined to comment on whether he had received as much as $100 million from his China business activities.[84] At a meeting of the Republican National Committee in 2012, calls were made for congressional hearings into the affair, but they were not pursued because it was believed an investigation would harm the party.[85]

The Sanya Initiative continues to flourish. In October 2018 it convened a meeting paid for by the CCP-linked China-United States Exchange Foundation (see chapters six and eleven) and 'private donors'. The CAIFC also collaborated.[86]

Of the high-powered guests who have appeared at functions organised by the China Arts Foundation International, Stephen Schwarzman, CEO of the Blackstone Group, stands out. A Palm Beach neighbour of Donald Trump, Schwarzman has been described by Michael Kranish of *The Washington Post* as Trump's 'China whisperer', because he has 'one of the closest relationships to Beijing of any American executive'.[87] Throughout 2017 and 2018 Trump zigzagged between being hard and soft on China, though he seemed to harden permanently in early 2019. Sometimes, Schwarzman's message to Trump to take a soft line has been overruled by more hawkish voices. But in Schwarzman Beijing has a sympathiser intimate with the president. Trump appointed him to head a White House business advisory panel, the sixteen-member President's Strategic and Policy Forum, which included the top executives from J.P. Morgan Chase, BlackRock, Boeing, Intel, Ernst & Young, and IBM. At its first meeting they told Trump that he had China wrong and should be more conciliatory.[88]

When the Blackstone group was publicly listed in 2007, a Chinese government entity, China Investment Corporation, bought 9.9 per cent of its shares, just below the threshold that would trigger a national security review. CIC is a sovereign wealth fund that manages part of China's foreign exchange reserves.[89] In June 2017 Blackstone pocketed $13.8 billion when it sold Logicor, owner of the largest portfolio of logistics and distribution properties in Europe, to CIC. In 2016 Blackstone sold a portfolio of luxury US hotels to the Chinese insurance and banking firm Anbang Group for $5.5 billion, then tried to buy them back three years later when the firm was crippled by a corruption scandal. Schwarzman had become 'the go-to man for Chinese buyers'.[90]

Schwarzman has remarked that he is considered both the 'unofficial US ambassador to China' and the 'unofficial Chinese ambassador to the US'.[91] Although he was joking, his comment rings uncomfortably true. He's well known to top leaders in Beijing. At the 2017 World Economic Forum in Davos, President Xi pulled Schwarzman aside for a chat, confirming the billionaire's good standing at the highest levels of the CCP. Before Trump met Xi Jinping at Mar-a-Lago in 2018, Schwarzman told him, 'President Xi is a great guy.'[92] Schwarzman has endowed a new college at Tsinghua University in Beijing, the university regarded by many as the best in China; it's the alma mater of many top Party leaders, including Xi Jinping.[93] Schwarzman College teaches a master's program in global affairs for 'promising young leaders'. Nearly half of its students are drawn from the United States and it's all free of charge.

In February 2017 Schwarzman staged an opulent Silk Road–themed seventieth birthday party for himself. Guests included fellow friends of China and incoming Trump cabinet members Steve Mnuchin, Wilbur Ross and Elaine Chao, along with Jared Kushner and Ivanka Trump.[94]

Blackstone owns the major share of the big financial news and data analysis service Refinitiv (in partnership with Reuters). In June 2019 Refinitiv censored news stories on the thirtieth anniversary of the Tiananmen Square massacre, after demands from the Cyberspace Administration of China.[95] Three months later Schwarzman was playing the peacekeeper in the trade dispute, praising China's 'astonishing miracle' but urging it to change its trade and business practices to accommodate Western concerns. He characterised Beijing's massive program of tech theft as 'other approaches to intellectual property'.[96]

Canada's Beijing elite

For many years journalists have been fascinated by the extraordinary political influence of Power Corporation, the Canadian conglomerate owned by the Desmarais family. Much less well known is the way in which China, through Power Corp, has become closely integrated into a deep network of Canada's political-business elite, an elite that seems at times to run the country. This insinuation of Beijing's influence goes a long way towards explaining why the Trudeau government froze in reaction to the 2018 crisis over Huawei's Meng Wanzhou, and remained frozen. The story of how this network developed is told by long-serving foreign correspondent Jonathan Manthorpe in his important book of 2019, *Claws of the Panda*.[97]

One of the early events was the staging of a conference in 1977 that brought together what Manthorpe calls 'Canada's corporate aristocracy'. At a time when Washington had not yet formally recognised China, it led to Power Corp chief Paul Desmarais and CEO of Petro-Canada Maurice Strong to call for a permanent trade presence in China. (Strong, a member of the Liberal Party, later became president of Power Corp.) In 1978 the pair formed what would become a powerful business lobby, the Canada-China Business Council. Remarkably, among the ten officially listed founding companies was the China International Trust and Investment Corporation. Set up in 1979 on the orders of Deng Xiaoping, CITIC began operating in Hong Kong in 1987 and was soon swallowing up several large companies, growing into a huge conglomerate.[98] Its senior executive ranks included members of the red aristocracy. It had close links with the PLA and was 'swarming with secret agents'.[99] The president of CITIC, Wang Jun, whose father had been vice president of the PRC and a close friend of Deng Xiaoping, was an intelligence operative; he was later intimately involved in the Chinagate scandal that engulfed the Clinton presidency, until the Monica Lewinsky affair took all the oxygen.[100]

It was Paul Desmarais, as the new chair of the Canada-China Business Council, who drew CITIC into the lobby group, and thus into the most senior levels of Canada's business elite. Power Corp channelled most of its China investments through the military-linked company.[101] Desmarais then offered CITIC a 50 per cent share in one of Power Corp's paper mills, an offer that gave CITIC its first important overseas investment opportunity and began a process of heavy investment in Canada by China's state-owned enterprises. The Desmarais family, with Paul succeeded by his son André, has maintained tight links to China's business and political elites ever since. (Paul Desmarais has named Mao Zedong as one of the four historical figures he most admires.[102])

Until 2012 the Desmarais family's closest friend in the CCP hierarchy was the high-flying Bo Xilai, the rival of Xi Jinping, whose spectacular fall in a corruption and murder trial did not dent the deep connection between Power Corp and the Canada-China Business Council. Bo Xilai's son, Bo Guagua, a Columbia University law graduate, began work at Power Corp in 2018.[103]

The Liberal Party, the dominant party of Canadian government for many decades, is intimately linked with Power Corp. A revolving door has cycled dozens of political advisers, ministers and provincial governors through the corporation, but here we focus only on the top. Paul Desmarais was an adviser to Pierre Trudeau both before he became prime minister and during his tenure of office (1980–84). After Trudeau left parliament, Desmarais paid him to advise Power Corp.[104] The conservative Brian Mulroney, prime minister from 1984 to 1993, had been a lawyer for Power Corp. 'I loved him like a brother,' Mulroney said on Desmarais's death.[105] After the arrest of Meng Wanzhou, Mulroney weighed into the debate over Beijing's bullying, supporting a plan for Ottawa to appease Beijing.[106]

Liberal Prime Minister Jean Chrétien (in office 1993–2003) had served on the board of a Power Corp subsidiary in the late 1980s, and in 1981 his daughter married André Desmarais. Along with being the future president of Power Corp, André also chaired the Canada-China Business Council and today he maintains strong links with Beijing's ruling elite, including a position on the board of CITIC Pacific Ltd, a Hong Kong affiliate of CITIC.[107] Two months after he left office, Chrétien made a secret visit to China, organised by CITIC, to arrange personal business deals.[108] He was accompanied by his son-in-law André. Chrétien's successor as prime minister, Paul Martin (in office 2003–06), had worked for Power Corp for thirteen years before buying from Desmarais the Power Corp subsidiary he'd been running.[109]

In 1999, while the Chrétien government was in power, the sensational Sidewinder report was leaked to *The Globe and Mail*.[110] (Jonathan Manthorpe provides the best discussion of this.[111]) Secretly prepared in 1997 by officers of the Royal Canadian Mounted Police and the Canadian Security Intelligence Service, the report argued that a 'new triumvirate' had established itself in Canada, an alliance of China's intelligence agencies, triad gangs, and Chinese tycoons who were buying up local companies.[112] The three groups were cooperating in operations to steal Canadian technology, acquire influence over the economic levers of the country, and exercise political sway through building associations with powerful politicians. The report also warned of growing CCP interference in universities, and of Beijing-linked tycoons building political influence through real estate investments.

The report further noted that the acquisition of Canadian firms was led by CITIC, and that it had developed close links with Power Corp. It noted that CITIC had become a substantial donor to the main political parties.

The Chrétien government, more interested in actively pursuing closer economic links with China, had no interest in looking closely at the claims in the Sidewinder report. The report was denounced and buried.[113]

Manthorpe describes Power Corp as 'the premier gatekeeper' of Canada's formal relations with China. CCP bosses had come to believe they would always get what they wanted in Canada, so much so that they responded to Meng Wanzhou's arrest as if betrayed. And they badly wanted Meng back.

In 2016 it was reported that Justin Trudeau, elected prime minister in 2015, had been visiting the homes of wealthy Chinese-Canadians for private fundraising events. Some of the hosts had close connections with the CCP and had been actively promoting Beijing's takeover of islands in the South China Sea.[114] One donor lobbied the prime minister to loosen the immigration rules for wealthy Chinese. Another, Zhang Bin, who *The Globe and Mail* described as a 'Chinese billionaire and Communist Party official', with his business partner donated C$50,000 to University of Montreal for a statue of Trudeau's father, Pierre. Buying favour does not get much more blatant, but for good measure they threw in C$200,000 for the Pierre Elliott Trudeau Foundation, a charity honouring Justin's father.[115] The donors knew they had a friend in Justin; after all, in 2013 he had confided to another fundraiser that he admired China's 'basic dictatorship' because it could get things done.[116] It was the deep misfortune of Michael Kovrig and Michael Spavor, the Canadians seized on fake charges by Beijing in retaliation for the arrest of Meng Wanzhou, that their government was led by a man so unwilling to confront the CCP.

This network of elites in Canada and China has also seen the election of trusted Chinese-Canadians to political office, including a number in federal parliament. One of those most often mentioned for his closeness to Beijing is Michael Chan, a minister in the Liberal Party government of Ontario from 2007 to 2018. As early as 2010 Canada's spy chief, Richard Fadden, had warned that government ministers in at least two provinces were 'under the influence of a foreign government', and were shifting government policy.[117] Although he did not name China, Fadden endured a storm of criticism for implicitly singling out Chinese-Canadians as disloyal. A parliamentary committee demanded that the government apologise and put a gag on Fadden.

In 2015 *The Globe and Mail* reported that Chan was one of those whom Fadden had had in mind.[118] Chan denied the claim and sued the paper.[119] The Ontario premier dismissed concerns about Chan as baseless. Clearly, no-one in power in Canada was willing to take the CSIS concerns seriously, either because they were under Beijing's sway or were too scared of accusations of racism and Sinophobia.

In 2016, after China's foreign minister testily rebuked a Canadian reporter for asking questions about human rights, Minister Chan defended China's human rights record in a Chinese-language publication.[120] After leaving parliament, in the midst of the 2019 Hong Kong riots, Michael Chan spoke at a pro-Beijing rally urging Hong Kong police to deal severely with protesters. He later echoed Beijing's criticisms, claiming that outsiders were responsible for stirring up the trouble, and inflaming feelings of historical humiliation.[121]

During the Huawei crisis, Justin Trudeau, having sacked ambassador John McCallum for becoming in effect Beijing's envoy in Ottawa, replaced him with someone even more deeply entangled with Beijing's elites. Dominic Barton was a managing director of McKinsey & Co from 2009 to 2018, during which time he spent five years in Shanghai as the company's Asia chairman. McKinsey has been described by *The New York Times* as having 'helped raise the stature of authoritarian and corrupt governments across the globe'.[122] The company has extensive involvement with China's government; for example, it signed up a client that was helping build artificial islands in the South China Sea.[123]

Barton has also served on the advisory board of the state-owned China Development Bank and is an adjunct professor at Tsinghua University. He has been said to write glowingly about China's 'success story'.[124] When he left McKinsey in 2018 it was to chair the board of Teck Resources, one of Canada's biggest mining companies. Part-owned by the CCP-controlled China Investment Corporation, and with China its biggest market, Teck raised eyebrows in 2016 when it took an unprecedented step in appointing to its board a Party member, Chong Quan, a former member of the National People's Congress.[125]

In a move that will doubtless draw him further still into Beijing's net, in early 2019 Barton married Geraldine Buckingham, head of Asia-Pacific operations for BlackRock, the giant US investment fund that has been working hard to build its presence in China (see chapter six).

The diplomatic appointment of Dominic Barton reflects a common political mistake in the West, the belief that it's always an advantage for ambassadors to have long experience in China. Governments forget that, in the process of getting to know China and some of its powerful players, many succumb to Beijing's subtle influence techniques, so that an ambassador may in practice serve as a conduit for Beijing's messaging back to the Western capital.

After his re-election in October 2019, Prime Minister Trudeau appointed a new foreign minister, to whom Barton answers. François-Philippe Champagne appears to be as enamoured with the CCP regime as Barton and Trudeau, and his mentor Jean Chrétien.[126] In an interview with CGTN in 2017, Champagne was full of praise for Xi Jinping. China and Canada, he gushed, 'stand out as [a] beacon of stability, predictability, a rule-based system, a very inclusive society'.[127]

All this explains the cone of silence that has descended over Canada's elites in response to the litany of Beijing's outrages—in Xinjiang, Hong Kong and in Canada itself, where there have been kidnappings, cyber attacks, trade bans, blatant united front activity and frequent diplomatic insults. During his 2019 election campaign, Trudeau cancelled the traditional foreign policy debate and said nothing about the deepest diplomatic crisis the nation has faced since the end of the Second World War.[128]

4
Political elites at the centre: Europe

Party-to-party diplomacy

The Chinese Communist Party has a long history of cultivating friendly relations with political parties abroad, beginning with its membership of the Soviet Union's Communist International; the latter had helped found the CCP in 1921. Until the 1980s, fraternal contacts were largely confined to parties with a communist ideology, but since then, all parties have become targets for influence. While the United Front Work Department is responsible for guiding overseas Chinese and suppressing dissident voices, the task of pursuing party-to-party diplomacy, as well as links with foreign NGOs and other political groups, lies with the CCP's International Liaison Department.[1] The department's deputy head quoted Xi Jinping: 'Party-to-party diplomacy is an important battlefront for our Party, and an important component of the nation's overall diplomacy.'[2]

The ILD has been growing for a couple of decades and has been further strengthened in the Xi era. Its broad outreach has allowed it to build relations with other countries' governments, opposition parties and potential future governments.[3] Following the 2016 dispute over Beijing's annexation of islands in the South China Sea, the ILD claimed that China had the support of over 240 parties from 120 countries, plus that of 280 well-known think tanks and NGOs.[4] This particular number may be inflated, or the importance of supporters exaggerated, but by and large party-to-party diplomacy has produced some impressive results.

In November 2017 the ILD staged a huge conference in Beijing called 'CPC [Communist Party of China] in Dialogue with World Political Parties High-level Meeting'. It drew 600 representatives from 300 political parties from around the world.[5] There were delegates from the UK's Conservative Party, Canada's Liberal Party and the US Republican Party, with the latter represented by Tony Parker, treasurer of the Republican National Committee.[6] At the conference's conclusion delegates put their names to the 'Beijing Initiative', declaring that they 'commend the immense efforts and important contribution of the Communist Party of China with General Secretary Xi Jinping as the core'.[7] They endorsed Xi's vision for an alternative to a liberal, rules-based order, an option that Party messaging calls 'the building of a community of a shared future for mankind'. The declaration called for respect for each country's own values, CCP code for the rejection of universal human rights.

As Julia Bowie of the Party Watch Initiative notes, this does not mean that the US Republican Party or the UK Conservative Party secretly worship Xi Jinping.[8] These events are valuable because of the opportunity they provide for the CCP to befriend individuals, who then return home to inject Beijing's viewpoint into their parties' deliberations. Such events also have substantial symbolic value for the CCP, in showing that the Party and its policies enjoy international support.

Like other official CCP organisations, the International Liaison Department presents itself using the language of 'peace', 'development' and 'progress'.[9] It regularly publishes reports on its meetings with various foreign entities.[10] In May 2019 the head of the ILD, Song Tao, met with Manfred Grund, a delegate of the German Bundestag and member of its Committee on Foreign Affairs. According to the ILD, Grund offered assurances that his party, the Christian Democratic Union, 'actively supports the Belt and Road Initiative' and 'stands ready to strengthen exchanges and mutual learning with the CPC'.[11] When later asked to comment, Grund said that he did not recall saying this, but that he did see common interests for Europe and China in Central Asia.[12]

Publishing statements by foreign politicians belongs to the ritual of *biaotai*, 'expressing allegiance', whereby foreigners, as we saw in chapter two, are induced to repeat CCP phrases. In another instance of this, Norway's foreign minister, Ine Eriksen Søreide, said in December 2018 that the 'Norwegian Government respects China's core interests and major concerns and will take concrete actions to safeguard the political foundation for bilateral relations.'[13] And the president of the Hungarian Socialist Party, Tóth Bertalan, declared that his party 'is willing to learn from the successful experience of the CPC in party building and state governance'.[14]

Some are content to be cited like this, while others may be unaware that they have been quoted or paraphrased in ways that support the CCP and its policies. Either way, since the purpose is to create the impression of a broad pro-CCP consensus among foreigners, the goal is achieved, as long as people who feel they have been misquoted don't demand to have the record corrected; doing so can cause loss of face on both sides, with material consequences for the complainant.

The ILD meets with nearly all political parties in Europe, established and new. Not everyone is willing to give enthusiastic endorsements, but almost all high-level politicians are happy to meet, usually resulting in reports in which assurances of support for China are attributed to them.[15]

The ILD has put enormous effort into promoting the Belt and Road Initiative, with the objective of persuading parties around the world to endorse it. Nations that have been worked on most intensively include Japan, Greece and the United Kingdom.[16] One of the more loyal friends of the ILD is Peter Mandelson, former senior cabinet member in the Blair government and honorary president of the Great Britain-China Centre.[17] In May 2019 Mandelson was reported as saying that relations with China are very important to Britain, which 'hopes to actively participate in the building of the Belt and Road Initiative'. In words that read as if composed by a Party propagandist, he added: 'The UK is ready to continue to work with China to well conduct the UK-China dialogue between political parties, strengthen exchanges between political parties of the two countries and promote the building of a "Golden Era" of UK-China relations.'[18]

A month later, Mandelson was writing in the *Sunday Times* that the United States had launched a trade war against China to quash a rival, and that Britain should not take sides.[19] Claims about the security risks of Huawei were 'completely overblown' and aimed at strangling the company, he wrote. Britain, not being in geopolitical competition with China, should instead be influencing China as a trade partner. Mandelson is among those who still believe that, with a bit of persuasion, CCP leaders can become good international citizens. The tenor of his article is that there is no downside to the CCP, and Britain should welcome China's rise and engage enthusiastically. Mandelson is a fellow of the 48 Group Club (see below).[20]

Grooming Europe

The same process of grooming that worked so well with Canada's John McCallum may have shaped the thinking of the Swedish ambassador to China, Anna Lindstedt,[21] who in January 2019 was reported to have aided attempts to silence Angela Gui. Angela's father, Gui Minhai, a Swedish citizen, was working as a bookseller in Hong Kong in 2015 when he was kidnapped by Chinese authorities in Thailand and imprisoned in China without trial, as part of the crackdown on Hong Kong booksellers. Like many others, he was paraded on Chinese state television, where he made a forced confession. Angela had been campaigning vocally for his release.

Ambassador Lindstedt asked Angela Gui to meet with her and several Chinese businessmen, who claimed to be well connected in Beijing and promised to help have her father released.[22] At that meeting, in a Stockholm hotel, the businessmen used flattery, bribes and threats, all in Lindstedt's presence, to induce Gui to stop speaking out about her father's detention. Angela claims that the ambassador told her that if she did as she was told and her father was released, then she, Lindstedt, would 'go on Swedish television and speak of the bright future of Sweden-China relations'.[23]

After Gui went public about her experience, Ambassador Lindstedt was stood down.[24] The Swedish Ministry of Foreign Affairs claimed it was unaware of the meeting. It would have been violating all protocol if Lindstedt, without informing her employer, had travelled to Sweden to engage in negotiations with Beijing's proxies. Swedish prosecutors began a criminal investigation into Lindstedt's actions and in December 2019 she was charged with the obscure offence of 'arbitrariness during negotiations with a foreign power'.[25] When PEN Sweden awarded Gui Minhai a prize, which was presented by culture minister Amanda Lind, China's ambassador in Stockholm, Gui Congyou, said China would punish Sweden with trade restrictions.

Anna Lindstedt is not the first European diplomat to have come under scrutiny for being too close to Beijing. In 2013 Mikael Lindström became an adviser to Huawei after leaving his post as Swedish ambassador to China.[26] Elsewhere, Serge Abou, head of the EU Mission to China from 2005 to 2011, was hired as a consultant for Huawei in Brussels. This prompted the European Commission to make the rare move of imposing a cooling-off period on Abou until the end of 2012 and placing additional restrictions on his activities in Brussels, including a ban on 'engaging in any lobbying activity in relation to the [European] Commission'.[27] In early 2014 Abou withdrew from his role at Huawei.[28]

Other former ambassadors have lent their support to Xi Jinping's Belt and Road Initiative. Michael Schaefer, Germany's ambassador to China from 2007 to 2013, was praised by Xinhua for being 'among the first German politicians to advocate China's BRI'.[29] Schaefer has said that the BRI is 'an amazing project of the 21st century'. Well connected to Germany's elite circles, Schaefer is on the board of the German-Chinese Business Association and he chairs the board of the BMW Foundation Herbert Quandt.[30] He is also on the board of Europe's leading China-focused think tank, the Mercator Institute for China Studies.[31] In 2016, echoing the CCP's messaging, Schaefer called on the European Union to embrace Beijing's 'new kind of diplomacy based on inclusiveness, equal opportunity, and the respect for the diversity of cultures and political systems', terms that the CCP uses to reject universal human rights and the idea that democratic forms of government are to be preferred over authoritarian ones.[32]

Schaefer, an honorary professor at the China University for Political Science and Law in Beijing, has praised China's 'enormous progress' in social and economic rights, arguing that freedom of expression and freedom of the press 'hardly play a role' in countries like China.[33] He has also expressed his personal admiration for Xi Jinping, calling him 'the most impressive Chinese leader' he has ever met.[34] It goes without saying that his words were highlighted in Chinese media, specifically in an article reporting the praise of important foreigners for Xi, dubbed by journalist David Bandurski as China's new science of sycophantology.[35]

The EU-China Friendship Group

According to Peter Martin and Alan Crawford, writing for US news agency Bloomberg News, China's network of friends throughout the European Union, including politicians, officials and businesspeople, is extensive.[36] Along with the ILD, the influence operation has been spearheaded by the Chinese People's Association for Friendship with Foreign Countries, which focuses on building influence networks at local levels. These Party outfits promote Beijing's position and try to marginalise its sceptics. One sympathetic group is Germany's BGA trade association, which in 2019 warned that 'there is no basis for the current China phobia'.[37] Beijing is happy to cross political boundaries, from 2017 making successful overtures to populists, including the far-right Alternative for Germany (AfD), and Italy's 'anti-establishment' Five Star Movement. The deputy chair of the German–Chinese group in the Bundestag is AfD politician Robby Schlund. After meeting with the vice president of the CPAFFC he pledged to deepen cooperation and promote sister-city relationships between the two countries.[38]

Beijing reportedly took a close interest in the 2019 European Parliament elections, and how the results might influence Europe's stance on China.[39] The Chinese Mission to the EU is very active and has so far faced very little backlash. As we will see in chapter eleven, it sponsors almost all think tanks working on China and Asia in Brussels, quite a few of which are headed by former EU officials. Many of the mission's activities are jointly organised with departments of the European Union.[40]

As well as a range of EU institutions, Brussels hosts NATO's headquarters. The city is a hub for diplomats, military brass, journalists and political leaders, and attracts intense interest from Beijing's influence and espionage agencies. In fact, Brussels is described by Belgium's intelligence agency as a 'chessboard' for spies, notably from China.[41]

Die Welt reported in early 2019 that the European External Action Service estimates there are around 250 Chinese spies in Brussels, and urges diplomats and military officers to avoid certain eateries in the capital.[42] (China's EU mission was 'deeply shocked' at the accusation, claiming it never interferes in the internal affairs of other countries.[43]) In January 2020 Germany's Federal Prosecutor's Office launched an investigation into a former EU official and diplomat, Gerhard Sabathil, suspected of passing information to China.[44] Belgium is an easy target for China's spying and influence because of its fractured political system and lackadaisical attitude.[45] And the government wants to cultivate Beijing for greater investment. If Italy is Beijing's southern entry point into Europe, Belgium is its northern gateway.

Some of the CCP's most unapologetic supporters are found in the EU-China Friendship Group of the European Parliament in Brussels. In 2019 the group claimed a membership of forty-six MEPs from some twenty countries, making it the parliament's largest friendship group.[46] (Jichang Lulu, who has published an important study of the group, suggests that active members are fewer.[47]) It has been a staunch advocate of closer relations between Europe and China and has worked to stop the parliament criticising China's human rights abuses, including thwarting a 'plot' by MEPs for an EU boycott of the 2008 Beijing Olympics.[48] Delegations from the group frequently visit China, and also Tibet, where they are shown the CCP's efforts to protect Tibetan culture.[49] After one such visit the *China Daily* proclaimed: 'Friendship group praises Tibet after 3-day field trip'.[50]

Founded in 2006 by Nirj Deva, Conservative member of the European Parliament for South East England, the group was also chaired by him until the 2019 elections. It keeps a low public profile in Europe, but its existence is evident in Chinese media. The *Global Times* describes Deva as a 'famous friend of China', high praise indeed.[51] The power behind the throne, as it were, is Gai Lin, secretary-general of the friendship group and an accredited assistant of Deva's at the European Parliament. According to the Czech research collective Sinopsis, Gai Lin is affiliated with the provincial branch of the CPAFFC in his home province of Liaoning.[52] Chinese media claim that in 2009 he became the first and only Chinese national to work as an EU civil servant.[53]

According to a report by China Radio International, Gai Lin began working for Deva after he ran into him in a bar in Brussels in the summer of 2004, while Gai was studying hotel management. The two struck up a conversation and Deva suggested that Gai Lin do an internship at the European Parliament. In the summer of 2005, Deva wrote to the president of the European Parliament requesting special permission to employ Gai Lin. The MEP wanted to employ a Chinese citizen because he felt that nobody at the European Parliament properly 'understood' China. Gai was soon hired as a consultant.[54]

Writing in the *People's Daily* in 2014, Gai Lin claimed it had been his idea to found the EU-China Friendship Group in 2006.[55] It would, he said, allow members of the European Parliament to better 'understand' China by providing some 'positive propaganda', and Nirj Deva had agreed. Gai boasted of drafting and amending legislation put before the parliament, trying to stop the parliament welcoming the Dalai Lama, and convincing delegates that China was still a developing country, resulting in 128 million euros of development aid.[56]

The EU-China Friendship Group seems to have had quite an impact in shifting the discourse on China at the European Parliament, including on human rights. Deva himself frequently echoes Beijing's talking points.[57] He has dismissed security concerns about Huawei as 'nonsense'; defended China's human rights situation, arguing strongly (and successfully) against a boycott of the 2008 Beijing Olympics; and supported China's crackdown in Xinjiang in 2009.[58] When the Uyghur businesswoman and activist Rebiya Kadeer spoke at the European Parliament in September 2009, Deva questioned how she could have become so rich, have eleven children, and speak Uyghur fluently if China suppressed Uyghurs.[59] In 2018 Xinhua reported on a visit to the parliament by a Tibetan delegation from the National People's Congress; the delegation explained the rapid growth and social cohesion in Tibet and criticised the Dalai Lama's 'splittism'. The report also quoted Deva as saying that the 'EU-China Friendship Group will continue to objectively present China's efforts in promoting the development of Tibet in the European Parliament'.[60]

Deva and the members of his group receive better access to top leaders in China than the EU's official delegation, despite the fact they have no formal role.[61] Deva has repeatedly advocated for China in the European Parliament, lambasting the EU for 'treating China as a small child'.[62] He has been presented on Chinese state television as a 'UK expert'. In July 2016 he questioned the legitimacy of The Hague Tribunal's ruling on the South China Sea, reciting Beijing's position that the Philippines should have tried to resolve the issue through bilateral discussions.[63] Deva stated that in over fifteen years of China-watching he could not think of one big mistake the Chinese government had made.[64]

Deva and Gai Lin have also launched a range of other initiatives. On Gai Lin's suggestion, some members of the friendship group set up an NGO called the EU-China Friendship Association in order to reach segments of society beyond the parliament.[65] Among other things, the association has formed a partnership with the Chinese province of Liaoning to help its government cooperate with various EU institutions and companies.[66]

Deva failed in his re-election bid at the 2019 European elections, as did the friendship group's vice chair, the British Labour Party MEP Derek Vaughan.[67] The group has had no trouble surviving, however, and according to Chinese reports is now led by Czech MEP Jan Zahradil.[68] Zahradil is a significant player in Europe, having been runner-up for presidency of the European Parliament in 2019.[69] As CCP analyst Jichang Lulu points out, he is a strong supporter of the BRI and he seems as committed as his predecessor to bringing China into Europe. Gai Lin continues to be the group's organiser.[70]

In March 2019 the friendship group launched the Policy Co-ordination Committee of the Belt and Road Initiative in Europe.[71] In October 2019 several MEPs hosted an event called 'Sustaining an open global digital ecosystem with Huawei: a European perspective'. The event, organised with Huawei, took place just days after the European Commission had issued a 5G network security risk assessment, which warned of risks posed by 'states and state-backed actors'.[72] One of the event's hosts was Jan Zahradil, the new head of the EU-China Friendship Group, but his ties to the group were not disclosed.[73]

The problem is not limited to the EU. Friendship groups have been formed in a number of Europe's national parliaments.[74] In France, both houses of parliament have France–China friendship groups, dominated by Republicans and members of President Macron's party. One of the more China-friendly groups is the left-wing party La France Insoumise (France Unbowed), led by Jean-Luc Mélenchon.[75]

In Britain, the All-Party Parliamentary China Group was established in 1997. In 2006 it signed an agreement to deepen ties with the China-UK Friendship Group of the Chinese National People's Congress. The group does not give uncritical support to everything done by the CCP, but it works closely with the Great Britain-China Centre and the China-Britain Business Council, both in Beijing's orbit.[76]

In the next four sections, we examine some of the ways in which the CCP has insinuated itself into the highest levels of decision-making in Europe. While it's not possible to provide a comprehensive review of these, by focusing on certain influence efforts in Britain, France, Italy and Germany we will illustrate the significance and *modus operandi* of CCP operations.

Britain's 48 Group Club

In 1954, a group of forty-eight British businessmen travelled to Beijing to establish trade relations with the PRC. On their return they founded the 48 Group of British Traders with China, chaired by Jack Perry. The current list of those in China and Britain who play a role in the 48 Group Club, which grew out of the original 48 Group, is a who's who of power elites.[77]

The well-known names on the British side include former prime minister Tony Blair; former deputy prime minister Michael Heseltine; former deputy prime minister John Prescott; the billionaire Duke of Westminster; foreign minister in the Blair government Jack Straw; Alex Salmond, former first minister of Scotland; former Labour Party powerbroker and European trade commissioner Peter Mandelson; and Nirj Deva. There are also five former British ambassadors to Beijing, masters of colleges at Oxford and Cambridge, a retired general, the chairman and director of the British Museum, the chief executive of the Royal Opera House, the chair of British Airways, a director of Huawei, and people closely linked to the Bank of England, Goldman Sachs and JP Morgan.

Among the less prominent members who appear elsewhere in this book are Lady Katy Tse Blair, Tony Blair's well-connected sister-in-law; Tom Glocer, former CEO of Thomson Reuters; Professor Peter Nolan, University of Cambridge; and Professor Hugo de Burgh, University of Westminster.

On the Chinese side are Li Yuanchao, former head of the CCP's powerful Organisation Department, and vice premier of the PRC; Madam Fu Ying, vice minister of Foreign Affairs, and former ambassador to the UK; Ji Chaozhu, former ambassador to the UK (and formerly Mao Zedong's interpreter);[78] Jiang Enzhu, former chairman of the Foreign Affairs Committee of the National People's Congress; Liu Mingkang, chairman of the China Banking Regulatory Commission; and Zha Peixin, former UK ambassador, and chair of the NPC-European Parliament Relations Group. Clearly, Beijing rates the 48 Group Club very highly in its overseas influence effort. Huawei Director Victor Zhang is also a member.

In 1991 the 48 Group of British Traders with China had merged with the Sino-British Trade Council to form the China-Britain Trade Group, which later became the China-Britain Business Council, a powerful lobby group bringing together some of Britain's largest companies.[79] The board of the CBBC is stacked with powerful business figures, especially from banking and accounting firms. In 2019 one of its board members, John McLean, said that the council has been 'at the heart of UK-China trade relations for over 65 years'.[80] Among many activities, the council promotes the Belt and Road Initiative and works closely with the All-Party Parliamentary China Group.[81]

Following the merger, the 48 Group Club was launched to broaden the membership of the original group beyond business elites. Today it is chaired by Jack Perry's son, Stephen. As a sign of the 48 Group Club's importance to China's leadership, when Stephen Perry visits China he is granted unmatched access, from Xi Jinping down.[82] Perry has praised Xi's concept of a community of shared future as a 'new approach to a philosophy to underwrite international norms'. He also reproduces Party propaganda in statements like this one: 'China does not seek empire. It seeks a socialist state where the benefits of economic activity are shared reasonably, where the people's lives are cared for, and culture and social development will be vital in developing the moral base of the nation.'[83]

In 2018 Perry was honoured with a most prestigious award, the China Reform Friendship Medal, conferred on him personally by President Xi Jinping and Premier Li Keqiang.[84] (A fellow medal recipient, American public intellectual Robert Kuhn, who wrote a hagiography of Jiang Zemin, was described in a Xinhua magazine as 'one of the all-time top-ten influential supporters of China's ruling party'.[85])

While the 48 Group Club is feted at banquets in Beijing, it keeps a very low profile in the United Kingdom. With over 500 members, it serves as a meeting place and networking hub for friends of China, through which Beijing grooms Britain's elites. (We will see its members cropping up elsewhere in this book.) Chairman Stephen Perry's stream of commentary on the group's website is a robotic repetition of CCP propaganda.[86] He defends the abolition of limits on the term of China's presidency, and sees increased Party control as necessary to give the government the power it needs to bring change. He says Xi Jinping is responsible for freeing our minds. In a Xinhua interview he said it's time for the world to fully embrace the BRI, which he claims is about sharing, which 'is the essence of Socialism with Chinese characteristics'.[87] In November 2019 he told New China TV that China's system of democratic governance, that of 'hearing the people, listening to the people and … serving the people', will lead the world in the twenty-first century.[88]

No group in Britain enjoys more intimacy and trust with the CCP leadership than the 48 Group Club. On the face of it, this is puzzling, but if we look behind the club's airbrushed origin story, we begin to understand why the Party's top leaders place so much confidence in it.[89]

In the early 1950s, due to its involvement in the Korean War, China was the subject of an embargo on strategic goods by the United States and Britain. The Soviet bloc was also subject to a trade embargo and, to get around it, in 1952 Moscow created a front group called the International Committee for the Promotion of Trade. It held an international economic conference in Moscow that same year and Jack Perry was a delegate. He returned to Britain to found, with others, the British Council for the Promotion of International Trade, whose aim was to help the USSR and China get around the trade embargo. Also in 1952, on the instructions of Premier Zhou Enlai, the CCP formed the China Council for the Promotion of International Trade, which then 'carried out external work under the personal care and guidance of Zhou Enlai'.[90] Its first task was to persuade foreign businessmen to begin trading with China and to convince their governments to lift the embargo. (A 1957 CIA dossier, declassified in 1999, noted that the CCPIT was closely affiliated with Moscow's ICPT.[91])

The two most senior office holders in CCPIT also served on the committee of the Soviet International Committee for the Promotion of Trade.[92] The chairman of the CCPIT was the governor of China's central bank, Nan Hanchen.[93] From the late 1930s Nan had been deputy director of the United Front Work Department, and he also held various senior positions in United Front organisations subsequently.[94] CCPIT's vice chairman and secretary-general was Ji Chaoding, who came to be regarded as 'the principal architect ... of close relations between China and the UK'.[95] With excellent English, perfected in the United States, Ji was a secret member of the CCP in the 1930s and 1940s. He was also a brilliant spy and worked directly under Zhou Enlai; according to some accounts, he played a vital role as a double agent in the destruction of the Nationalist government, of which he was a senior official.[96] (Zhou Enlai was revered in the Party for his leadership of CCP intelligence from its early days.[97])

In 1953 Jack Perry helped organise a major conference in Moscow, staged by the Soviet International Committee for the Promotion of Trade. Perry attended the conference as chairman of his new company, the London Export Corporation; he had been encouraged to give up his job and establish the corporation by Ji Chaoding, who he had met in Europe in 1951. The Chinese delegation was led by Nan Hanchen and Ji Chaoding.[98] At the conference, Nan Hanchen invited Perry to bring a delegation of sixteen British businessmen to China to open up trade, which Perry did a month or so later. Although barely mentioned by the 48 Group Club today, there were two others involved in the London Export Corporation, Roland Berger and Bernard Buckman; these two led the visit to China, hosted by the CCPIT and its secretary-general Ji.[99]

Roland Berger had been a civil liberties activist and in 1953 was the secretary of the British Council for the Promotion of International Trade. He was also a secret member of the Communist Party of Great Britain. Bernard Buckman, a textile merchant, was another secret member of the CPGB, and a Labour Party entrist.[100] Buckman became a frequent visitor to China, and when he died in 2016 the *China Daily* reported that no other Westerner had enjoyed his level of access to top leaders.[101]

At Ji Chaoding's invitation, Jack Perry returned to China in 1954 with a larger delegation, this time forty-eight British businessmen. According to the 48 Group Club's own account, Perry was prompted to set up the 48 Group, which was also known as The Icebreakers, by a discussion with Premier Zhou Enlai. Back in London the businessmen, led by Perry, went about building trade between the two nations.

From the earliest days of the British Council for the Promotion of International Trade, the British government suspected it was a Soviet front closely linked to the Communist Party of Great Britain.[102] Soviet front groups had proliferated in the West since the 1920s, and especially after the Second World War. When some of the forty-eight businessmen who visited China in 1954 were questioned by trade officials on their return, one said of Perry, Berger and Buckman, 'If they are Communists they manage to disguise the fact successfully.'[103] It seems fitting to discover now that Jack Perry, along with Berger and Buckman, was also a member of the Communist Party of Great Britain.[104] In 1963 and subsequently he was active in the split of Maoists from the CPGB, in reaction to the latter's 'revisionism'. Perry was reported, along with the 48 Group itself, to be funding the new Maoist newspaper *The Marxist,* first published in 1966.[105]

In short, at the instigation of a member of the Standing Committee of the Politburo, Zhou Enlai, the 48 Group was the work of three secret members of the Communist Party of Great Britain. From this foundation the club quickly developed an unrivalled level of trust and intimacy with the top leadership of the CCP, and has built itself into the most powerful instrument of Beijing's influence and intelligence gathering in the United Kingdom. Reaching into the highest ranks of Britain's political, business, media and university elites, the club plays a decisive role in shaping British attitudes to China.

Four years after its inaugural trip to China in 1954, 48 Group members were returning from Beijing to report on the 'extraordinary prestige' of the group in China. Puzzled but pleased at the solicitous treatment they'd received, they began to speak of the group's 'mystique'.[106] Today the 48 Group Club is playing an even greater role, enthusiastically fostering the interests of the CCP in the United Kingdom or, as Xinhua prefers to put it, 'promot[ing] positive UK-China relations'.[107] In October 2018 the China Council for the Promotion of International Trade hosted a grand banquet in Beijing to celebrate the sixty-fifth anniversary of the original group's visit.[108] Stephen Perry had an audience with Xi Jinping, something Britain's diplomats cannot achieve, signalling that the CCP leadership sees the 48 Group Club as central to its influence efforts in Britain. Xi applauded the work of the 48 Group Club, and Perry lauded China's 'tremendous achievement' and praised Xi's idea of a 'community with a shared future for humanity'.[109]

Stephen Perry's son, another Jack, leads the Young Icebreakers, set up by the 48 Group Club for promising young British businesspeople with an interest in China. The formation of the Young Icebreakers seems to have been the suggestion of Premier Wen Jiabao on a visit to Britain in 2006.[110] Stephen Perry, who studied law at University College London, told the *China Daily*, 'I read about Marxism, Leninism and Mao Zedong thoughts more than law books.'[111]

One event is especially revealing about the role of the 48 Group Club. After the 19th Party Congress in 2017 voted unanimously to incorporate 'Xi Jinping Thought' into its constitution—with China's parliament inserting it into the nation's constitution a few months later—Party members across China joined study sessions to absorb the paramount leader's ideas. In April 2019 the Chinese embassy in London held a study session, Xi Jinping Thought on Diplomacy.[112] Over seventy people were present, including many from the 48 Group Club and its sister organisation the China-Britain Business Council. Ambassador Liu Xiaoming gave the opening speech. After acknowledging 'Chairman Stephen Perry', he urged participants to engage in 'earnest study and accurate interpretation' of Xi Jinping Thought in order to 'strengthen the bond between the people of the two countries'.[113] He finished by echoing Xi-ism's central concept: 'I count on your contribution to the building of a community with a shared future for mankind!'

The speeches by other eminent persons at the study session are not recorded, but the embassy reported that Stephen Perry was followed by Professor Martin Albrow, honorary vice president of the British Sociological Association and the author of *China's Role in a Shared Human Future*, which argues that Xi Jinping Thought can heal the divisions in the world and promote global peace. Published in 2018 by a CCP-linked company, the book was greeted enthusiastically by Party media in China.[114] Anthony Giddens, a prominent sociologist and theorist for the Blair government, lauded Albrow's 'remarkable' book for explaining how China 'not only can, but must, assume a pivotal position in shaping world society for the better'.[115] (In 2019 Albrow and Giddens were full of praise for the launch of the international edition of *China Daily*, the CCP's primary English-language newspaper, whose journalism is 'infused with the spirit of the party'.[116] Peter Frankopan, professor of global history at Oxford University, joined in the praise.)

Another who was invited to speak at the embassy study session was Martin Jacques, author of the bestselling 2009 book *When China Rules the World: The end of the western world and the birth of a new global order*. While at the G20 summit in Osaka in June 2019, he gave an interview at a forum organised by the *China Daily* in which he laid all the blame for the breakdown of Sino-US relations at the feet of Washington. Jacques identified the rise of American nationalism as the problem. China, he wrote, will be unique in history as a great power that only wants peace.[117] The following month, in an interview with state broadcaster CGTN, he attacked the protesters in Hong Kong as militants whose actions should not be tolerated by the authorities.[118] Beijing is not trying to exert control over Hong Kong, he said, and those who fear otherwise show a 'lack of trust'; the people of Hong Kong are too Western in their thinking and are 'extraordinarily ignorant' about China.

Among the other participants at the embassy study session were the chair of the House of Lords international relations committee, Lord Howell; the chairman of the CBBC, Lord Sassoon; the director of the Confucius Institute at the School of African and Asian Studies,

Dr Nathan Hill; the chairman of Asia House, Lord Green; and Ian MacGregor, former editor of *The Telegraph* and *The Sunday Telegraph*.[119]

In our judgement, so entrenched are the CCP's influence networks among British elites that Britain has passed the point of no return, and any attempt to extricate itself from Beijing's orbit would probably fail.

The Italian conversion[120]

In March 2018 Italy joined with Germany and France to call for an EU investment-screening mechanism to keep Chinese companies out of strategic sectors, and so moderate Beijing's geopolitical push into Europe.[121] Thirteen months later Prime Minister Guiseppe Conte joined with President Xi to witness the signing of Italy onto the Belt and Road Initiative.[122] Europe's third-biggest economy had decided to ignore security issues and look east. What happened?

The *volte-face* was due to the formation in June 2018 of a new coalition government dominated by Eurosceptics and right-wing populists, and also to the outsized influence of a previously obscure finance professor, Michele Geraci, who had recently returned from a decade in China. Over a dinner in 2017, Geraci's views on China impressed the leader of the League party, Matteo Salvini.[123] When Salvini became deputy prime minister, he appointed Geraci undersecretary of state for economic development. Geraci soon set up Taskforce China, overseen jointly with economic development minister Luigi Di Maio, to facilitate Chinese investment in Italy. Geraci wanted Italy to be the leading European partner in the Belt and Road Initiative, and was given primary responsibility for negotiating the memorandum of understanding with Beijing.[124]

Italy, in a coup for Beijing, was the first major industrial power to join the BRI. According to Ding Chun, director of the Centre for European Studies at Shanghai's Fudan University, Beijing saw Italy's debt crisis as an opportunity to expand the BRI into 'the heart' of Western powers, and the outcome was of 'huge significance' to China as it met stronger headwinds with the United States.[125] Strategists in China had been taking close note of the fractures in the EU over the debt crisis, the austerity imposed by Germany, conflicts about migration, and Britain's decision to leave. A divided Europe was much easier to tempt and subvert. A senior Chinese academic and former diplomat, Wang Yiwei of Renmin University, said that the Euroscepticism of the new Italian government made it willing to defy Washington and move closer to China.[126]

China scholar Lucrezia Poggetti has noted Beijing's pattern of presenting itself as an alternative economic partner to European countries with economic vulnerabilities and rising Euroscepticism.[127] Before Italy, Beijing had succeeded in persuading several Central and Eastern European nations to join the BRI—Poland, the Czech Republic, Bulgaria and Hungary—as well as Portugal, Greece and Malta in Southern Europe. Italy's joining reinforces the impression that Beijing is pursuing a strategy in Europe of 'use the countryside to surround the city'.[128]

China was already a substantial investor in Italy, with a Chinese chemical company buying Pirelli, and Huawei buying mobile phone operator Wind.[129] As China specialist François Godement points out, previous Italian governments were happy to sign a series of science and technology cooperation agreements that were 'essentially a carbon copy' of the priorities laid out in *Made in China 2025*, Beijing's blueprint for becoming the world's dominant technological power.[130] This was no accident; the government had said it wanted to make Italy Europe's leading partner in *Made in China 2025*, despite fears that the program was one of continued industrial theft.[131] In March 2019 Italy and Britain were the only two EU states to abstain from a second vote to introduce an investment-screening mechanism, the same proposal that Italy had put with France and Germany in 2017.[132]

Before taking power in Italy in 2018, the League and Five Star parties opposed China's expansion in Europe, but once in government the new prime minister and his senior ministers began trekking to Beijing for talks.[133] Michele Geraci's links and views have been influential, perhaps decisive. In Italy, some see China as an 'obsession' for him.[134] His public utterances indicate that he sees no political risks from BRI.[135] For him, Sino-European economic integration is natural and desirable. Huawei is just another equipment provider. Asked about the company's potential for cooperating with Chinese intelligence, he said that China is misunderstood, that it is a 'very peaceful nation' and just wants to 'feed its people'.[136] He encourages his staff to communicate using the

Chinese social media app WeChat, which is monitored in Beijing.[137] He brushes off criticism from Italian politicians and journalists that he is kowtowing to Beijing.

In June 2018 Geraci wrote an opinion piece that is a paean to the wonders of modern China. He claimed that China is the answer to all of Italy's major problems—national debt, migration, population ageing and even, because China's justice system is better than Italy's, public security—and will also provide the funding for a flat tax, the recovery of manufacturing, and the greening of the economy.[138] The article attracted a scathing open letter from a group of Italian China scholars, who derided Geraci's views as naive and unethical for endorsing the Chinese government.[139]

Geraci was an investment banker before moving to China. He spent ten years as a part-time professor at universities in Zhejiang, including Nottingham University's Ningbo campus, source of a number of pro-CCP Western academics with a global influence.[140] When in 2016 the Ningbo campus co-hosted a forum with the Center for China and Globalization, a think tank whose president is a top United Front official, Michele Geraci was invited to speak.[141] Geraci had been writing 'reverential' opinion columns for the Beijing business news outlet *Caixin*, praising President Xi and the 'win-win' for countries joining the BRI.[142] He was also a regular commentator in the Party outlets CCTV and *China Daily*.

When Geraci returned to Italy in 2017, his pro-Beijing views found an environment that had been well prepared. Among other activities, an Italy China Cooperation Week had been staged in Rome in 2017 to promote the BRI. It was organised by the CCP's Chinese People's Association for Friendship with Foreign Countries; the Italy China Friendship Association, formed in 2013 under the CPAFFC's auspices; and pro-Beijing groups such as the Italy China Link Association.[143] Carlo Capria, a top civil servant, former undersecretary for economic development, and strong supporter of the BRI, was present. In 2019 Capria referred to the BRI in the *China Daily* as 'a last call for Italy'.[144]

Local united front groups had been actively promoting the BRI among the Chinese diaspora, and making links with senior business and political figures. In December 2017 Zhao Hongying, deputy secretary-general of the All-China Federation of Returned Overseas Chinese, a United Front agency, led a delegation to Rome where he held a forum titled 'Take advantage of the role of overseas Chinese, promote OBOR'. (One Belt, One Road, or OBOR, is another name for the BRI.) Key members of the China Italy Chamber of Commerce, most of whom had United Front links, vowed to contribute to the great cause.[145] And, underlining Beijing's determination, in August 2017 the head of the Overseas Chinese Affairs Office, Qiu Yuanping, arrived in Italy to organise Chinese-Italians to back the BRI more actively.[146]

CPAFFC, AFROC, OCAO: a trifecta of the top United Front bodies (see the organisation chart on pages 124–5) was actively preparing the ground in Italy for the sign-up to the BRI.[147]

The year 2017 also saw the formation of the Italian OBOR Institute, with enough funding to employ thirty staff in offices in Beijing and Rome.[148] The head of the institute, Michele de Gasperis, has said that the BRI is all about cooperation, not political interference, and represents a new 'politically stabilizing' paradigm in international relations.[149] By joining the BRI, the institute's website claims, Italy will be 'renewing the relations between China and Europe'.[150]

In April 2019, a month before President Xi and Prime Minister Conte oversaw the signing of the BRI memorandum, the EU issued a report labelling China (among others) a 'systemic rival'.[151] At the signing ceremony, Xi thanked Italy for its 'deep friendship'. Conte said he looked forward to greater 'connectivity' and reviving 'the ancient Silk Road'. Twenty-nine separate agreements were signed by Italian ministers and business leaders.[152] Among them was an agreement between Italian state bank Cassa Depositi e Prestiti and the Bank of China for the Italian bank to sell 'Panda' bonds—loans to Chinese investors denominated in renminbi—one more step towards Beijing's aspiration of internationalising China's currency.

The Conte government has allowed a Chinese firm to buy into the nation's electricity network, and Italy's ports are also expected to feature strongly in the flow of BRI investment, especially in Trieste, which Geraci has said 'must be open to Chinese investments'.[153] Trieste's port enhances Italy's role as China's gateway to Europe. (The city also boasts many of the nation's top scientific research institutions.)

If, as some believe, the BRI is a Trojan horse smuggling CCP influence into a country's political system, some seemingly innocuous provisions in the Italian memorandum of understanding hint at what is hidden in its belly. Along with promoting sister-city networks—and specifically the twinning of Verona and Hangzhou—the memorandum agreed that 'Parties will promote exchanges and cooperation between their local authorities, media, think tanks, universities and the youth', including cooperation between Italy's national public broadcaster, RAI, and the China Media Group (overseen by the CCP's Central Propaganda Department).[154] These provisions open the door for greater CCP influence activity.

Matteo Salvini, the leader of the League party and Michele Geraci's political patron, was absent from the BRI signing ceremony. Perhaps influenced by Steve Bannon, former White House chief strategist, he'd had a late change of heart and had begun to warn about Italy's 'colonialisation' by China.[155]

In July 2019, in a move that gave the appearance of blackmail, Huawei offered to invest $3.1 billion in Italy while simultaneously leaning on the government to ensure Huawei's participation in the country's 5G network.[156] The head of Huawei's local subsidiary said that it planned to cut 1000 jobs in the United States and create the same number in Italy. The offer came a week after the Italian government had adopted a decree giving it more power to protect the security of the 5G network. The decree needed to be ratified by parliament within sixty days, but it took only a week for the government to quietly announce that it would not be pushing through the legislation.[157]

Elite entanglement in France

The intermingling of French and Chinese business and political elites is well advanced. An investment firm known as Cathay Capital has built a remarkable web of political contacts in both countries. Careful detective work published by the Paris-based *Intelligence Online* has managed to unravel some of it, and this section draws partly on its report.[158]

Cathay Capital was formed in 2006 by Chinese national Cai Mingpo and Lyon-based financier Edouard Moinet, with the support of the state-owned China Development Bank and the French government's investment bank, Bpifrance. The company, a vehicle for French investors in China, is especially well networked in the business community of Lyon, and also has offices in New York, San Francisco and Shanghai. Cai Mingpo has recruited several former senior civil servants to the firm. Bruno Bézard, former director general of the French Treasury, is a managing partner of Cathay Capital.[159] Bézard also spent two years as minister counsellor in France's Beijing embassy, and worked closely with Jean-Pierre Jouyet, now France's ambassador in London and a confidant of President Macron.[160]

Cai Mingpo is also close to Lyon businessman Thierry Delaunoy de La Tour d'Artaise, who sits on the board of a Chinese company with senior CCP members.[161] Another associate is Frederic Beraha, who was an executive with the military helicopter maker Eurocopter, a predecessor of Airbus Helicopters. Cai's complex network in Lyon and Paris includes links to President Macron's office, to his political party, and to former and current Chinese diplomats. He is also connected to senior CCP officials in China, including Li Yuanchu of the Hubei Provincial High Technology Investment Company, who is involved in organisations accused of economic espionage.[162]

Cai himself is vice president of the Shanghai branch of the Yangtze River International Chamber of Commerce, a united front organisation founded in Hubei in 2014, which later expanded into a network of chambers of the same name across China, North America, Europe and Australia.[163] He is a graduate of the Shanghai-based China Europe International Business School, founded in 1994 by the Chinese government and the European Commission. It is said to be 'a haunt of prominent French nationals who have an interest in China'.[164] Cai has funded a chair in accounting at the school and is a member of its advisory board. Joining him at meetings of this board are top French CEOs and the director of a subsidiary of the Aviation Industry Corporation of China. AVIC is a massive, state-owned enterprise and the main supplier of military aircraft to the PLA Airforce, including stealth fighters and attack drones.[165]

When long-time president of the business school Pedro Nueno retired in 2018 he received a friendship award from the government of China and was praised by Xi Jinping. (The school has a European and a Chinese president.[166]) Professors at the school have included former World Trade Organization head Pascal Lamy, and former French prime ministers Dominique de Villepin and Jean-Pierre Raffarin.[167]

Raffarin is worth particular attention. His enormous value to the Party was confirmed on 29 September 2019, ahead of the seventieth anniversary of the founding of the PRC, when he was named as one of only six foreigners to receive the ultimate symbol of Party gratitude, a Friendship Medal, awarded by Xi Jinping himself. (The only other Westerner was Isabel Crook, a Canadian anthropologist, KGB spy and long-time friend of China.[168]) According to Xinhua, Xi stressed that the medals were for 'loyalty to the cause of the Party and the people'.[169]

Raffarin was prime minister from 2002 to 2005. On a state visit to China in 2005 he endorsed a law authorising China to invade Taiwan.[170] In 2008 he intervened to smooth the path for the Olympic torch through Paris. In 2010 a book he authored praising China's achievements was published by a CCP publishing house, in Chinese only.[171] A Silk Road enthusiast, he is a director of a number of Chinese companies and is on the board of the Boao Forum, the CCP's version of the World Economic Forum at Davos.[172]

Raffarin's establishment credentials are unmatched. In addition to serving as prime minister, he was France's vice president from 2011 to 2014, and chairman of the Defence and Foreign Affairs Committee from 2014 to 2017. In 2018 he was appointed as the Macron government's special representative for China.[173] A *lao pengyou* or 'old friend' of China, he claims that China merely wants dialogue and cooperation in the trade war with the United States.[174] Together with former Chinese diplomat Xu Bo, Raffarin set up the Club Paris-Shanghai and appointed as its director the former head of Huawei Healthcare, Patrice Cristofini.[175] In June 2018 the club held a meeting for the 'European-Chinese community' to promote 'mutual understanding for the benefit of all'. It was held in France's National Assembly building.[176]

Raffarin is said to have initiated the prestigious France China Foundation, launched in 2012, the official partner of which is the Chinese People's Institute for Foreign Affairs, a united front organisation that has for many years regularly invited politicians, policy-makers and journalists to China and drip-fed them Beijing's line; some regurgitate it when they return home.[177] (Larry Diamond and Orville Schell write: 'CPIFA is a so-called united front organization, similar to those found in the former Soviet Union and other Leninist states that seek to opportunistically build alliances wherever they can.'[178]) Cathay Capital was until recently listed as a partner of the France China Foundation.[179] The 'strategic committee' of the foundation is a who's who of the rich and powerful of the two nations.[180] The French side includes the CEO of L'Oréal, Jean-Paul Agon; the chairman of insurance giant AXA, Denis Duverne; author and intellectual Jacques Attali; former prime ministers Laurent Fabius and Edouard Philippe; the chair of the investment committee of France's sovereign wealth fund, Patricia Barbizet; and film director Jean-Jacques Annaud. In 1997 Annaud earned Beijing's wrath for making *Seven Years in Tibet*, a film about the PLA's brutal invasion that treated the Dalai Lama sympathetically. Annaud was banned from China (as was co-star Brad Pitt), but after he underwent a self-criticism the ban was lifted, and in 2015 he made a Party-approved film called *Wolf Totem*.[181]

The Chinese side features a stellar cast of internet billionaires—Jack Ma of Alibaba, Pony Ma of Tencent, Wang Yan of Sina.com, and Ya-Qin Zhang of Baidu. All are Party members. They are joined by the CEO of PLA-linked corporation China Everbright Ltd, Chen Shuang; the chairman of PLA-linked company CITIC Resources Holdings, Peter Viem Kwok; and a former foreign minister, Li Zhaoxing.[182] Clearly, the CCP views the France China Foundation as its foremost avenue of influence on France's elites. In this respect, it is similar to Britain's 48 Group Club.

The France China Foundation sponsors the Young Leaders Forum, a club that each year since 2013 has brought together twenty French and twenty Chinese 'high potential' leaders.[183] Emmanuel Macron has been a member, as has the president of Radio-France, Sibyle Veil, and Prime Minister Edouard Philippe.[184]

There is another France China Foundation (with the same name in Chinese), which was set up in 2014 by 'a group of Chinese and French entrepreneurs' to promote mutual understand and cooperation.[185] It operates under the auspices of the China Association for International Friendly Contacts, a PLA front group.[186] CAIFC is reported as a 'key member' of the foundation, along with the huge conglomerate HNA Group, which often acts for the Party.[187] The 'Honorary President for China' of the 2014 France China Foundation is Sun Xiaoyu, director of the Development Research Center of the State Council, China's central administrative authority. The foundation's honorary president for France is the disgraced former boss of the International Monetary Fund, Dominique Strauss-Kahn.[188] The website of the foundation is packed with pro-Xi and BRI propaganda.[189]

China's friends in Germany

When former German chancellor Helmut Schmidt passed away in 2015, China Central Television let it be known that an 'old friend of the Chinese people' had died. The first item on the seven-o'clock evening news reported messages of condolence from both Xi Jinping and Premier Li Keqiang.[190] In life as in death, Schmidt received the full treatment as a *lao pengyou*.

Schmidt had earned his title. He first travelled to China before Germany took up formal relations with the PRC in 1972. In fact, he claimed that after this trip he privately advised then chancellor Willy Brandt that Germany needed to establish diplomatic relations, which, as Schmidt noted in an interview, 'he did, seven years ahead of the Americans'.[191] Whether or not Schmidt was actually responsible for Germany breaking ties with Taiwan and recognising the PRC, Beijing had many reasons to be grateful.

In 1975, he became the first German chancellor to visit China. He was also the first German politician to travel to China after relations had been frozen following 1989's Tiananmen massacre.[192] Indeed, Schmidt was infamous for justifying the bloody crackdown by saying that the Chinese military had been provoked, and that European standards should not be used to measure other countries.[193] When the CCP needed someone to endorse Xi Jinping's book *Governance of China*, Schmidt was happy to oblige, describing it as an 'inspirational piece of work'.[194] He was also the official patron (*Schirmherr*) of the Hamburg Summit, a high-level biennial summit on economic relations between China and Germany, organised since 2004 by the Hamburg Chamber of Commerce and the China Federation of Industrial Economics.

While the CCP liaises with all of Germany's major political parties and has won over politicians in each, Schmidt's Social Democratic Party (SPD) has played a large role in building and maintaining Sino-German ties, from the time the CCP decided to forge closer relations with socialist parties in Europe. In 1984, while the Christian Democratic Union was in power, the SPD was one of the first non-communist parties the CCP began liaising with. The SPD-affiliated Friedrich Ebert Foundation was the first German political foundation to establish a presence in China.[195]

In a provocative 2013 essay titled 'The China sympathisers and their democratic enemies', journalist Sabine Pamperrien noted that German support for China tended to emanate from two distinct camps—'left-wing politicians and publicists', often fuelled by anti-Americanism; and powerful businesspeople who don't want to see their 'flourishing trade' with China impeded by concerns over human rights.[196] These two need not necessarily contradict each other. For some, sympathy for nominally left-wing regimes and profit motives go hand in hand.

Few embody this mix better than former chancellor Gerhard Schröder. Schröder is mainly known in Germany for having sold out to Russia after leaving office in 2005, and for becoming chairman of the board of the state-owned oil giant Rosneft in 2017.[197] But he is also firmly in Beijing's orbit, so much so that in 2009 *Der Spiegel* published a photo of him literally hugging a panda.[198] Well before his 2007 public attack on Angela Merkel for meeting the Dalai Lama, he was held in high regard in Beijing.[199] In 1999 he was the first politician to travel to China to apologise for the accidental NATO bombing of the Chinese embassy in Belgrade.[200] In the fall of 2001, before visiting China, he told German media that he was tired of bringing up lists of political prisoners with the Chinese side.[201] While in office (1998–2005) he was a strong proponent of lifting the arms embargo imposed by the EU on China after the 1989 Tiananmen Square massacre.[202]

On leaving office, Schröder was appointed as an adviser to the Chinese Ministry of Foreign Affairs, albeit in a minor role helping transform an old Chinese embassy building in Bonn into a centre for traditional Chinese medicine.[203] Today he spends much of his time in China, brokering contacts between CCP officials and European businesses. For example, he introduced the Swiss Ringier media group to the Politburo member in charge of media and propaganda work, Li Changchun.[204] When asked about China's re-education centres in Xinjiang, he feigned ignorance: 'I'm not sure; I'm very careful because I have no information.'[205]

After Helmut Schmidt died, Schröder became the official patron of the Hamburg Summit[206] and won the summit's China-Europe Friendship Award.[207] Predictably, Schröder has used the summit to express his strong support for the BRI.[208]

Rudolf Scharping, former chairman of the SPD (1993–95) and former German minister of defence (1998–2002), also turned China into a career after politics. Following a path blazed by other senior politicians, he established a consultancy to help German companies gain a foothold in China, and Chinese companies to enter the German market. His company is also registered in Beijing. According to German media reports, he spends more than a third of each year in China and has told German businesses that, as long as they don't question the rule of the CCP or China's territorial integrity, 'there is much freedom' that companies can use for themselves.[209] Unsurprisingly, he is seen as an 'old friend' in China rather than a business consultant.[210] In 2013 'old friend' Scharping was appointed as economic adviser to the governor of Guangdong, and in 2018 he received the Yellow River Friendship Award from the provincial government of Henan.[211]

Scharping has been a major asset for the CCP in promoting the BRI in Germany, and regularly appears alongside Chinese diplomats to give talks about it.[212] A local SPD branch reported, after hosting him, that 'his love and enthusiasm for China were visible. He skilfully avoided a handful of critical questions.'[213] More importantly, his company has teamed up with the China Economic Cooperation Center to organise an annual Sino-German Belt and Road Conference. Founded in 1993, the CECC is under the International Liaison Department of the CCP and can be understood as the economic arm of the vast party-to-party diplomacy machine (that is, united front work for people not of Chinese descent).[214] It brings together business leaders from companies like Siemens, Daimler, Volkswagen and many others. Despite being organised by a private consultancy, the Sino-German Belt and Road Conference has attracted high-level participants from German ministries and the Bundestag.[215]

While the SPD may stand out for its prominent ex-politicians who have become China enthusiasts, it would be unfair to paint the party as China's only supporters in Germany. The governing Christian Democratic Union, ever mindful of the interests of German industry, worries about offending China. Chancellor Angela Merkel's determination to ignore security advice, and critics in her own party, to allow Huawei equipment into Germany's 5G network is an excellent example.[216] Politicians from other parties have also been cultivated. After leaving office, former vice chancellor and chairman of the Free Democratic Party, Philipp Rösler, became the chief executive of the Hainan Cihang Charity Foundation in New York, which is run by the huge, mysterious and probably corrupt Chinese conglomerate, HNA Group.[217] (Rösler moved there from the Beijing-friendly World Economic Forum. He resigned from the foundation in 2019.)

In the German Left Party (Die Linke), scepticism towards the United States has led many to instinctively embrace CCP talking points. On the party's official website is an article demanding that Germany protest in the UN Security Council against weapons exports to Taiwan.[218] Another calls the arrest of Huawei's Meng Wanzhou a 'politically motivated kidnapping'.[219] There's also an interview with the first of its members to have joined the party from China. Identified only as 'Norbert', he praises Xi Jinping's social reforms for having improved the 'lives of people in the countryside in West China'.[220] (The website makes no mention of Xinjiang in west China.) And at a public hearing on religious minorities in China, held at the German Bundestag, the expert invited by the Left Party argued that the problem needs to be put in historical context and external threats felt by China need to be taken account of.[221]

Most significantly, it was reported in January 2020 that a new group called the China Bridge (China Brücke) had been formed to serve as a network of German elites to boost ties with China. According to its initiators, it is modelled on the Atlantic Bridge, which promotes transatlantic ties. It is headed by Hans-Peter Friedrich, a politician in the conservative Christian Social Union, the Bavarian sister party of the Christian Democratic Union. Friedrich is also vice president of the German Bundestag and a former minister of the interior. He claims he had the idea during a visit to China. Reuters paraphrased him saying: an export nation like Germany cannot afford to lack close personal networks with China.[222] It remains to be seen whether the network will take on the role of mobilising pro-Beijing elites in the way the 48 Group Club and the France China Foundation do.

While the CCP's policies gain mainstream legitimacy from the backing they receive from top political figures and parties, fervent support also emanates from the fringes. The Schiller Institute has been particularly active in boosting Beijing's influence in Europe. It was founded in 1984 in Wiesbaden by Helga Zepp-LaRouche, the wife of controversial American conspiracy theorist Lyndon LaRouche, and is linked to the right-wing LaRouche Movement.[223] The Chinese media regularly features Zepp-LaRouche expressing her support for the CCP's policies and ideas.[224] The Schiller Institute's main focus is promoting the BRI. It strongly advocates the 'China model' and Xi's concepts as alternatives to the current global order. In election campaigns, Zepp-LaRouche's political party, BüSo (Citizens' Movement Solidarity), promotes the BRI as the 'future of Germany'.[225]

The Schiller Institute also promotes the BRI elsewhere in Europe. The LaRouche Movement's main organisation in Italy is Movisol, which has been very active. Movisol has teamed up with the local government of the Lombardy Region to organise a BRI conference in Milan. Speakers included the architect of Italy's BRI agreement, Michele Geraci, who highlighted the importance of the agreement to Italy's future.[226] During a visit to the Chinese embassy in Stockholm, the head of the Swedish Schiller Institute told ambassador Gui Congyou he would be promoting BRI cooperation between the two countries 'through seminars, media campaign, courses targeting Swedish companies, and visits of Swedish business delegations to China'.[227] In May 2018, jointly with the China-Sweden Business Council, the institute launched the Belt and Road Initiative Executive Group in Stockholm.[228]

So while the LaRouche Movement is on the fringe in Germany, it has managed to get much closer to the centre of Italian, and possibly Swedish, politics.

5
Political elites on the periphery

Subnational work

When it comes to CCP influence activities, a wide knowledge gap typically separates central government from local and state or provincial governments. But even central governments can find it difficult to track a sprawling organisation like the CCP, which works through a confusing array of Party and front groups whose agendas are hidden, as we saw in chapter two. Western leaders can believe they are dealing with leaders of genuine Chinese civic organisations, whereas in fact they are dealing with Party operatives or people guided by agencies in Beijing.

Local politicians typically know little about China and have no responsibility for national security, and because their Chinese interlocutors present themselves as offering people-to-people exchanges and 'opportunities for local business', these politicians have a strong incentive to remain uninformed. The focus is typically on economic and cultural ties, and it's easy to pretend that there is no political element. As we will see, however, these local ties are in fact highly political, and where necessary they can be leveraged to pressure national governments. This is the tactic of 'use the countryside to surround the city'.

CCP analyst Jichang Lulu has explored the localisation of united front influence activities in the Nordic countries, where local officials with considerable decision-making power are targeted for 'friendly contact' because they are insulated from strategic debates in the capital cities and do not have the expertise to understand Beijing's intentions and tactics.[1] He notes that Beijing has been actively cultivating political influence in Greenland, which Beijing sees as important for resource supply and for being an Arctic state. The strategy includes investments, an attempt to acquire a derelict naval base, and political work on Greenland's elites, activities that have rung alarm bells in Denmark. However, due to the small-scale, decentralised nature of much of the CCP's work at the local level, alarm is the exception rather than the rule.

Wilful ignorance, and the influence of united front agents at top levels of state government, help explain why the state of Victoria in Australia signed on to the Belt and Road Initiative, despite the federal government having expressly declined to do so, and the fact that the issue had been widely discussed in the media.[2] The Victorian premier, Daniel Andrews, often photographed with united front figures in Melbourne, said that he wants the state to be 'China's gateway to Australia'.[3]

In San Francisco, the board of the Municipal Transport Agency named a new subway station in Chinatown after a prominent Chinese-American community leader, Rose Pak, despite the fact that she had deep, demonstrable links to the CCP going back decades, links that had been exposed in the media.[4] After detailing the various ways that Beijing had showered honours on Pak, the executive director of the Human Rights Law Foundation, Terri Marsh, urged the board not 'to honor someone who has been closely associated with China's dictatorship'.[5] Although some local Chinese-Americans expressed fierce opposition to the name choice, Pak's united front work had given her high status in the mainstream as a community leader. The board voted four to three in favour of honouring Pak, with one member saying that 'as a woman of color' she wanted 'to elevate a person of color who fought really hard to make something happen'.[6] The majority chose to ignore Pak's close links to Beijing.

In Sweden, a small municipality was more cautious. The town of Lysekil was approached by a Chinese consortium offering to build a new port, new infrastructure and a health resort.[7] The chairman of the consortium had strong links to the United Front and the PLA, indicating that the offer was part of Beijing's maritime strategy of acquiring ports around the world. (In Australia a state-linked Chinese company was allowed to take out a 99-year lease on the strategically vital Port of Darwin.) Although the consortium pressured the Lysekil municipality for a rapid answer, news of its links to the CCP leaked out and the proposal died.

Beijing's logic for subnational influence is straightforward. First, friendly relations at this level can help smooth the way for investment in strategic assets—ports, regional airports (including pilot training schools), satellite dishes (as in New Zealand), developments adjacent to military bases, certain agricultural developments and the like. Second, Beijing knows that some subnational leaders will graduate to national parliaments, where the friendship can pay even higher dividends. Finally, they understand that local leaders can exert political pressure on the centre.

A salutary example of the latter occurred in August 2019 in the middle of the China–US trade war. Xinhua featured a story titled 'U.S. state and local officials are seeking to enhance cooperation with China despite simmering trade tensions between the world's two largest economies'.[8] The story was built around a video clip from a forum held at the Brookings Institution in the capital on 29 July, where Oregon's governor, Kate Brown, complained about the 'chilling effect' of the trade war on Oregon's exports to China. She blamed Washington, and said, 'It's been extremely detrimental particularly in the agricultural sector, which is a huge driver of the Oregon economy.'[9] The deputy mayor of Los Angeles, Nina Hachigian, reinforced the message by detailing the impact of the trade war on exports from LA ports. (In August LA mayor Eric Garcetti told the *South China Morning Post* that a continued trade war would see children starving in his city.[10])

The most striking comments featured by Xinhua were made by Bob Holden, former Democratic governor of Missouri (2001–05). He said that agricultural producers 'are very scared' that the relationship with China will break down.[11] Holden is a Beijing favourite, and for good reason. According to the *China Daily*, on a visit to China in 2004 he had a revelation: Chinese people and American people share common values.[12] Appointed a professor at Webster University after he lost the governorship, Holden was instrumental in setting up Missouri's first Confucius Institute in 2005.[13]

Bob Holden is also the chairman of the United States Heartland China Association, formed to build bridges of friendship and cooperation with China, and which brings together twenty Midwest states. It was reconstituted in 2018 and 'welcomed the support' of the China-United States Exchange Foundation.[14] As we will see in chapter eleven, CUSEF is funded and chaired by Tung Chee-hwa, a Hong Kong shipping tycoon and major CCP player.[15] During the 2019 Hong Kong protests, Tung accused Washington of 'orchestrating' events, defended police accused of brutality, and said there should be no compromise. In December 2019 Tung Chee-hwa was named by Hong Kong democracy advocates as one of the territory's eleven top-tier perpetrators of human rights and democracy abuse.[16] The advocates identified CUSEF as an attempt by the Chinese government to interfere with US politics and called for Tung to be sanctioned. CUSEF is registered as a foreign principal for China in the United States, where some organisations, such as the University of Texas at Austin, have rejected its funding offers because of its CCP links.[17]

None of this seemed to worry Bob Holden when he arrived at the fifth annual U.S.-China National Governors Collaboration Summit, held in Kentucky in May 2019 at the height of the trade war. The event raised concern in Washington because the National Governors Association had organised the summit jointly with the Chinese People's Association for Friendship with Foreign Countries, a united front agency whose top leaders are often drawn from the red aristocracy.[18] Its 'people's diplomacy' is a covert element of Beijing's official diplomacy and foreign influence work.[19] Its president, Li Xiaolin, the daughter of a former president of China, Li Xiannian, addressed the summit. CPAFFC has particular responsibility for cultivating links at subnational levels, through building sister-city relationships and promoting the BRI.[20]

The CPAFFC also has responsibility for strengthening friendship societies in Western countries, including donating substantial sums to reinvigorate moribund societies, as occurred in New Zealand.[21] The U.S.-China Peoples Friendship Association was founded in 1974 and has thirty-five chapters across the US. It has drawn in many Americans with the best motives, but in recent years it has come under more direct influence from the Party, through the CPAFFC.[22] Barbara Harrison, active in the USCPFA since the 1970s and its president for five years until 2005, was in 2004 made a Friendship Ambassador, the CPAFFC's highest accolade.[23]

While the Kentucky governors' summit was ostensibly designed to facilitate investment deals and drew 'prestigious investment firms',[24] it was an ideal opportunity for the CCP to bypass Washington and build personal relations with significant players across the US. China's ambassador in Washington, Cui Tiankai, took time off from trying to manage the trade war to tell the 400 gathered at the summit that he hoped it would 'identify win-win opportunities'.[25] He said, 'I always find true friendship, not groundless suspicions.' And a PRC foreign ministry spokesperson expressed enthusiasm for the summit because it showed the two countries could benefit by 'deepening sub-national and across-the-board exchange and cooperation'.[26]

If, according to a leaked email, the White House was 'not happy' about the summit, Kentucky governor Matt Bevin was sure that the suspicion and misunderstanding driving the trade war would vanish 'when people talk'.[27] This was precisely Beijing's desired message and, as always, such statements of support were amplified in China's official media.[28] (Matt Bevin was happy two months later when a Chinese company announced plans to invest $200 million in rural Kentucky to build a new paper-and-pulp recycling facility, creating 500 jobs.[29]) Commenting on the role of the CPAFFC at the governors' summit, John Dotson of *China Brief* observed that the Americans involved 'might think they're dealing with a representative of a civic organisation but they're not. They're actually dealing with … functionaries of the Chinese Communist Party'.[30] These relationships are points of leverage: Chinese diplomats leant on the governors to lobby Washington to dial back the trade war.[31]

The summit put into practice the strategy elaborated in March 2019 by the influential Fudan University scholar Huang Renwei. Drawing on Mao's essay 'On protracted war', he argued that to 'resolutely fight back' against Washington, China should establish 'deeper economic and trade relations with the 50 US states'.[32]

The CPAFFC was on a roll. In July 2019, two months after the Kentucky governors' summit, it was in Houston co-hosting the fourth U.S.-China Sister Cities Mayors' Summit with the US peak body, Sister Cities International. Ambassador Cui Tiankai sent a message: 'Subnational cooperation and people-to-people exchanges are the highlights of the history of China-U.S. interactions and the driving force for the growth of our relations.'[33] The 277 US–China sister-city friendships—and the fifty sister-state pairings—had led to win-win cooperation, he said. As if reading from the Beijing script, the vice chair of Sister Cities International, Carol Lopez, told the delegates, 'Our people are so intertwined. We believe when people connect—people to people, community to community—we just become stronger together.'[34] Delegates talked up the Maritime Silk Road (the 'road' of BRI) and smart cities. In China, 'smart cities' technology is inseparable from the CCP's surveillance state, but the CCP trades on the naivety of well-meaning people and benefits from the covert support of others.

The curious case of Muscatine

In 2018 the elite Zhejiang Symphony Orchestra made a brief tour of the United States. It put on only four concerts, in Detroit, Chicago, San Diego and … Muscatine. A struggling, soybean-farming town on the banks of the Mississippi River in Iowa, Muscatine has a population of 24,000. What was the attraction for the orchestra? The town's special relationship with China began in 1985 when an official from Hebei province led a trade delegation to farms and towns in Iowa, including Muscatine. The same official returned in 2012, except this time he was China's vice president and soon to be president, Xi Jinping. He praised his 'old friends' in Iowa, Hebei's sister state, for their 'agrarian common sense, family values and hospitality'.[35]

Having built on these early links, a network of prominent businessmen from the state refer to themselves in Beijing as the 'Iowa mafia'. They are backing Xi's Belt and Road Initiative as a way of getting more Chinese investment in Iowa.[36] In 2018 they welcomed a former governor of the state, Terry Branstad, as the new US ambassador to China. Branstad had been governor during both of Xi Jinping's visits and counts himself a friend.[37]

Another of President Xi's old friends is Sarah Lande, who got to know him in 1985 and hosted him in her living room in 2012. She first met Xi in her role with the Iowa Sister States organisation. She went on to become its executive director. In 2013 another delegation from the CPAFFC arrived in town.[38] Some eighty people, including journalists from official Chinese media, had come to award a gold medal to Sarah Lande and bestow on her the title of Friendship Ambassador, one of only eight awarded to Americans.[39] She and her husband Roger, who was director of the Iowa Department of Natural Resources, were part of the 'old friends' group that travelled to China in late 2012 to meet with the nation's new leader.[40]

Xi Jinping's links to Muscatine are well known in China. Groups of Chinese school students go to visit the town, and a number of Chinese businessmen have bought up property there, hoping to cash in on the association with Xi.[41] The visit of the symphony orchestra was funded by businessman Lijun 'Glad' Cheng, who has made Muscatine his second home, buying various properties and refurbishing an old hotel.[42]

When in 2018 Beijing retaliated against Donald Trump's tariffs, it was aware that by restricting US soybean imports the impact would be felt in Iowa. Iowa was among the Midwest farming states that switched to Trump from the Democrats in the 2016 presidential election, another reason why, during the early weeks of the trade dispute, Beijing paid the *Des Moines Register* to publish an insert from the *China Daily*. But the move backfired: rather than persuading Iowans to pressure Washington, it raised ire in Washington, with Trump denouncing the insert as foreign interference.

Malleable mayors

The CCP has 'useful idiots' (a term, attributed to Lenin, that described naive foreign enthusiasts for the revolution) in many places, enabling the intensification of local influence activities as resistance to its practices rises in the centre. Anne-Marie Brady has noted that the CPAFFC has for some years organised an annual China–New Zealand mayoral forum where tourism, education and agriculture are discussed.[43] At the 2018 forum a ninety-strong delegation, including seven cadres from the CPAFFC, arrived in Wellington.[44] The Wellington

Council spent NZ$100,000 on a banquet. The mayor declared it a 'resounding success'.

In Canada, the Chinese consulate general in Vancouver, British Columbia, has for some years been hosting cocktail receptions at the annual convention of local government leaders, the Union of BC Municipalities.[45] No other foreign government appears to have sought to exert influence over these politicians, so why does Beijing bother? As one close observer put it, China's diplomats were 'sizing up the chumps'.[46] After a number of such receptions without controversy, in 2019 several BC mayors, including Vancouver's, announced they would boycott the next one. They were responding to media reports and pressure from a public angered by China's bullying after the arrest of Huawei's Meng Wanzhou. The mayor of Port Coquitlam, Brad West, denounced China's involvement in the receptions as unethical and 'cash for access'.[47]

As Vancouver's mayor from 2008 to 2018, Gregor Robertson built an impressive reputation as a leader committed to sustainable urban living in a green city. Visiting Shanghai in 2010, a few months after China had torpedoed global climate negotiations in Copenhagen, he said that China's policies were greener than those of Western countries. But what attracted more attention back in Canada was his claim that these better policies were due to China's superior form of government. *The Globe and Mail* observed that Robertson was echoing those who once praised Mussolini because he made the trains run on time.[48]

Gregor Robertson is proud to be descended from one of the most revered 'old friends' of China, Norman Bethune.[49] In 2018, after agitation by united front groups, Robertson issued an apology on behalf of the city for past injustices to people of Chinese heritage.[50] Canada, like many other Western nations, had a lot to apologise for, but the apology was also an excellent opportunity for Beijing's propagandists to reinforce the sense of grievance among Chinese people, including overseas Chinese. Beijing stokes nationalist resentment for past wrongs, and presents the Party as the answer to historical humiliation. Robertson's words of contrition were aired by Beijing's official broadcaster, CCTV.

It was an example of how the CCP cynically exploits legitimate social-justice discourses in the West. It's no accident that united front groups were responsible for erecting memorials to the 1937 Nanjing Massacre.[51] The memorials are less a means of quiet remembrance of the victims of an atrocity, and more a way to whip up jingoistic resentment against foreigners. The CCP's treatment of China's minorities, meanwhile, has much in common with Western nations' treatment of Chinese people in the nineteenth and early twentieth centuries, and we can expect that one day monuments will be erected to their persecution.

In 2019 Gregor Robertson was appointed a roving ambassador for the Global Covenant of Mayors for Climate and Energy. Formed in 2015 in reaction to the failure of national governments to grasp the nettle, the group represents 9200 cities around the world, all pledged to strong action to reduce greenhouse gas emissions.[52] Robertson will be touring the world, meeting international and local environmental groups, putting a positive, sincere and friendly spin on the achievements of the CCP.

No event at the local level is too trivial for the CCP to exert its power over. In 2018, in the remote Australian town of Rockhampton (population 80,000), the local council joined with the beef industry to propose the creation of a large papier-mâché bull decorated with fish-shaped flags, to be painted by schoolchildren to represent the variety of nations they hailed from. The bull would thus be a celebration of the cultural diversity of the town. Two students painted small Taiwanese flags because that's where their mother was from. When the bull was put on display they were dismayed to discover that, alone among the other children's flags, theirs had been painted over by council workers. It transpired that the council had received a complaint from the Chinese vice consul in the state capital, Brisbane. The students' mother, Amy Chen, said her children were 'very sad and disappointed' by the decision to erase their flags.[53]

Rockhampton's mayor tried to excuse her council's behaviour by saying the action was in line with Australia's 'one China policy', as if that had any bearing on a children's art project in a remote town. Moreover, Australia's one China policy only 'acknowledges' that China claims Taiwan; it does not endorse it, contrary to the repeated assertions of the CCP and its sympathisers.

BRI support in Germany's 'countryside'

In her 2019 exploration of united front organisations in Germany, the first in that country, journalist and united front expert Didi Kirsten Tatlow found over 190 Chinese groups 'with direct ties to the United Front bureaucracy'.[54] These included Chinese professional associations, business organisations, media outlets and Chinese aid centres, among others (see also chapter seven).[55]

As is the case elsewhere, German organisations often partner with Chinese organisations without knowing they are dealing with the CCP. For instance, the Deutsch-Chinesische Wirtschaftsvereinigung (German-Chinese Business Association) partners with the Party-run China Council for the Promotion of International Trade.[56] One of the most important umbrella organisations identified by Tatlow is the Federation of German China Friendship Associations (Arbeitsgescheimschaft Deutscher China-Gesellschaften). Its groundwork was laid in 1993, when a musical centre in Mainz received an invitation from the Chinese People's Association for Friendship with Foreign Countries to host a *pipa*, or Chinese lute, ensemble. Kurt Karst, the founder of the musical centre, did not know at the time what the CPAFFC was and he accepted.[57] Today Karst is the chairman of the German-Chinese Friendship Association of Mainz-Wiesbaden as well as president of the Federation of German China Friendship Associations, which ties together the friendship associations across Germany. Its launch in 2016 was attended by Chinese diplomats, representatives from the CPAFFC, and German officials.[58] Two years later, the federation signed a cooperation agreement with the CPAFFC in Beijing.[59] This is a classic example of a genuine civil society organisation cooperating with a CCP-led organisation headed by a cadre of ministerial or vice-ministerial rank. The national federation has reprinted verbatim Chinese propaganda on the BRI, including Xi Jinping's speeches and his claims that the initiative is 'marked by peace and prosperity'.[60]

The vice president of the Federation of German China Friendship Associations is Johannes Pflug, a Social Democrat and from 1998 to 2013 a member of the German Bundestag. He is now on the board of the newly founded elite networking club, China Bridge.[61] In 2016, in the presence of the Chinese consul general, Pflug was appointed honorary China representative of the city of Duisburg. In the press release announcing this appointment, Duisburg labelled itself 'an integral part' of the Belt and Road Initiative.[62] Pflug has appeared in promotional videos for the BRI run by local German press, and has been interviewed in CCP-linked media targeted at Europe, such as *Nouvelles d'Europe* and the German online version of the official CCP mouthpiece, the *People's Daily*.[63] Pflug also heads the China Business Network of Duisburg, which brings together local businesses with interests in China but also works with the local Confucius Institute.[64]

Most local German governments have ties to China, but some stand out for their intensive contact and economic engagement. The state of North-Rhine-Westphalia has several cities with close ties and that argue for deeper Sino-German relations. One is the state capital Düsseldorf; the site of a Chinese consulate, it is referred to by the city's mayor as 'Germany's most important China business location'.[65] Duisburg, also based in the state, selected Huawei to turn it into a 'smart city', including the provision of cloud computing solutions and e-government infrastructure.[66] This decision followed a visit by Duisburg's mayor, Sören Link, with a nineteen-strong government delegation, to Huawei's headquarters in Shenzhen.[67] Duisburg has refused to disclose its memorandum of understanding with Huawei, despite requests, claiming that Huawei has threatened legal action if the document were to be made public.[68]

Another important hub is Hamburg, a German city-state where over 550 Chinese companies have set up shop. Hamburg, host to the Hamburg Summit discussed in chapter four, is sister cities with Shanghai and has hosted an office of the Chinese Chamber of Commerce in Germany since 2017.[69] Hamburg's parliament holds regular exchanges with Shanghai's Standing Committee and the city's People's Political Consultative Conference.[70] The mayor of Hamburg, Peter Tschentscher, has praised the BRI, declaring that, as a centre of international trade, Hamburg is 'a natural node and endpoint of the New Silk Road'.[71] Adjacent to Hamburg is the state of Lower Saxony, the home of Volkswagen, which sold over 4 million cars in China in 2018. At a meeting with the Chinese consul general in Hamburg, the state's economics minister, Bernd Althusmann of the Christian Democratic

Union, said that China is not only an important cooperation partner for Lower Saxony but also 'a significant force for world peace'.[72]

In sum, while the German federal government has been apprehensive about the Belt and Road Initiative and careful not to endorse it, the CCP has found more than enough local politicians willing to do so. They are used to pressure the central government to change its stance. It's a tactic that has been deployed around the world.

Sister cities

Sister-city and sister-state agreements have been very effective for the CCP in gaining influence in local communities, and cities across the world continue to sign new agreements. But here, too, most municipal governments lack even a rudimentary understanding of the CCP's political goals in these arrangements.

While in the West a decision to enter a sister-city partnership is made by a municipal council or city government, in China the process is coordinated by the CPAFFC, described by Jichang Lulu as 'the main "people's diplomacy" organisation within the CCP foreign-affairs system'.[73] Behind the sister-city banner, the CPAFFC systematically advances the Party's political and strategic goals. Officials build personal relationships that can then be 'weaponised' when a city plans an activity the CCP does not like, such as dealings with Taiwan (including cultural activities) and with the Dalai Lama.[74]

A decade or so ago, after some years in the doldrums, the CPAFFC was reinvigorated in order, in Brady's words, 'to coopt foreigners to support and promote China's foreign policy goals'.[75] In Xi Jinping's China there is no 'people' in the sense of an independent civil society, so what is really being built in sister agreements are Party-to-people relationships. Thousands of well-meaning citizens in Western nations who have worked hard to foster genuine understanding and harmony with Chinese people are having their commitment exploited by the CCP.

Sister-city/state relationships provide another opportunity for deploying the tactic of 'use the countryside to surround the city'. Despite the soothing language of international cooperation and world peace, for the CCP 'all exchanges have a political character and hopefully a political harvest'.[76]

The state of Maryland is an instructive case study. Adjacent to Washington D.C., Maryland hosts many federal government research centres, security organisations and intelligence establishments, from NASA's Goddard Space Flight Center to the National Security Agency and the Internal Revenue Service.[77] It also hosts fourteen military installations, ranging from U.S. Cyber Command at Fort Meade to the Naval Surface Warfare Center. Tens of thousands of personnel employed at these centres, some with high-level security clearances, live and work in Maryland.

Maryland has longstanding ties with China, including immigration, stretching back to an era when relationships were more innocuous. It signed a sister-state agreement with the Chinese province of Anhui in 1980, the first of its kind in the United States, and is the base for the USA-China Sister Schools Association, which organises educational and cultural exchange programs in secondary schools in the D.C. area.[78] Rockville, in the county of Montgomery, Maryland's largest, is home to some 50,000 Chinese-Americans and has been described as the region's 'new Chinatown'.[79] (The county government even once considered declaring Chinese New Year a holiday for public schools.[80])

The University of Maryland was one of the earliest to build ties with China, and in 2004 became the first university in the US to host a Confucius Institute (and only the second in the world).[81] It now hosts a large number of students from China, teaches several courses aimed at Chinese officials, and has many research collaborations. When in 2017 a Chinese student, Yang Shuping, used her commencement address to praise the 'fresh air of free speech' in the United States, the Chinese Students and Scholars Association launched a campaign to denounce her harshly for betraying the motherland.[82] The *People's Daily* accused her of 'bolstering negative Chinese stereotypes'.[83] Chinese embassy officials praised the CSSA and encouraged others to engage in similar activity. Yang's family in China was harassed and she was bombarded with threats. She was forced to issue a grovelling apology. To its credit, the university spoke in defence of the right of students to speak (although it could hardly do otherwise).[84] Perhaps in retaliation, the university's lucrative programs to train Chinese officials appear to have experienced a sharp decline in enrolments, and student numbers also appear to have fallen off.[85]

Howard County, also in Maryland, is home to Columbia, a city of 100,000 people. A high proportion of its residents work in sensitive federal government agencies. When Columbia decided to partner with a city in China, it set up a committee to find a suitable candidate.[86] Liyang was seemingly selected from eight Chinese cities, although delegations from Liyang had been lobbying for it over some years.[87] The initiator of the Columbia–Liyang sister city partnership was Clarksville resident Wu Chau. He served as vice chair of Columbia's China Sister City Planning Committee.[88] While a doctoral student at the University of Maryland in the 2000s, Wu served as the president of the Chinese Students and Scholars Association. In 2008 he and his comrades organised students to make complaints about the pro-Tibet movement, and campaigned against those making negative remarks about Beijing's hosting of the Olympic Games.[89]

The agreement was brokered by a woman named Han Jun, who runs an organisation called Success International Mutual Liaison Services in Rockville.[90] She was reportedly 'hired by China to find a sister city on the East Coast', indicating she may have links with the CPAFFC.[91] She also has close connections with senior government officials in Liyang, including the mayor and the provincial office of the Ministry of Foreign Affairs, which manages the CPAFFC.[92]

In 2016 Wu Chao and Han Jun were nominated as Outstanding Chinese in the Greater D.C. Area at an event hosted by Alliance Cultural Media Inc., a pro-Beijing media outlet with links to CCP media.[93] Wu Chao was also presented by the CCP's Overseas Chinese Affairs Office as a role model for *huaren canzheng*, the Party's program of encouraging trusted Chinese-Americans to become active in politics.[94] In 2018 he was elected to the Howard County Board of Education.[95]

Maryland has been fertile ground for united front activity. A number of prominent citizens—including the director of a medical centre, an engineer at Georgetown University, and a scientist at the National Institutes of Health—have links to the CCP or CCP-run organisations.[96] Maryland political activist He (Helen) Xiaohui was in 2018 appointed president of the National Association for China's Peaceful Unification in Washington D.C., the Washington chapter of the China Council for the Promotion of Peaceful National Reunification, an agency of the CCP (see the organisation chart on pages 124–5).[97] Accepting the position, she promised to 'work tirelessly for the great rejuvenation of the Chinese nation'.[98] Helen He has been heavily involved in promoting China's influence activities in Maryland and is often presented as a spokesperson for the local community when criticising the 'anti-China' moves of the US government.[99]

Noting that her appointment ceremony was presided over by a senior official from the Chinese embassy, Bethany Allen-Ebrahimian wrote that Helen He now 'serves as a top point of contact between the Chinese Communist Party in Beijing and the Chinese-American community in greater Washington, D.C.'. As a sign of her importance, in 2009 she served as an overseas delegate to the Chinese People's Political Consultative Conference, an honour reserved for those of proven value to the Party.[100]

The case of Prague also shows that the CCP views sister-city agreements as an instrument of political influence. In 2019 Prague City Hall voted to terminate its partnership with Beijing, after Beijing refused to remove a 'one China' policy clause from the agreement.[101] Prague's recently elected mayor, Zdenek Hrib of the progressive Pirate Party, argued that the partnership was supposed to be a cultural one, and that the 'one China' clause was a matter of international politics. Beijing, accustomed to getting its way in the Czech Republic under the slavishly pro-Beijing presidency of Milos Zeman, was enraged. The embassy demanded that Prague reverse its decision or 'it will be their own interests that will be hurt'. In China, concerts by orchestras that had 'Prague' in their names were cancelled. Two months after ending its sister-city relationship with Beijing, Prague announced that it would partner with Taipei instead.[102]

In its reaction to Prague's decision, Beijing gave the game away.

6
The Party-corporate conglomerate

The Party and business

When President Trump began a trade war with China in 2018 he cited a long list of Beijing's infractions of the standards of free-market behaviour, including manipulating the currency, dumping subsidised goods in American markets, and forcing US companies to engage in joint ventures that resulted in their technology being stolen. In 2016 the same practices had led industrialised nations to refuse to grant China the status of market economy under WTO rules, something Beijing badly wanted.

In any Chinese embassy's mapping of a nation's centres of power, business elites feature prominently. Both Chinese companies operating abroad and Western companies with economic interests in China are important vectors of CCP influence. While most Chinese businesses operating abroad have commercial reasons for doing so, at the same time they are required to serve the interests of the Party-state. These businesses benefit materially from cultivating good relations with senior CCP cadres, and are punished if they do not obey the Party. In 2017 the requirement for such businesses to assist China's intelligence agencies abroad was formalised in Chinese law.[1]

When the CCP opened up the Chinese economy to market forces it did not mean that government withdrew. It would be more accurate to see the process as one in which aspects of modern capitalism were grafted onto a Leninist state apparatus, creating a new model of Leninist capitalism. The spread of market forces did not weaken the power of the Party-state; in fact, today it is more powerful than ever *because of* market forces.

Historically in the West, the spread of private property and markets saw the development of an independent legal system that could adjudicate disputes according to legislated principles. Along with criminal law, this gave rise to the notion of the rule of law. It cannot be stressed enough that there is no rule of law in China. What the country has is rule *by* law; that is, the use of law as an instrument to govern.[2] The Party is quite clear about this: it's the Party that decides on the laws, and the interests of the Party trump all interests that are in conflict with it. Judges must serve the Party's interests. Lawyers who act as if there is rule of law find themselves in prison.[3]

State-owned enterprises, responsible for around a third of China's industrial output, are being strengthened. Their top executives are appointed by the Party's powerful Organisation Department. President Xi declared in 2016 that SOEs should 'become important forces to implement' the Party's decisions, and their boards are now expected to take guidance from the internal Party committee before making major decisions.[4] Party control is not confined to SOEs. Virtually all large and medium-sized private enterprises, including foreign-invested companies and sensitive ones, such as internet firms, now have Party committees operating within them.[5] The Party secretary can often appoint and dismiss senior managers and nominate board members, and may chair the board or hold an executive position.[6] In 2016 it was reported that henceforth the secretary of the Party committee and the chairman of the board must be the same person.[7]

When it was reported that the boards of the four largest banks in China are required by their articles of association to take account of the opinions of the Party committee before making important decisions, David Webb, an independent investor and shareholder-activist in Hong Kong, observed: 'This is a reminder to investors they are buying into a party machine.'[8] The same applies to foreign firms operating in China, which may need Party approval for the appointment of senior managers.[9]

In the words of one close observer, Yi-Zheng Lian, the modern Chinese economy is 'a party-corporate conglomerate'.[10] Whereas several years ago it was plausible to argue that the CCP would permit continuing economic liberalisation, today, it's apparent that the Party has been moving decisively in the opposite direction.

The links between senior Party officials and Chinese companies are personal as well as political. Officials typically have financial interests in Chinese corporations, usually through family members and shell companies. Even the family of corruption-busting Xi Jinping has enormous wealth hidden offshore.[11] Certain companies, such as the mysterious HNA Group (whose chairman reportedly died when he fell off a wall in France in 2018), are believed to be vehicles for hiding, protecting and growing the wealth of top Party officials and their families.[12]

An academic study published in 2018 found that when firms linked to the twenty-five or so members of the Politburo purchased land owned by local governments, they paid less than half the price paid by buyers without political connections.[13] Firms connected to the seven-member Standing Committee of the Politburo received a 75 per cent discount. The obliging local officials all expected promotions in return. As Minxin Pei shows at length in his 2016 book, those promotions are in turn monetised through the extraction of bribes from lower-level officials and businessmen.[14] The 2018 study shows that President Xi's anti-corruption crackdown led to only a small decline in the discounts provided to Party leaders.

Comrade billionaire

Some executives and business commentators in the West, and even some academics, still argue that the role of the Party in private companies is merely a formality, but in the Xi era nothing could be further from the truth. Any CEO of a major company who refused to abide by a direction from the Party would soon find themselves in trouble, with their assets confiscated. The claim by Huawei's founder, Ren Zhengfei, that he would defy any order from the Party to install backdoors in the company's equipment does not pass the laugh test.[15]

While the 2017 National Intelligence Law obliges all citizens and organisations to comply with any direction to cooperate in 'national intelligence work', it only formalises a practice going back many years. (By putting it explicitly into law, CCP leaders have shot themselves in the foot, as the law is regularly cited in the West to argue that a company like Huawei cannot refuse to assist China's intelligence agencies.[16])

It stretches credulity when China's most powerful tycoons pledge their undying allegiance to the Party, as Richard Liu of JD.com—China's 'Jeff Bezos'—did when he said 'communism would be realised in his generation'.[17] Loyalty to the Party is a condition of doing business. When Xu Jiayin, chairman and Party secretary of the country's largest property developer, declared that 'everything the company possessed was given by the party', and when heavy-industry tycoon Liang Wengen said his life 'belonged to the party', both were speaking a truth, though not the one intended.[18]

From the early 2000s the CCP adopted a policy of drawing capitalists and corporate executives into the Party apparatus and subjecting them to its chain of command in exchange for official favours. Billionaires, bankers and chief executives have in this way been rewarded with appointment to the Chinese People's Political Consultative Conference. Even a superstar entrepreneur like Jack Ma—the revered founder of the ecommerce behemoth Alibaba, who was worth $42 billion at the end of 2019—succumbs to the Party's wishes, publicly saying, for example, that sending in the tanks to crush the students in Tiananmen Square was the 'correct decision'.[19]

As a measure of how deep is the fusion between Party-state and private business, the delegates at the 2018 meeting of the CPPCC included the CEOs of the biggest tech firms in the country, including Tencent's Pony Ma and Baidu's Robin Li.[20] The *People's Daily* revealed late that year that Jack Ma has been a member of the Party since the 1980s.[21] So are most of the other CEOs of major tech firms.[22]

Whether they participate in top Party events for opportunistic, ideological or patriotic reasons, by doing so they signal their deference to the CCP. In 2018 the CEO of tech giant Sogou, Wang Xiaochuan, told business leaders that they were entering an era in which their companies would be 'fused together' with the Party, which may ask them to allow state companies to buy a share. They should not resist, for if they were to think that their interests differ from the state's then they would 'probably find things are painful, *more painful than in the past*' (our emphasis).[23]

The marriage of business and the Party-state in China is especially apparent in the CCP's policy of 'civil-military fusion'.[24] A pillar of China's military modernisation, this fusion is deeper and more far-reaching than the US military-industrial complex. Since Xi Jinping ascended to power in 2012, civil-military fusion has been part of nearly every major strategic initiative, including *Made in China 2025*, the Next Generation Artificial Intelligence Plan, and the Belt and Road Initiative.[25]

America's 'globalist billionaires'

In November 2018 Peter Navarro, the White House trade adviser who at the time was intimately involved in President Trump's trade war with Beijing, launched a scathing attack on what he called the 'globalist billionaires' of Wall Street.[26] He accused the 'self-appointed group of Wall Street bankers and hedge fund managers' of engaging in their own 'shuttle diplomacy' with the Chinese side, and attempting to sabotage US trade negotiations by putting enormous pressure on the White House to give way to Beijing. Navarro further accused the financial elite of being 'unregistered foreign agents' acting as part of Beijing's influence operations in Washington.

It was strong stuff, but was there any foundation to it?

When Navarro referred to the bankers' shuttle diplomacy, he was probably thinking of a meeting in September 2018 between executives from Goldman Sachs, Morgan Stanley, the Blackstone Group and others, and Xi Jinping's powerful right-hand man, vice premier Wang Qishan. And he would have been aware that each time China's chief trade negotiator, Liu He, arrived in the US for talks, his first meeting was with the top Wall Street bankers.[27]

Beijing has been working on Wall Street for a long time. When Prime Minister Zhu Rongji visited the US in 1999, he holed up in New York's Astoria Hotel and spent days in back-to-back meetings with business leaders. 'Zhu seems never to tire of courting Corporate America', reported *The New York Times*.[28] The titans of US finance have for decades been guiding the nation's China policy. Whenever presidents Clinton, Bush or Obama threatened to take a tougher stance on China's trade protectionism, currency manipulation or technology theft, Wall Street chiefs used their influence to persuade them to back off.[29] And it was pressure from Wall Street that proved decisive in the Clinton White House's decision to support China's admission to the World Trade Organization, despite China's serial violation of trade rules.[30] Twenty years later, *The New York Times* was writing: 'In Washington, on Wall Street and in corporate boardrooms, Beijing has used the country's size and promise for decades to quell opposition and reward those who helped its rise.' Financial institutions have been Beijing's most powerful advocates in Washington.[31]

In recent times, Beijing has 'encouraged' US investors to buy into Chinese-listed companies. Writing in *The Washington Post* in June 2019, Josh Rogin noted that US capital markets are 'drastically increasing their holdings of Chinese companies, giving Beijing massive leverage inside the United States'.[32] Billions of dollars from US institutional investors like pension funds are now invested in Chinese companies. And Wall Street has for years been helping Chinese companies obtain investor funds from the US stock markets—companies whose accounts are opaque and shielded from foreign scrutiny, exposing the US economy to higher risk.

The finance sector—the big banks, hedge funds and investment vehicles—is thus in the centre of the map of power in the US, and occupying pride of place is Goldman Sachs. No organisation has been more important to the CCP's campaign to penetrate US elites, or more willing.[33] For the CCP, titans of finance are easy targets, as there's a concordance of interests. Wall Street executives, anticipating an Eldorado when Beijing opens up its vast finance markets to foreigners, have been advising Chinese companies on which American companies to buy, and lending them the money to do it, taking a cut from the sales.[34] In the words of a senior White House official, 'People who like making deals really like the Chinese Communist Party.'[35] The CCP is pushing on an open door. But the alignment of interests may not be long term, if it's Beijing's intention to displace New York and the City of London, and eventually make Shanghai the financial capital of the world. As Lenin reputedly said, 'The capitalists will sell us the rope with which we will hang them.'

By 2003 Goldman Sachs 'had become the lead underwriter for major Chinese state-owned companies'.[36] In 2006 Henry Paulson moved from CEO of Goldman Sachs to Treasury secretary under George W. Bush, taking with him one of the best contact books on the Chinese elite. Paulson had visited the country some seventy times. He asked the president if he could take charge of America's China economic policy, and Bush agreed.

But Henry Paulson, in the judgement of Paul Blustein, screwed up. Blustein argues that if Paulson had responded more forcefully to Beijing's currency manipulation, tight control of state-owned enterprises, mistreatment of US enterprises in China, and program of technology theft, then the conditions that led to the trade war might not have arisen.[37] Instead of recommending retaliatory actions to protect US companies, Paulson worked to head them off in Congress, proposing to hold a 'Strategic Economic Dialogue'. Needless to say, this gave the advantage to Beijing.

Paulson, a good friend of Beijing's then mayor, Wang Qishan, and already inclined to look benignly on the Party's efforts to open up the economy, was being manipulated. The CCP was drawing him further into its inner circle, stoking his perception of his own influence. He was granted a private, one-on-one briefing with President Hu Jintao.

After Paulson left office in 2009—having overseen the global financial crisis, during which he phoned Wang Qishan and begged him to order a state-owned Chinese bank to bail out Bear Stearns—the Goldman Sachs alumnus set up the Paulson Institute, dedicated 'to fostering a US-China relationship that serves to maintain global order'.[38]

John Thornton is another influential graduate of Goldman Sachs. He led Goldman's entry into China, and when he retired as the bank's chairman in 2003, he became director of the Global Leadership Program at Beijing's Tsinghua University. Thornton is a strong supporter of Stephen Schwarzman's scholarship program at Tsinghua and sits on the board of a number of top Chinese and American corporations. In 2006 he put his money into a new China Center at the Brookings Institution, where he is chairman of the board of trustees. In 2008 the Chinese Communist Party gave him its highest award for foreigners, the Friendship Award of the People's Republic of China.[39]

This part of the Wall Street story would not be complete without mentioning the US investment fund BlackRock, the world's largest, with $6.5 trillion worth of assets under management. In 2019 its CEO, Larry Fink, told the company's shareholders that he planned to turn BlackRock into one of China's leading asset managers, saying he would be ready to take advantage once Beijing opened up its capital markets to foreigners, and that he aimed to become one of the first foreign-asset managers to raise renminbi funds in China.[40] To this end, Fink has set out to Sinicise the company, and has recruited Tang Xiaodong (Tony Tang) to head its China operations. A veteran investor, with stints at J.P. Morgan, RBS Greenwich and CITIC Group, Tang has an MBA from the University of Chicago. After being recruited through the Thousand Talents Plan, he spent five years as a top finance regulator in Beijing.[41] BlackRock's head of Chinese equities is Helen Zhu. Based in Hong Kong, she joined the company in 2014, after being poached from Goldman Sachs. She studied engineering at MIT.[42] The head of strategy and innovation at BlackRock is Amelia Tan, who's based in the City of London and who joined the company from Citibank.

While the power of Wall Street in setting China policy has been real enough, in 2017 something changed. US manufacturers decided they had had enough of their intellectual property being stolen and they were no longer willing to wait for Beijing to honour its promises to liberalise China's economy and provide a level playing field for American firms. The U.S. Chamber of Commerce published a report saying so, driving a wedge between finance and manufacturing, a gap that allowed the Trump administration, backed by the Democrats, to muscle up to Beijing. This prompted intensified lobbying by the finance sector, and closer coordination with its allies in Beijing.

The princelings of Wall Street

The CCP has not been content to rely solely on a concordance of interests between Beijing and big finance in the West. One important avenue of influence are the princelings—the sons and daughters of top Party leaders, past and present. For years, the giant state-owned investment company CITIC has been dominated by princelings, as has China Poly Group, the conglomerate that was built around arms manufacturing.[43] China's burgeoning private equity sector is controlled by the 'red aristocracy' and their children.

For Western hedge funds, insurance companies, pension funds and banks, a prerequisite for doing business in the emerging, highly lucrative Chinese capital markets is a network of connections to the families that control the largest companies and dominate the Party hierarchy. Giving jobs to the sons, daughters, nephews and nieces of these families brings immediate *guanxi*. The offspring need not be well qualified or even especially bright; it's their connections that count. An ideal career path for a princeling is an undergraduate degree at a prestigious university, preferably an Ivy League college or Oxbridge, then straight onto the trading floor of a big bank or hedge fund in New York or London, and after a few years there, an MBA and then a Wall Street firm.

An unusual insight into how this works was provided by an inquiry by the U.S. Securities and Exchange Commission in 2016, which led to J.P. Morgan paying $264 million for violating the *Foreign Corrupt Practices Act*. J.P. Morgan had been caught hiring Chinese princelings to win business, something the commission described as 'systematic bribery'.[44] The company operated what it called the Sons and Daughters Program, which provided dozens of jobs in Hong Kong, Shanghai and New York to children of the Party elite.[45]

One was Gao Jue, the son of China's commerce minister, Gao Hucheng. A recent graduate of Purdue University, Gao Jue landed a job after a meeting between his father and senior J.P. Morgan executive William Daley. (Daley was a former US commerce secretary under Clinton, and pushed for China's entry into the WTO. He later served as President Obama's chief of staff.) Gao Jue interviewed poorly but was offered a coveted analyst position with the bank. Prone to falling asleep at work, he was soon judged to be an 'immature, irresponsible and unreliable' employee. When, as part of a general downsizing, the bank later wanted to lay him off, his father took the head of the bank's Hong Kong office, Fang Fang, to dinner and pleaded for his son to be kept on, promising to 'go extra miles' for J.P. Morgan in its China deals.[46] Fang was persuaded and a senior executive in New York agreed to keep Gao Jue on, even though the executive's own son had been laid off. Business is business. When Gao Jue was eventually let go, he took other finance jobs before winding up at Goldman Sachs.

As one equity executive told the *Financial Times*, 'You don't say no to a princeling,' which begs the question of what else the banks do for the Party elite, besides employing their children.[47] Another J.P. Morgan hire brokered by Fang Fang was Tang Xiaoning, the son of Tang Shuangning, a former senior bank regulator and chairman of the Everbright Group, a Fortune 500 banking and financial services group owned by the Chinese government. Tang Xiaoning had previously worked for Goldman Sachs and Citigroup. J.P. Morgan also provided an internship for the daughter of Leung Chun-ying, Hong Kong's former chief executive (and member of the CPPCC), while she was still a high-school student. The bank had created a 'summer camp' for the children of well-heeled and well-connected elites.[48]

There are, of course, many mainland Chinese working in US finance who are highly competent and deserve their positions, often very senior ones. Fang Fang is one example. Fang graduated from the prestigious Tsinghua University in the 1980s and then studied for an MBA at Vanderbilt University in Nashville. In 1993 he took a job at Merrill Lynch, working in New York and Hong Kong, and in 2001 he began a thirteen-year career with J.P. Morgan, rising to the position of chief executive for China investment banking, based in Hong Kong.[49] In that time he brokered the appointment of many sons and daughters to positions within the bank.[50] He also gained intimate knowledge of the personal finances of some of China's ruling elite. Fang is said to have a 'deep network of contacts in Chinese government and business circles'.[51]

While not CCP royalty, Fang is on very close terms with the red aristocracy. *Fortune* describes him as 'a media-friendly executive with close ties to the Communist Party'.[52] In 2011 he founded the Hua Jing Society in Hong Kong, a social club for the children of mainland elites who had studied abroad and returned to Hong Kong.[53] The society has been described as the Princeling's Club, and the Hong Kong branch for CCP princelings.[54] A sign of the trust and regard in which Fang was held by the ruling elite was his appointment in 2008 to the Chinese People's Political Consultative Conference, which gives direct access to the top Party leadership.[55] He was also made vice chairman of an important, Party-linked think tank, the Center for China and Globalization.[56]

There was nothing unique about J.P. Morgan's Sons and Daughters Program; all the big American finance companies had something similar. It was claimed in 2013 that Goldman Sachs had employed twenty-five sons and daughters, including the grandson of Jiang Zemin, the all-powerful CCP boss until the early 2000s.[57] Merrill Lynch (and before it, Citigroup) employed the daughter-in-law of former premier Zhao Ziyang, Margaret Ren. In 2012 she was promoted to managing director, China country executive, and chairman of Bank of America Merrill Lynch. She has an MBA from the MIT Sloan School of Management and is a council member at the Center for China and Globalization.[58] Merrill Lynch also employed the son-in-law of Wu Bangguo, who for a decade until his retirement in 2013 was ranked second in the Party hierarchy. Janice Hu, granddaughter of former Party head Hu Yaobang, also worked at Merrill Lynch before joining Credit Suisse, where she rose to the position of head of investment banking in Hong Kong.

Morgan Stanley hired the son of former premier Zhu Rongji. It also employed Chen Xiaodan (Sabrina Chen), the daughter of Chen Yuan, chairman of the massive China Development Bank before he was appointed vice chairman of the CPPCC.[59] Chen Yuan's father was one of the 'Eight Immortals' who fought alongside Mao Zedong.[60] Sabrina was educated at a Massachusetts private school before attending Duke University and gaining a Harvard MBA. (When the China Development Bank offered summer internships, applications were accepted only from graduates of Harvard and MIT.[61] Other Ivy League graduates did not make the cut.) Her brother, Chen Xiaoxin, was employed by Citigroup. He too went to a private school in Massachusetts, then Cornell, then Stanford for an MBA.[62] And Citigroup also employed Li Wangzhi, the son of purged Party boss Bo Xilai.[63]

For the CCP elite, entanglement with the masters of Wall Street through the placement of scores of princelings serves a more important purpose than employment for their kids.[64] It is a means of gathering intelligence and exerting influence because it places its informants and agents in the heart of American power. The entire workings of a US firm may be sent back to a father or an uncle in China, along with confidential information on the personal and financial affairs of the wealthiest people in North America.

CCP in the City of London

European financial institutions were not slow to recruit princelings either. In the 2000s Deutsche Bank, Germany's biggest, used bribes and corrupt practices to gain access to China, including showering expensive gifts on leaders, especially the family of then premier Wen Jiabao, and then mayor of Beijing Wang Qishan, now a member of the Politburo's inner cabinet, the Standing Committee.[65] In 2009 Deutsche Bank beat J.P. Morgan to a deal because it had employed the daughter of the client's chairman.[66] The bank also had an active program of employing the children of powerful officials. Among them was the son of then propaganda minister Liu Yunshan, and one of the daughters of Li Zhanshu—now one of the seven on the Politburo Standing Committee—even though both were rated unsuitable for the job.[67] Wang Xisha, whose father Wang Yang is now vice premier and a Politburo Standing Committee member, was also hired by Deutsche Bank. She is married to Nicholas Zhang (Zhang Xinliang), the grandson of PLA general Zhang Aiping. Nicholas Zhang was an investment banker at UBS and Goldman Sachs before setting up his own hedge fund, Magnolia Capital Management.[68]

In Zurich, Credit Suisse employed the daughter of Wen Jiabao, who as China's premier until 2013 ran economic policy. Credit Suisse kept a spreadsheet that tracked princeling hires against how much money they brought in. It hired over a hundred sons, daughters and friends of senior government officials.[69] One 'princess' was employed after Credit Suisse bankers helped massage her résumé. Once on the payroll, she often didn't show up for work. When she did, she was judged 'rude and unprofessional' and sometimes brought her mother with her. Nevertheless, she was paid US$1 million a year and given a number of promotions because her family awarded deals to the bank. (In 2018 Credit Suisse agreed to pay US$77 million to US authorities to avoid prosecution on bribery charges.[70])

While the placement of princelings and promises of access to China's huge financial market have been the foremost avenue of influence in

Wall Street, in the City of London the situation is different. London's financial district—the square mile east of St Paul's Cathedral known as the City of London, or simply the City—is also the financial hub of Europe, giving big finance an inordinate influence in British politics. Brexit has many wondering whether the City can retain its dominant position or will be displaced by its rivals in Frankfurt or even Paris. The mandarins of the City have been working hard to ensure its pre-eminence, which provides a golden opportunity for Beijing. It would be an exaggeration to say that if Beijing could control the City it could control Britain, but not a large one. An ominous, if small, sign of the influence Beijing already wields came in May 2019 when the City of London Corporation, the district's municipal government, banned the Taiwan office from contributing a float to the annual lord mayor's parade.[71]

At the centre of the CCP's ambitious strategy for global economic domination is the push for China's currency, the renminbi or RMB (also known as the yuan), to become the foremost global currency, replacing the US dollar. The size of China's economy and the fact that the RMB is the second most used currency for trade helps, but financial markets know that China's financial system is not robust, and that the government manipulates it, which creates distrust. So rather than liberalise its markets, Beijing has embarked on a campaign to influence key decision-makers abroad in favour of the RMB. As far back as 2011, *Der Spiegel* was criticising China for pursuing 'economic hegemony' by 'forcing other countries to maintain reserves of Chinese money'.[72] More recently, Beijing has shown more subtlety but also greater determination.

To explain its approach, we are indebted to the excellent work of Martin Thorley of Nottingham University, who has exposed the influence network of an organisation called the International Monetary Institute.[73] Based at Renmin University in Beijing, the institute claims to be independent, but Thorley has shown that its senior staff have strong Party and united front links. Its founder and executive director, Ben Shenglin, is a very significant operative.

Ben Shenglin's involvement in united front bodies includes being a committee member of the All-China Federation of Industry and

Commerce, and a member of the Zhejiang Provincial Committee of the Chinese People's Political Consultative Conference. If not a red aristocrat, Ben Shenglin is certainly a senior courtier. He has worked assiduously at cultivating links and partnerships with respectable organisations in the West. In 2016 the Brookings-Tsinghua Center co-hosted with the IMI a seminar discussing whether the renminbi would supplant the US dollar.[74] The Penn-Wharton China Center was also involved. The panel included both the director and the deputy director of the IMI, and the moderator was a reporter for China's state broadcaster CCTV. In 2018 publishing house Palgrave Macmillan lent legitimacy to the IMI and its claims by publishing *Currency Internationalization and Macro Financial Risk Control*, a book produced by the institute. A perusal shows it to be Beijing monetary propaganda.[75]

The Cato Institute republishes on its website the IMI's journal, the *International Monetary Review*, which is full of articles promoting the rise and rise of the RMB. Cato Institute senior fellow Steve Hanke is a member of institute's international committee.[76]

Foremost among the IMI's influence networks is the Official Monetary and Financial Institutions Forum, a London-based think tank focused on central banking and financial market regulation. It has links to British sovereign wealth and pension funds. Martin Thorley has uncovered the close interweaving of people associated with these two organisations. At least seven people hold positions in or contribute to both, including the chairman and co-founder of the forum, David Marsh, who is a member of the IMI's international advisory committee and sits on the board of its journal. The journal's editor, Herbert Poenisch, also writes for the forum. In 2018 Poenisch was arguing that Beijing should adopt a bolder RMB expansion strategy.[77] Ben Shenglin is a member of the forum's advisory council, giving this top united front operative direct access to senior players in the City.

One such player is Labour Party peer Lord Davidson of Glen Clova. He has been Beijing's most effective advocate for the internationalisation of the RMB, speaking in the House of Lords and writing opinion pieces urging the Treasury to open itself up to the RMB. [78] In 2014 he berated the Treasury for its timidity and lack of imagination in failing to include the RMB in the UK's foreign currency reserves; he wanted to make London *the* major offshore centre for China's foreign currency.[79] His wish came true in 2018 when London accounted for 37 per cent of all RMB transactions outside China, the largest of any overseas financial centre.[80]

Davidson is a well-known friend of China. When in 2013 he participated in a human rights forum in Beijing, a leading German human rights lawyer described him as the 'most vocal human rights relativist at the Forum'.[81] In 2014 Davidson travelled to Lhasa for a 'Development Forum', where, breaking with Labour Party policy, he condemned the Dalai Lama and praised the CCP government for bringing social harmony and happiness to Tibet.[82] In 2018 he suggested in the House of Lords that it was more important for the British government to strike a post-Brexit free trade deal with China than to indulge in 'bellicosity' by sending a Royal Navy ship to the South China Sea.[83]

Predictably, Davidson is a fellow of the 48 Group Club.[84] He's also well connected in the United States. When he travelled to Beijing in 2018, his expenses were paid by the Berggruen Institute.[85] This California-based think tank, set up by German-American investor Nicolas Berggruen, advocates for closer China-US ties (see chapter eleven). Berggruen spent $25 million on a China centre at Peking University to promote cross-cultural 'dialogue'.[86]

Today, the City of London Corporation can't get enough of China. In March 2019, two months before he banned Taiwan's float in his parade, Lord Mayor Peter Estlin joined a delegation to China to promote 'fintech and green finance' links, along with the City's role in the Belt and Road Initiative. While there, Estlin talked about the important part the City plays in China's success.[87] Interviewed on Phoenix TV, he revealed that the City would be hosting a banquet the following September to celebrate the seventieth anniversary of the PRC.[88] The lord mayor praised the BRI's 'win-win culture', and said he sees the City playing a vital role in helping to finance 'a fantastic initiative' and a 'very exciting' vision.

The delegation was led by John McLean, a board member of the China-Britain Business Council, who declared that 'London is open for business for Chinese financial and tech companies'.[89] Earlier in

2019 the chair of the City of London's policy committee, Catherine McGuinness, welcomed the launch of the global edition of the CCP's *China Daily*, noting that the paper 'is based in the Square Mile and is a good friend of the City of London Corporation'.[90]

The International Monetary Institute also has its eye on Frankfurt, the most important financial centre in continental Europe, and has teamed up with the House of Finance of Goethe University to launch the Sino-German Center of Finance and Economics at the Frankfurt School of Finance and Management, a training school for German bankers. It promotes RMB internationalisation and is supported by the central banks of China and Germany. The IMI's Ben Shenglin, in his capacity as a dean of Zhejiang University, is on the board of trustees.[91]

Among top Party operatives, Ben Shenglin has perhaps the best connections into official and academic finance networks around the world. As a further example, the IMI's close connections bring him into contact with the US chairman of the Official Monetary and Financial Institutions Forum, Mark Sobel, formerly a top official at the US Treasury Department and now an associate with a Washington think tank, the Center for Strategic and International Studies.[92]

Shaping economic perceptions

Bridgewater Associates, the world's biggest hedge fund, had been trying to build its business in China for some years. In 2015 Ray Dalio, Bridgewater's founder, confidentially advised his clients that the debt crisis in China was reaching a critical point and they should divest as soon as they could.[93] When his advice was leaked to the *Financial Times*, Dalio changed his tune. His advice had been 'taken the wrong way', he said. China's debt was not such a big problem because it was denominated in its own reserves, he claimed, and in the longer term the outlook was good.[94]

Two years later Dalio's reassessment paid off. Bridgewater became the first wholly foreign-owned enterprise to establish a Chinese asset management company permitted to invest in China's markets.[95] In 2018, while expressing pessimism about world economic prospects, Dalio waxed lyrical about China. 'China's been tremendously successful ... I'm excited about China—I can't understand how anybody couldn't be excited about China.'[96] In 2019 he wrote that senior leaders had explained to him that China is a kind of family-state, with the state having 'paternal' responsibility for the citizens, which is what the social credit system is all about. By contrast, he wrote, the US is based on individual rights. 'I'm not saying which system is better.'[97] Dalio has been shameless in his cultivation of political favour, not least through charity work, going so far as to enlist his sixteen-year-old son to 'set up a charity called China Care to help special-needs orphans'.[98]

In global financial markets, perceptions rule. The opinion-makers—the senior bank economists who appear on the evening news, analysts at investment funds, financial commentators in newspapers, economists with subscription newsletters, experts at ratings agencies—play a critical role in shaping understanding and expectations of world markets. What they say can influence perceptions of, for example, the credibility of China's growth forecasts and the stability of its financial sector. They are therefore of acute concern to Beijing.

China's government is deeply concerned about any loss of confidence in the country's fragile financial markets, both legitimate and shadow. If a financial crisis were to cause the economy to crash, it would jeopardise the Party's hold on power, not to mention a huge writedown in the value of assets owned by the red aristocracy.

When China's stock market was crashing in June 2015, a directive was issued to state media ordering them to change their reporting so as to 'rationally lead market expectations'.[99] They were directed to halt all discussions and expert interviews. The directive went on: 'Do not exaggerate panic or sadness. Do not use emotionally charged words such as "slump", "spike", or "collapse".'

Two months after the crash, a reporter for the respected business magazine *Caijing*, Wang Xiaolu, was arrested on charges of 'spreading rumors'.[100] He'd done nothing other than his usual reporting work, but when he appeared on television confessing that his stock-market report was 'irresponsible', the message to other journalists was unmistakeable. Foreign journalists found that the Chinese experts they went to for analysis and quotes had clammed up. Officials pressured foreign journalists, criticising them for being too pessimistic and demanding 'more balanced' coverage of China's economy, even as data, always unreliable, became harder to get.[101]

Economists and market analysts specialising in China are concentrated in Hong Kong. Over the past decade or so, overseas-trained economists from the mainland now working in foreign or Chinese firms have come to be predominant in these ranks, but regardless of where they're from, most are subject to pressure from Beijing to suppress concerns they may have about China's economy and financial markets. Often the 'independent advice' offered by Hong Kong economists looks coordinated, but it may be that the commentators pick up the same cues from China's official media.[102] Those who behave may in time be rewarded. By influencing the private and public pronouncements of economists, Beijing shapes global perceptions of China's economic outlook.

When financial risks to the Chinese economy became serious in 2015, the CCP began exerting subtle influence on international banks not to rock the boat with bad news. UBS, the largest Swiss bank, has a long history in China and has been actively pursuing a deeper role in its financial system.[103] It too has been pressured to rein in its public commentary, and in 2018 one of its employees was detained in China, for no apparent reason, causing UBS management to bar travel by its staff to China.[104] Because Xi's anti-corruption drive has focused especially on the financial sector, its participants are nervous anyway.

Expectations can be manipulated downwards too, to punish those who annoy the Party. During Hong Kong pro-democracy protests in 2019, Cathay Pacific earned Beijing's ire when some of its staff members joined in. An analyst at an investment bank, Zhao Dongchen, advised clients that Cathay had done 'irreversible damage' to its brand and predicted that its share price would collapse. He rated the shares a 'strong sell'.[105] Of nineteen analysts tracked by Bloomberg, Zhao Dongchen was the only one with a 'sell' rating; thirteen were recommending 'buy' and five 'hold'. Zhao, who is expert in energy companies and not airlines, works for the giant state-owned Industrial and Commercial Bank of China. Other analysts have accused him of assigning harsh ratings to foreign companies and positive ones to Chinese companies.[106] (Rather than tumbling, Cathay's share price plateaued then rose.)

Yi shang bi zheng

As we have seen, getting foreign businesses to lobby their governments on Beijing's behalf is one of the CCP's most powerful tactics. Commenting on the debacle that followed the tweet by the Houston Rockets' manager in support of Hong Kong protesters, John Pomfret observed that rather than 'us' changing 'China'—the dream of those urging greater economic integration—China is increasingly changing us, and Western businesses are Beijing's decisive weapon.[107] During the NBA imbroglio, America's leading sports network, the ESPN channel, banned its presenters from any discussion of the politics of it. ESPN also displayed a map of China showing the Nine-Dash Line; this map includes disputed territory in the South China Sea and has been ruled contrary to international law. It is almost never used outside the PRC.[108]

In other examples, camera-maker Leica, spooked by patriotic netizens, immediately distanced itself from its own advertisement referencing the 'tank man' of Tiananmen Square fame. Marriott International fired a junior employee who 'liked' a Twitter post supporting Tibetan autonomy, and it changed the name of Taiwan to 'Taiwan, China' when Beijing expressed annoyance. In Stockholm the Sheraton Hotel, a Marriott subsidiary, banned the local Taiwan office (the de facto embassy) from celebrating Taiwan's national day at the hotel.

Perhaps the most prominent spot in the corporate hall of shame belongs to Apple. After challenging the US government in court when the FBI wanted access to Apple users' data, the corporation then handed over encryption keys and iCloud data to Chinese authorities.[109] Apple, whose iPhones are assembled in China, also came under fire for deleting an app that allowed Hong Kong people to avoid street clashes with the police. It acted a day after China's state media accused it of protecting 'rioters'. Soon after, Apple CEO Tim Cook was appointed to chair a business school advisory board at Tsinghua University.[110]

Beijing's economic statecraft has in Xi's 'new era' evolved into a powerful instrument of political influence.[111] One tactic deployed frequently is *yi shang bi zheng* (using business to pressure government). The tactic was used during Trump's trade war to persuade the administration to ease up. In June 2019 a coalition of some 600 companies and associations (with an inordinate number of producers of pet food and sporting equipment) wrote an open letter to the president warning him against 'tariffs that are hurting American families and communities'. It was part of a slick, disciplined and expensive campaign organised by a group called Tariffs Hurt the Heartland. Its website highlights how tariffs had caused one non-profit organisation to cut the number of cribs it was providing to 'low-income moms across the Midwest'.[112] The letter was duly featured in CCP news outlets.[113]

It's not clear whether any CCP-linked organisations are backing Tariffs Hurt the Heartland. However, the China links of its spokesperson, Charles Boustany, were exposed by Bethany Allen-Ebrahimian in *Daily Beast*.[114] As a Republican member of congress for Louisiana, Boustany co-chaired the U.S.-China Working Group. On leaving Congress in 2017, he joined the lobbying firm Capitol Counsel, in which role he registered as a foreign agent representing the U.S.-China Transpacific Foundation. The foundation paid him to introduce US members of congress to Chinese business and political figures in order to enhance their understanding of China.

In Germany, the government appears to have at times adopted a more critical position towards Beijing, only to revert back to a more 'business friendly' stance. The CCP's use of business to exert pressure here is essential to understanding why. When Chancellor Angela Merkel ruled out a law blocking Huawei from Germany's 5G network, *Handelsblatt* reported that she 'feared a rift with China'.[115] In 2018 the bilateral trade volume between the two countries was almost €200 billion, making China Germany's largest trading partner for the third consecutive year. Chinese imports of German goods that year totalled €93 billion.[116] Such has been the growth in Germany's economic relations with China in recent years that it is now, of all the EU countries, the most dependent on China.[117]

But while German exports to China have been growing, their size alone cannot account for the impact they have on Berlin's China policy. More particular industrial interests seem to be at play. The German automotive industry has for decades wielded disproportionate political influence.[118] In 2018 over 5.5 million German vehicles were sold in China.[119] In July 2019 BMW announced it was teaming up with internet giant Tencent to develop self-driving cars.[120] Although not the only pro-CCP voice in German business, the auto industry has been an invaluable and carefully cultivated asset for the Party. As a result, in the words of *Der Spiegel*, 'the heads of Germany's vaunted car companies want to do everything to avoid a conflict with Beijing'.[121]

To ingratiate themselves, German car manufacturers self-censor their comments on China. In an interview with the BBC, the chairman of the board of Volkswagen denied any knowledge of the concentration camps in Xinjiang, stating he was 'extremely proud' of the company's activities in the region.[122] Mercedes-Benz was quick to apologise after using an innocuous quote from the Dalai Lama in one of its Instagram ads (which was blocked in China anyway).[123] Audi promptly and 'sincerely' apologised for using an 'incorrect' map of China (one that did not include Taiwan as part of China) during one of its press conferences in Germany.[124]

The German industrial conglomerate Siemens has also tried hard to curry favour with Beijing.[125] It was an early embracer of the Belt and Road Initiative, signing agreements with ten Chinese partners, and in June 2018 staged its very own BRI international summit in Beijing.[126] Asked to comment on the Hong Kong protests, Siemens CEO Joe Kaeser argued that Germany should 'balance' its values and its interest: 'When jobs in Germany depend on how we deal with sensitive topics, one should not add to the general outrage but carefully consider all positions and measures in all their aspects'.[127] Kaeser had in February 2019 become the chairman of the influential Asia Pacific Committee of German Business.[128]

Hans von Helldorff, chair of the Federal Association of the German Silk Road Initiative (formally launched in Bremen in March 2019, though it had been active prior to then), has attacked Germany's policy on China on national television, calling for an end to the country's 'value-oriented' policies.[129] In other words, the government should stop criticising China's human rights violations and focus solely on business interests. Few express this position as openly as von Helldorff, but it's a common argument behind closed doors.[130]

The Belt and Road strategy

As of 2019 over sixty countries, accounting for two-thirds of the world's population, had signed on to the BRI or intended to do so.[131] Across Eurasia, Indochina and Southeast Asia, Chinese state-owned and state-linked companies are investing in roads, ports, airports, railways, energy networks and dams. Ports are particularly valued because of China's dependence on sea trade, and also for their strategic function, in times of peace as well as conflict. The building of infrastructure in the nations bordering the South China Sea helps create a fatalistic acceptance of China's annexation of islands in the sea.

As the think tank Council on Foreign Relations noted, 'the United States shares the concern of some in Asia that the BRI could be a Trojan horse for China-led regional development, military expansion, and Beijing-controlled institutions'.[132] And, it should be stressed, for the control of critical infrastructure. After 40 per cent of the Philippines' national electricity network was sold to the giant state-owned State Grid Corporation of China, the head of the national transmission corporation conceded that the Philippines' entire power supply could be shut down by the flick of a switch in Nanjing, the location of the monitoring and control system.[133] State Grid also owns a large share of the electricity networks in the Australian states of Victoria and South Australia.[134] Its bid for the New South Wales grid was rejected on national security grounds. (In 2016 Donald Trump's hotel company was negotiating with State Grid for the latter to manage a major development in Beijing.[135])

In Europe, Chinese companies now own airports, seaports and wind farms across nine countries.[136] (They also own the tyre-maker Pirelli, the Swiss agrichemicals company Syngenta, a large slice of Daimler, a slew of office towers in London's financial hubs, and thirteen professional soccer teams.) All or part of the ports of Rotterdam (Europe's largest), Antwerp and Zeebrugge are Chinese-owned. The state-owned China Ocean Shipping Company owns the major Greek port of Piraeus and has a majority share in the Spanish port-management firm Noatum, and so controls the ports of Bilbao and Valencia.[137] Barcelona's huge new container terminal is owned by a Hong Kong–based company.

While the UK, Germany and France have attracted the largest share of Chinese investment, Mediterranean Europe, alienated from the EU following the debt crisis, is receiving increased attention. The BRI is the perfect vehicle for winning over nations that feel hard done by, and these countries do not have the investment filters that some others use to keep foreign firms out of vital infrastructure.[138] China also has a growing naval presence in the Mediterranean. The PLA Navy has been conspicuous for its activity in the Eastern Mediterranean and in 2015 held joint manoeuvres with Greece's navy.

Although Beijing insists in public that its port acquisitions are about promoting trade, it has a long-term plan to build strategic pressure, including beneath-the-radar expansion of its military presence. According to a study by Devin Thorne and Ben Spevack for the security-analysis think tank C4ADS, 'Port investments are viewed as vehicles with which China can cultivate political influence to constrain recipient countries and build dual-use infrastructure to facilitate Beijing's long-range naval operations.'[139] The shift in strategic landscape is most advanced in the Indo-Pacific, but good progress is being made in the Mediterranean. In Chinese-language sources, PLA Navy experts put the strategy this way: 'meticulously select locations, deploy discreetly, prioritise cooperation, and slowly infiltrate'.[140] Beijing aims to build 'strategic support states' (that is, those that can be guided to fit China's 'strategic needs') by investing in infrastructure and 'making relevant countries believe China's benevolence'.

BRI as discourse control

The leading Chinese scholar Xiang Debao has written that through the BRI China 'is exercising its international communication and international discourse power'.[141] It is because of this role in shaping thinking that the BRI recurs throughout this book. The initiative is one of the main vehicles by which Beijing challenges existing regional orders and promotes alternative models of governance, including its authoritarian, state-directed capitalism, but is couched in language of 'equality' and 'coexistence'. In short, it's agitprop for the China model.[142]

This ideological contest between the CCP and the West takes the form not so much of competing ideas as alternative narratives, using language that frames social reality more subtly. Narratives are a source of power because they set constraints on what is imaginable and considered feasible.[143] As two Party theorists have put it, 'In the new era, the Chinese approach to global governance *represented by Belt and Road* must be reflected in the story of China, and China must send a deeply penetrating Chinese voice through Belt and Road.' (The emphasis is ours.)[144]

From the outset, the BRI has been presented as a model of 'inclusive globalisation' and aimed at those who feel shut out. The language plays to the dream of global harmony through trade and cultural exchange. When Xi Jinping uses the phrase 'community of shared future', the subtext is that China's new world order will replace the postwar American hegemony. The BRI can be seen as the CCP's principal vehicle for promoting and entrenching the Party's alternative discourse system for the world. To the outside world, Xi and other leaders talk about 'win-win cooperation', and 'a big family of harmonious co-existence' and 'a bridge for peace and East-West cooperation', but in discussions at home, the talk is of achieving global discursive and geostrategic dominance.[145]

So when a nation or a state signs on to the BRI it signs on to the CCP's narrative. Italy's memorandum of understanding on the BRI endorses 'common development and prosperity, deepened mutual trust and beneficial cooperation'.[146] The government of Victoria, the Australian state that ignored the federal government's repudiation of the BRI, has committed itself to 'the aspiration of promoting the silkroad spirit centering on peace, cooperation, openness, inclusiveness, mutual learning and mutual benefits and aspiration to further enrich such spirit in keeping with the new era'—that is, Xi Jinping's new era.[147]

Typically, after signing on to the BRI, political leaders and senior bureaucrats soon adopt the CCP's language, reinforcing the Party's way of presenting China to the world, in a kind of subliminal soft power. In the Party's eyes, they legitimise its ambitions and become part of Xi's community of shared future for humankind.

At the end of the Second Belt and Road Forum in Beijing in 2019, dozens of world leaders signed a communiqué declaring, 'The ancient Silk Road contributed to the strengthening of the connectivity and the expansion of the world economy in the spirit of promoting peace and cooperation, openness, inclusiveness, equality, mutual learning and mutual benefit.'[148] They went on to endorse the whole word-world that Party theorists and propagandists have developed to gift-wrap the promise of Chinese investment. Properly understood, the wrapping is more important, because it's more insidious than what's inside.

7
Mobilising the Chinese diaspora

Qiaowu: overseas Chinese work

Some 50–60 million people of Chinese descent live elsewhere, a population the size of Britain's. As would be expected, they are very diverse socially, politically, culturally, linguistically, and in their feelings about China. They hail not only from the mainland, but also Taiwan, Hong Kong, Malaysia and other places. Many emigrated before the Chinese Communist Party came to power.

Over the past two or three decades, united front work, which originally focused on building coalitions with non-communist organisations in China, has shifted to a larger number of groups, including overseas communities. More recent additions to them—referred to as *xinqiao* if migrants, and *huaqiao* if PRC nationals living abroad—are more likely to retain their links to China and to 'have an emotional and psychological need to participate in activities associated with their ancestral homeland'.[1] These links, including family and business connections, provide great leverage for the CCP. In 2015 Xi Jinping designated Chinese students studying abroad as a new and important focus for united front work.[2]

The Party has propagated a version of 'Chineseness' aimed at binding overseas Chinese to the 'ancestral homeland', in so doing mobilising for its own purposes national pride in China's achievements. In the face of Western criticism of human rights violations, for instance, the Party often defends its governing style as the Chinese way or the Confucian way. (By implication, in the propaganda of the CCP, Taiwanese have chosen a path that is unsuitable to Chinese people and are paying the price in the form of social and political chaos.)

New Zealand CCP analyst James Jiann Hua To has provided an extraordinarily detailed picture of the objectives and methods of united front work in Western countries, including programs directed at overseas Chinese.[3] Known as *qiaowu* (literally, overseas Chinese affairs), its purpose is to mobilise sympathetic or potentially sympathetic community groups to serve the interests of the CCP, while at the same time suppressing those deemed hostile. It also aims to disseminate Party policy among overseas Chinese and prevent the spread of 'poisonous western ideas' (including representative democracy, human rights and academic freedom). A teaching manual for United Front cadres notes: 'The unity of Chinese at home requires the unity of the sons and daughters of Chinese abroad.'[4]

Over the past twenty years the CCP has succeeded in suppressing many voices critical of it in the West—primarily those campaigning for democracy, Tibetan autonomy, Uyghur rights, Taiwanese independence, and the rights of Falun Gong practitioners. These voices are barely heard today, in either mainstream or Chinese-language media. Control of Chinese-language media overseas has been vital in this respect. In the 1990s in Australia, for example, there was a vibrant and diverse Chinese-language media; now virtually all newspapers and radio stations reproduce Beijing's position and promote loyalty to the motherland.

Again from the 1990s, trusted individuals sympathetic to the CCP, assisted by Chinese embassies and consulates, have taken over many if not most of the established Chinese community and professional associations in North America and Western Europe. And many new organisations with a pro-Beijing position have also been established, including in business and the sciences, professional bodies, community groups for ethnic Chinese, and, since 1989, students and scholars associations on campuses.

The result is that pro-Beijing elements are now seen as representing the entire Chinese community and are often reported that way by the mainstream media. This apparent legitimacy enables them to associate with mainstream political representatives. Beijing, through its embassies and consulates, tends to guide ethnic Chinese organisations rather than directly control them. In the words of a confidential government document, the aim is to 'infiltrate their inner workings without overtly intervening; and to influence through guidance, rather than openly leading them'.[5]

United Front: modus operandi and structure

James To writes that *qiaowu* work engages in 'a continuous and evolving effort to influence the choices, direction and loyalties of the OC [overseas Chinese] by dispelling their negative suspicions and misunderstandings concerning China, and replacing those thoughts with a positive understanding instead'.[6] The work appeals to patriotism and sentiment, and routinely associates criticism of the CCP with 'anti-China' sentiment. But there are other motives too. As Party expert Gerry Groot writes, 'targets are rewarded with enhanced status and in some cases material advantages as well'.[7] Coercive and threatening methods against dissenting overseas Chinese are typically left to the Ministry of State Security and consulate staff.[8]

The psychological techniques used by the CCP in united front work have been developed and refined over decades and are taught to cadres with the help of classified manuals. James To observes that the techniques are effective for 'intensive behavioural control and manipulation' while appearing to be 'benign, benevolent and helpful'.[9] Speaking to the Central United Front Work Conference in 2015, Xi Jinping emphasised that the art of 'making friends' must be practised because it is 'an important method of carrying out united front work'. He added, 'Party cadres, government officials, united front cadres should master this method.'[10]

Since the early 2000s, national and provincial offices of the Overseas Chinese Affairs Office have been hosting 'training sessions' and 'root-seeking summer camps' for young overseas Chinese, targeting those identified as future community leaders.[11] This next generation of leaders will have a strong command of the native language of their place of residence and be at ease with the local culture. The objective is to enhance their patriotic feelings and tie them into networks in mainland China. While data is scarce, it was reported by official sources that in 2006, 11,000 young overseas Chinese participated in training.[12]

An organisational chart of overseas united front influence activities for a generic Western country is shown on the organisation chart on pages 124–5.[13] The chart is not comprehensive, and does not show the PLA's influence agencies (notably the CAIFC), or influence operations in universities, think tanks and non-Chinese-language media. And the more diffuse work of Party agencies cannot be reflected in a chart. What the chart does show are the links between the CCP and domestic organisations in the West: the latter are shown below the line dividing China and the Western nation. Only the main implementation agencies—those that make their presence felt in Western nations and that appear in this book—are shown, rather than the policy development bureaucracy that sits above these agencies (such as the Foreign Affairs Commission and the Leading Small Groups).

United front work falls under the aegis of the CCP rather than state agencies (shown on the right of the chart), although the latter are controlled by the CCP and also engage in influence work. The United Front Work Department is a large department under the authority of a Central Leading Small Group. After a recent restructuring, the 3rd, 9th and 10th bureaus of the UFWD are tasked with carrying out influence operations among ethnic Chinese communities abroad.[14] Two other Party departments also engage in overseas influence work: the International Liaison Department (also known as the International Department) and the Propaganda Department. The UFWD set out its broad strategy in its 2004 Blue Book.[15] The aim is to foster the 'cohesion of the Chinese nationality' by emphasising the 'cultural identity' and patriotism towards country and hometown of non-communist overseas Chinese wherever they may be.

In August 1979 General Secretary Deng Xiaoping gave explicit directions to the 14th national conference on united front work: 'The united front work is a task for the entire party, it depends on the entire party to do it. Party committees at every level should include the united front in their agenda.'[16] This means that, in practice, united front work is less structured and more amorphous than suggested by the chart.

The UFWD guides the Chinese People's Political Consultative Conference, a large, high-level advisory council that draws non-Party elements into the CCP's orbit (more on this below). Overseas Chinese persons who serve the Party well are invited to join the national Political Consultative Conference or its provincial counterparts. One of the CPPCC's most important overseas agencies is the China Council for the Promotion of Peaceful National Reunification, which has some 200 chapters throughout the world. The All-China Federation of Returned Overseas Chinese is also formally a constituency body of the CPPCC, but is in practice controlled by the UFWD, and for this reason is shown in the box that captures the major agencies controlled by the UFWD—the Overseas Chinese Affairs Office, the China News Service, and the China Overseas Friendship Association, also referred to as the Chinese Overseas Exchange Association.

Chinese People's Association for Friendship with Foreign Countries

The CPAFFC is the primary organ of influence in Western countries for 'people's diplomacy' through state, provincial and local governments; sister cities, parliamentary friendship groups; and China friendship societies, among others. The CPAFFC is mentioned often in this book.

The location of the CPAFFC in the Party hierarchy is uncertain, but Jichang Lulu makes a persuasive case that it is managed, though not controlled, by the Ministry of Foreign Affairs, with 'management' being defined as 'political and thought leadership' rather than day-to-day management.[17] The CPAFFC is staffed by cadres from Foreign Affairs. As it is controlled by a powerful princeling, Li Xiaolin, daughter of one of the Party's 'Eight Immortals', Li Xiannian, it enjoys considerable autonomy.[18]

Overseas Chinese Affairs Office

The OCAO is responsible for overseas Chinese including guiding or supervising as much activity by overseas Chinese as it can. James To writes: 'The OCAO also has a clear soft power agenda through guidance, coordination, solidarity, and friendship with the OC [overseas Chinese] mass media, cultural societies, and schools to carry out cultural communications.'[19]

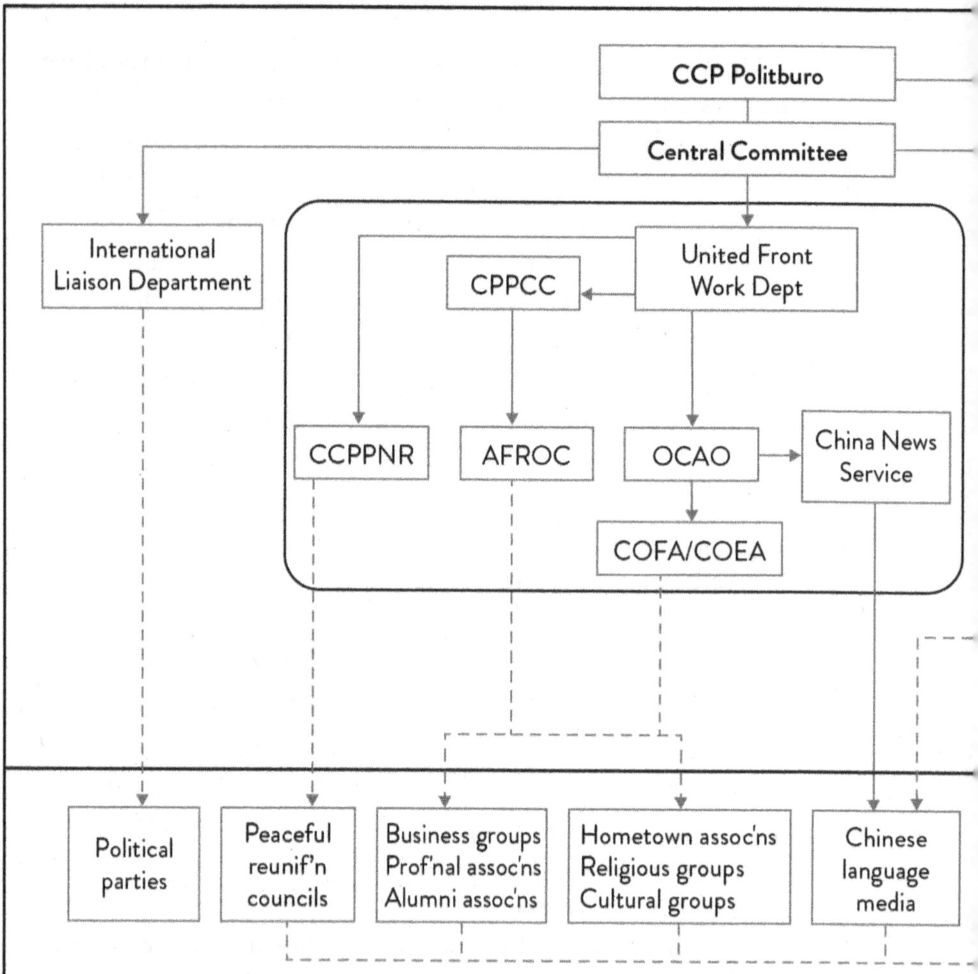

LEGEND

—— **directs/manages** - - - - **guides/influences**

AFROC – All-China Federation of Returned Overseas Chinese
CAIEP – China Association for International Exchange of Personnel
CCPIT – China Council for the Promotion of International Trade
CCPPNR – China Council for the Promotion of Peaceful National Reunification
CICIR – China Institutes of Contemporary International Relations
COEA – Chinese Overseas Exchange Association
COFA – China Overseas Friendship Association
CPAFFC – Chinese People's Association for Friendship with Foreign Countries
CPIFA – Chinese People's Institute of Foreign Affairs
CPPCC – Chinese People's Political Consultative Conference
CSSA – Chinese Students and Scholars Association
OCAO – Overseas Chinese Affairs Office
SAFEA – State Administration of Foreign Experts Affairs

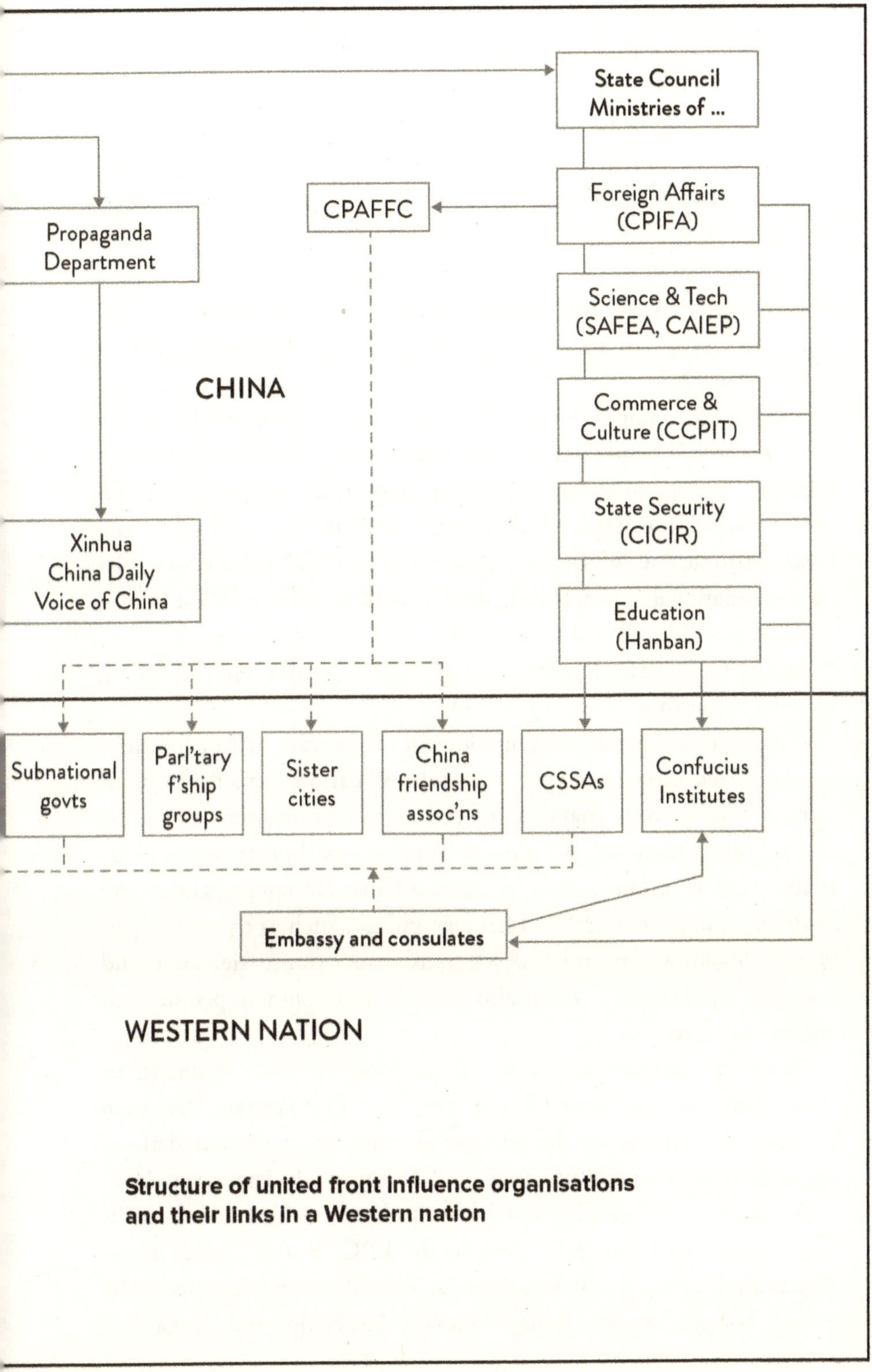

Structure of united front influence organisations and their links in a Western nation

In 2018 all of the functions of the OCAO were absorbed by the UFWD (into the 9th and 10th bureaus), but it still exists as a name for external use.[20] We retain its use here because the activities of 'OCAO officials' are reported in Western-oriented reports and commentary. Importantly, the OCAO and AFROC have provincial, city and county counterparts throughout China, and these have a direct role in cultivating and maintaining links with associations of overseas Chinese. Dozens of such organisations exist in most Western countries at the national, state and city levels, and all have links with the Chinese embassy or local consulates.[21]

As part of Xi Jinping's intensification of united front work, in June 2014 the OCAO unveiled its 'eight big plans for benefitting overseas Chinese', a program aimed at Chinese community groups, mutual aid centres, education, traditional Chinese medicine, cultural exchange, businesspeople and information services.[22] The OCOA also operates its own international news network, the China News Service. While official news agencies like Xinhua feed stories to Chinese-language media in the West, the CNS 'covertly runs overseas media organizations', including through ownership.[23]

The overseas Chinese organisations in the bottom half of the chart can be sorted into nine types: peaceful unification councils; business associations, such as chambers of commerce; professional, scientific and scholarly associations; alumni associations; hometown associations; religious groups, such as Chinese Christian congregations and Buddhist groups; cultural and heritage groups, such as dance troupes, writers' organisations and PLA veterans' associations; friendship and exchange associations, which also draw in non-Chinese people; and student associations.

Veterans' associations are worth dwelling on for a moment. In Western nations with large Chinese diasporas, PLA veterans have been forming associations for the purpose of renewing the camaraderie of the army days, as well as building *guanxi* for mutual advantage in business and social affairs. The nostalgia helps keep members emotionally, linguistically and culturally close to the PRC. But as United Front organisations, they also have subversive and influence functions.[24] The French Foreign Legion Chinese Veterans Association was established in 1996, although it did not become active in social events until 2004 when it registered with the Chinese embassy.[25] Its website notes that as long as PLA veterans can pass the test, they can join the French Foreign Legion, serve for five years and secure French citizenship.[26] In 2016 Chen Jianqing took over as president of the association, in the presence of various dignitaries and 'under the care of the Chinese Embassy in France'.[27] The outgoing president detailed a series of influence activities carried out by the association, including science and technology exchanges, BRI promotion, a forum on Chinese public security issues, and the facilitation of links between overseas Chinese and China. Among this last were cultural activities in China for Chinese-French children.[28]

In London, at the 2016 celebration of Army Day (held on 1 August to commemorate the establishment of the PLA), the president of the British Chinese Veteran's Association, Wang Jing, declared that the association would 'safeguard the dignity of the motherland' and 'respond to the call' of the motherland whenever it is needed.[29] In Canada, the founding of the Canada Chinese Veteran's Society in 2018 caused unease in sections of the Chinese-Canadian community.[30] The society has staged concerts in which veterans dressed in PLA uniforms sing patriotic military songs, and has held retreats where they are photographed goosestepping and saluting the flags of the PLA, China and Canada.

In Sydney, PLA veterans formed the Australian Chinese Ex-services Association in 2015. It too has staged events featuring army uniforms and patriotic songs, and has used military tactics to participate in welcoming ceremonies on city streets for Chinese leaders. On Army Day in Melbourne in 2018, uniforms were again donned, this time by the Australia-China Veterans Club, and there was marching to revolutionary songs.[31] In New Zealand, the role of the New Zealand (Chinese) Veterans Association has been more sinister. Its members have monitored events unsympathetic to Beijing and engaged in intimidation of critics.[32] Authorities in Western countries have done nothing in response to such behaviour.

Chinese People's Political Consultative Conference

One of the leading institutions of United Front work, the Chinese People's Political Consultative Conference is a high-level advisory body whose role is to integrate non-Party elements into the national decision-making process. Some years ago, it was opened up to business leaders and professionals, and has since become highly effective in co-opting wealthy and influential Chinese, abroad as well as at home, into the Party's sphere. Those invited into the CPPCC gain invaluable access to China's power centres. It has been reported that the 2013 national conference included fifty-two billionaires among its delegates.[33]

The CPPCC has provincial and municipal counterparts, allowing the net to be spread even wider. As a political body set up to draw in forces outside the CCP considered significant, it is arguably 'the most prominent national united front body'.[34] Overseas Chinese who participate in the CPPCC are usually trusted by the Party to advance its interests. Fred Teng, for example, president of the America China Public Affairs Institute (and also 'special US representative' of the China-U.S. Exchange Foundation), acted as convener of a session at the 2018 conference. While in Beijing, Teng told his hosts that 'a strong China is the most ardent hope of overseas Chinese'.[35]

China Council for the Promotion of Peaceful National Reunification

Established in 1988 to counter Taiwanese independence, the China Council for the Promotion of Peaceful National Reunification has since broadened its influence activities among overseas Chinese. In some countries the CCPPNR chapter is the foremost united front group. In a sign of its importance in the CCP hierarchy, the chair of the council, Wang Yang, is a member of the Politburo's Standing Committee. Its vice chair is the head of the UFWD. A thinly disguised front organisation of the UFWD, the council promotes CCP propaganda. John Dotson has listed ninety-one countries that host chapters of the CCPPNR, some with several regional chapters, and notes that it's 'an organisation that is becoming more active in covert political influence efforts on behalf of the Chinese government'.[36]

While the English names of the council's chapters vary, the Chinese characters are generally the same. In the United States, which has branches in most major cities, the national headquarters in Washington D.C. is called the National Association for China's Peaceful Unification. In the Chicago area, it's the Chinese American Alliance for China's

Peaceful Reunification. In Britain it's the UK Chinese Association for the Promotion of National Reunification.

The leaders of all of these groups around the world have close links to Beijing, and their work as agents of influence has been further elevated under Xi Jinping. The Sydney-based Australian Council for the Promotion of Peaceful Reunification of China has been very active in influence peddling, establishing deep links with the major political parties, not least through large donations. In 2018 the council's then president, billionaire Huang Xiangmo, was denied re-entry to Australia, in part because of his links to CCP operations.[37]

In the United States, CCPPNR affiliates have kept a lower profile. In D.C., efforts to cultivate politicians appear to be modest, confined mainly to moulding opinion within the ethnic Chinese community rather than wider public opinion or government policies. But here too, the increasingly prominent role of these Party affiliates means that dissident voices are drowned out.[38]

True to its name, the CCPPNR works towards excluding Taiwan from the international community. The European Association for the Peaceful Reunification of China has published an appeal to 'all compatriots in Europe' to oppose events organised by Taiwanese activists in support of Taiwan's participation in the World Health Assembly.[39]

Threats and harassment

Among the Chinese communities (and communities the CCP claims as Chinese) subjected to harassment, practitioners of Falun Gong have been at the sharp end. A peaceful spiritual practice based on tai chi and Buddhism, Falun Gong had millions of followers across China in the 1990s, perhaps in response to moral decline under CCP rule, lamented by many writers and intellectuals. Although it had no political interests, Falun Gong's rapid spread frightened the Party's leaders, and in 1999 Premier Jiang Zemin launched a ferocious crackdown. Many practitioners managed to escape from China, but wherever they've settled they have faced persecution, from the petty to the violent.

One of the more serious incidents took place in Flushing, in Queens, New York City, which has a large Chinese community. In 2008 Falun Gong practitioners were abused, harassed and attacked on the streets by patriotic 'anti-cult' activists led by a man named Michael Chu. Chu was the vice president of the New York Association for the Peaceful Reunification of China.[40] Falun Gong practitioners also received phone calls threatening them with death, and punishment for their families in China. It emerged that China's consul general in New York, Peng Keyu, had personally instigated the violence.[41]

In 2019, with repression in the 'autonomous region' of Xinjiang at an all-time high, including surveillance equipment in wide use and more than a million people interned in concentration camps, Chinese authorities intensified their harassment of Uyghurs living outside China. In France, Chinese police have been contacting expatriate Uyghurs by phone and WeChat, demanding they provide such information as scans of their French ID cards and marriage certificates, along with their home and work addresses. In Germany, when the sister of exiled Uyghur Abdujelil Emet phoned him from her home in Xinjiang to beg him to stop his activism, a security agent took the phone and told him, 'You're living overseas, but you need to think of your family while you're running around doing your activism work in Germany. You need to think of their safety.'[42] Persecution of Uyghurs is occurring in many countries and foreign citizenship provides no protection from the Chinese police.[43]

Uyghur students in the West have been threatened by their Han Chinese classmates for expressing their opinions. A Uyghur student in the US was told he would be reported to the Chinese embassy for using the term 'East Turkistan', the name preferred by many Uyghurs for their homeland.[44] Denouncing him as a separatist, the Chinese students were heard to say, 'We cannot allow you to speak against China in our class!' (The teacher told them that if they reported him to the embassy, the Uyghur student would be entitled to report them to the FBI. They backed down.) Uyghurs in Canada, Britain, Sweden and Germany have been told that unless they agree to spy on fellow Uyghurs they will never see their families again.[45] 'Some might think that once you flee China, you are free,' said a Canadian Uyghur leader. 'But you are never free.'

Wen Yunchao, a human rights activist based in New York, has said that Chinese authorities took photos of his son on his way to school. 'They just wanted to let me know that at any time they can harm my child,' he said.[46] Many other Chinese people living abroad, including human rights lawyers Teng Biao and Chen Guangcheng, report receiving death threats.[47] Democracy activist Sheng Xue from Toronto said that Chinese authorities were tracking her and had threatened to kill her if she didn't stop criticising China's leaders. She has also been harassed online, including having her head photoshopped onto nudes which were then posted to escort sites, along with her phone number and address, resulting in countless phone calls.[48]

In Germany, Chinese artist Yang Weidong said, '... it's getting to the point where they are treating Germany as if it were the Chinese Communist Party's backyard.'[49] Didi Kirsten Tatlow recounts an incident at a memorial service for Nobel Peace Prize laureate Liu Xiaobo in Berlin in 2018, where a number of Chinese guests 'with unemotional expressions' started filming everyone, frightening anyone familiar with the methods of Chinese state security.[50] The sense of insecurity and fear felt by many Chinese, Uyghur, Hong Kong and Tibetan people residing in the West, along with Falun Gong practitioners, is reinforced when law enforcement authorities collaborate with China's police and intelligence services, as will be seen in chapter thirteen. As if to remind CCP critics that the Party-state can find them anywhere, patriotic Chinese in Western cities have taken to kitting out their cars to look like Chinese police vehicles.[51]

Huaren canzheng

Beijing began pushing its policy of *huaren canzheng*, or 'ethnic Chinese participation in politics', around 2005.[52] Often exploiting the narrative of a 'century of humiliation' and continuing anti-Chinese racism, it was a new tactic in the Party's united front strategy, and over the following years it saw ethnic Chinese people supported by Beijing joining political parties and running for office in Canada, the United States, New Zealand, Australia, Britain and beyond.[53]

United front organisations are increasingly following the advice laid out in 2010 by a CCP strategist—build ethnic Chinese-based political organisations, make political donations, support ethnic Chinese politicians, and deploy votes to swing close-run elections.[54] The approach is related to the 'mixing sand' tactic used by Chairman Mao; that is, planting trusted people in the enemy's camp.[55] Its program is most advanced in Canada but has been building in Germany, France, New Zealand and Australia.[56] In September 2019 Australian news outlets reported that a newly elected member of federal parliament, Gladys Liu, had links to a number of united front groups, in both Australia and China.[57] Most damningly, evidence emerged that she had been a member for several years of the council of the Guangdong Overseas Exchange Association, a chapter of the China Overseas Exchange Association, a UFWD agency (see the organisation chart on pages 124–5). Liu won selection as a Liberal Party candidate because she was a prolific fundraiser in the Chinese community (A$1 million, or US$700,000).[58] After she was elected to parliament, the prime minister, Scott Morrison, dismissed the allegations of Liu's CCP links as a smear with racist undertones.[59]

In November 2019 a leading Australian investigative reporter, Nick McKenzie, broke an explosive story about a Chinese spy ring attempting to recruit a luxury car dealer in Melbourne to run for federal parliament.[60] Bo (Nick) Zhao was promised A$1 million towards his campaign. The spy ring was reportedly led by Melbourne businessman Brian Chen, described as 'a suspected senior Chinese intelligence operative' (a claim Chen rejects). The plan was to back Nick Zhao as the Liberal Party candidate for the seat of Chisholm (the seat subsequently won by Gladys Liu). Zhao reported the attempt to recruit him to the Australian Security Intelligence Organisation in late 2018, and in March 2019 he was found dead in a motel room in mysterious circumstances.

People of Chinese heritage living in the West are often under-represented in politics, and more should be done to encourage their participation. However, the situation is being exploited by the CCP to push forward candidates sympathetic to it. Democratic elections are used to advance the Party's authoritarian influence, and again, a history of anti-Chinese sentiment is often used to unite voters.

Another avenue for gaining political influence is the formation of ethnic Chinese ginger groups within mainstream political parties. In Western Australia, for example, the Australian Chinese Labor Association is influential within the Labor Party, and has promoted favoured candidates into political office.[61] The WA Chinese Liberal

Club has done the same on the conservative side. Candidates recruited and supported by such organisations are expected to put ethnic Chinese voters' interests first. United front organisations appear to be grooming a new generation of Chinese-Australians for entry into politics, either through mentoring or 'educational seminars'.

In France, representatives of the Association des Chinois Residant en France travelled to Beijing in 2017 to meet the deputy head of the Overseas Chinese Affairs Office, Tan Tianxing. The association's president, Ren Limin, told Tan that his organisation would nurture young ethnic Chinese community leaders and encourage young people to participate in local politics.[62] The following year Ren Limin was invited to the Chinese People's Political Consultative Conference, a measure of the Party's trust in him.[63]

Huaren canzheng in the United Kingdom

Some prominent Britons of Chinese heritage are office holders or members of united front organisations that meet in China.[64] In May 2018 the OCAO in Beijing encouraged Chinese-Britons to get out and vote, and praised the large number of them standing for election.[65] Two Chinese-Britons are particularly noteworthy.

Christine Lee is a solicitor whose firm has offices in Beijing, Hong Kong and Guangzhou, as well as London.[66] In 2006 she founded the British Chinese Project (the Chinese name for which translates as 'British Chinese Participation in Politics'). At the time, she was a member of the China Overseas Exchange Association.[67] Her links to the CCP go deep. She has been the chief legal adviser to the Chinese embassy in London and a legal adviser to the Overseas Chinese Affairs Office. Lee is also an overseas member of the Chinese People's Political Consultative Conference.[68] These positions are unmistakable signs of her importance to the Party. Yet she is also the secretary of the Inter-Party China Group of the British parliament.[69]

Lee's involvement in British politics appears to have begun during the prime ministership of Tony Blair, when she formed an alliance with London Labour MP and minister Barry Gardiner, more recently Labour's shadow international trade secretary.[70] Exposing these links in 2017, Hannah McGrath and Oliver Wright wrote in *The Times*: 'What followed ... was a fruitful association that eventually led Ms Lee to donate more than £200,000 to both the MP and his constituency party.'

In 2007, while a Blair government minister, Barry Gardiner became the chair of Christine Lee's British Chinese Project and the two of them embarked on a program of making friends in Westminster, boosted by Gardiner's formation in 2011 of 'an all-party group ... to represent Chinese citizens in Britain'. One of Lee's children, Michael Wilkes, became its vice chairman.[71]

Another son, Daniel Wilkes, began working in Gardiner's parliamentary office, with his salary paid by his mother's law firm. Gardiner has been a strong advocate of closer Sino-British relations and investment in Britain by China's sovereign wealth fund. He was a strong advocate for the construction of a nuclear power station at Hinkley Point by a state-owned Chinese corporation, which Theresa May's government put on hold due to concerns about national security. According to *The Times*, 'A Labour source said that he [Gardiner] strongly opposed internal party criticism of Chinese involvement in the Hinkley Point project.'[72]

On her blog Christine Lee describes the CCP's *huaren canzheng* program and gives advice to British people of Chinese heritage on how to gain influence. She writes that the British Chinese Project is working with former Tory MP Edmond Yeo (originally from Malaysia); the chair of Chinese for Labour, Sonny Leong; and the co-chair of the Chinese Liberal Democratic Party, Merlene Emerson.[73] Lee's work has won praise from official CCP media, with the *China Daily* reporting in 2011 that she had made great efforts to promote the rights of Chinese in the UK.[74]

Lee has organised many events for visiting Chinese delegations and met with Beijing's top leaders, including Xi Jinping. She appears to have developed a good relationship with David Cameron while he was prime minister. In 2012 she led the largest ever *huaren canzheng* delegation to Beijing. She was accompanied by Sonny Leong and the chairwoman of the Liberal Democrats and they were received by Tan Tianxing, then deputy head of the OCAO.[75] In 2016 Lee and Sonny Leong again met with Tan, this time with the vice president of the Chinese Liberal Democrats. Tan encouraged British-Chinese to join the political mainstream.[76] The following year, Lee, Leong and a group of UK *huaren canzheng* promoters were back in Beijing to consult with Tan.[77]

In 2015 Lee was again lauded for her *huaren canzheng* work, this time by the *People's Daily*, which reported that she 'led the door-to-door encouragement of Chinese to vote, popularise electoral knowledge, and help Chinese to fill in the voting cards'.[78] In 2016 an official *qiaowu* website said of Lee's work, 'the Chinese must control their own destiny'.[79] On 31 January 2019 Christine Lee received a Points of Light Award from Prime Minister May, in recognition of her contribution through the British Chinese Project.[80] A photo of Lee in front of 10 Downing Street shows the iconic door draped with red banners displaying New Year couplets in Chinese characters and announcing the 'Golden Era' of Sino-British relations. The symbolism is blunt and powerful: Lee at the heart of Britain's government, being embraced by it.

One of the founders of Chinese for Labour was Katy Tse Blair, the Chinese-American sister-in-law of Tony Blair, who was prime minister at the time the group was established in 1999.[81] It's affiliated with the Labour Party, is represented on the National Executive Committee and the National Policy Forum, and regularly meets with the leader, deputy leader and shadow cabinet.[82] Chair Sonny Leong is a member of the 48 Group Club and also of the Labour Party 1000 Club (which provides access for donations), and an executive committee member of BAME Labour—the Black, Asian and Minority Ethnic Labour group affiliated to the party.[83]

The second Chinese-Briton of particular relevance to this book is involved with the other side of politics. Li Xuelin arrived in Britain in 1989 and after some years entered the real estate business.[84] In 2009 she became the founding president of the Zhejiang UK Association, which carries out united front work.[85] She continues to serve as ZJUKA's honorary chair.[86] In the same year, she was appointed vice president of the council of the Zhejiang Overseas Exchange Association, an affiliate of the United Front Work Department.[87]

In one of the clearest signs of the CCP's faith in her, Li Xuelin is executive vice president of the UK Chinese Association for the Promotion of National Reunification, the British chapter of the CCPPNR. In 2013 she was also appointed as an overseas council member of AFROC, and was reappointed in 2018 (see the organisation chart on pages 124–5).[88]

In 2009 Li Xuelin attended a five-day leadership workshop in Hangzhou. Organised by the OCAO, its purpose was to 'promote the sustainable development of *qiaowu* work'.[89] The next year she was back in Hangzhou meeting with top Party officials, where she 'reported to leaders of her home country and hometown' on her work. The Zhejiang UK Association was praised for its achievements.[90]

Li had quickly become an enthusiastic campaigner for the Conservative Party on arriving in Britain, and for David Cameron in particular, meeting him on many occasions.[91] By 2015 Cameron began speaking of 'a Golden Era' in the Sino-British relationship.[92] At the same time, Li was working as a 'pro bono advisor' to Lord Wei (Nathanael Ming-Yan Wei), a social entrepreneur and the first British-born Chinese-heritage peer. Li Xuelin accompanied Wei to China, where she reportedly enhanced Lord Wei's understanding of the PRC.[93]

In 2011 Li met the Conservative peer and sometime minister of state Lord Michael Bates. In that same year she introduced him to Li Xiaolin, president of the CPAFFC and a top Party cadre.[94] Li Xuelin and Michael Bates married in 2012.[95] Lord Bates had been a friend of China for some years, so much so that when Xi Jinping addressed the British parliament during his 2015 state visit he singled out Bates for praise. And Bates was present at Xi's meeting with the elite of the CCP's British friends, along with a number of prominent faces from the 48 Group Club, of which Bates is a fellow.[96] In 2019 Bates gave a TED talk in which he professed his love for China and the amazing achievements of its government, reeling off a string of statistics and telling his audience that China only wants peace.[97] In April that same year, Li Xuelin, now Lady Bates, attended a seminar, Xi Jinping Thought on Diplomacy, hosted by the Chinese embassy and also attended by several 48 Group Club luminaries, including Chairman Perry.[98]

The marriage to Bates opened more doors. Over the years, she has actively facilitated access by Chinese businesspeople to Britain's elite circles, receiving praise in united front outlets in China.[99]

In 2014 Xuelin Bates was caught up in a property development scandal involving Boris Johnson, then mayor of London, with whom she had developed a friendship. A deal she facilitated between Johnson and a Chinese company she worked for, Advanced Business Park, to redevelop a part of London's Royal Albert Dock was worth £1 billion and described as 'China's largest property investment in the UK'.[100] It was claimed that Johnson gave preferment to ABP because of Bates's donations to the Conservative Party—£162,000 between 2010 and 2012. Lady Bates said the money had not come from ABP but from her own pocket.[101] It seems that in 2015 she persuaded Johnson to back another development by a Chinese firm, this one in Crystal Palace Park and worth £500 million.[102] Lord Bates failed to declare a financial interest in the scheme, which subsequently collapsed.[103]

Xuelin Bates pays £50,000 a year to be a member of the Leader's Group, which was set up by David Cameron for top donors to the Conservative Party.[104] Members have special access to senior politicians. In May 2014, at a Conservative Party luncheon that she co-organised, Xuelin Bates introduced her Chinese guests one by one to Cameron, in order, it was said, to lay a foundation for future Sino-British cooperation.[105] In 2017 she campaigned with her husband for Theresa May in the forthcoming general election, sitting next to the prime minister as May made phone calls to voters. ZJUKA's newsletter emphasised that its president Xuelin stood next to May when the prime minister delivered her campaign speech.[106] Lady Bates was again rubbing shoulders with the prime minister at a Two Cities Luncheon in 2018.[107] In 2019 Lord and Lady Bates campaigned enthusiastically for Boris Johnson.

In February 2019 ZJUKA held the UK-China 'Golden Era' New Year Dinner in the Houses of Parliament, where British politicians, Chinese diplomats and businessmen mingled. At a charity auction session, a piece of papercut art made by Theresa May was bought by Beijing businessman Yao Yichun.[108] A few days later, at the Conservative Party's annual black-and-white fundraising ball, Xuelin Bates informed Theresa May that Yao Yichun had paid £2200 for her artwork. The prime minister was reportedly very pleased and thanked Yao for his generosity.[109] Two years earlier, Yao Yichun had donated £12,000 to a charity event hosted by Lady Bates.[110]

On the same day that Christine Lee was draping the door of 10 Downing Street with Chinese banners, Xuelin Bates and three other figures linked to CCP agencies were decorating the inside of Number 10 for a celebration of Chinese New Year with Theresa May.[111] Christine Lee and Xuelin Bates had both succeeded in positioning themselves close to Britain's top elites, where they could spread a 'Chinese perspective'.

Lord Michael Bates is an enthusiastic hiker and has undertaken several 'Walks of Friendship' through China. In August 2019, with Lady Bates in attendance, he took a month-long hike around Zhejiang province. The walk was co-organised by the Chinese People's Association for Friendship with Foreign Countries and the Walk for Peace Foundation (chaired by Lady Xuelin Bates).[112] A soft-soap documentary was made of Bates's meet-the-people walk by a subsidiary of the China Foreign Language Bureau, part of the CCP's external propaganda machine.

Whether seen as pathetic or sinister, Michael Bates's activities are ideal for the CCP tactic of 'use the foreigner to tell good China stories'. Interviewed by the *People's Daily* in 2019, he once again gushed about modern China, stressing how much it has contributed to world peace and prosperity.[113]

At a screening of the documentary at the Chinese embassy in London, the ambassador told those gathered: 'On their journey, [the Bates's] tried to find out about the connection between Xi Jinping Thought on Socialism with Chinese Characteristics for a New Era and different places and people in China, and what kind of guidance it offered to local development.'[114] Agreements have been reached to air the documentary on CNBC, *The Wall Street Journal* website, China Central Television, and a number of new media outlets.[115]

More importantly for the CCP's influence work in Britain, in December 2019 it was reported that Bates had signed an agreement with Li Xiaolin, president of the CPAFFC, to establish the UK China Friendship Association, scheduled to be launched in February 2020.[116] The agreement was made at a meeting in the Beijing office of the CPAFFC with Li Xiaolin. During the same visit, Lord and Lady Bates were presented with an award for 'spreading the Brilliance of China' by the deputy minister of the CCP's Propaganda Department.[117]

8
The ecology of espionage

Influence and spying

In 1996 President Bill Clinton's re-election fund received a large donation from the Chinese–Indonesian company Lippo, and further donations from the Chinese–Thai group Charoeun Popkhand and the Macau company San Kin Yip. Lippo had been partly acquired by China Resources Group, a company that was owned by the Ministry of Foreign Trade and Economic Cooperation. All up, these donations amounted to $4.5 million. They had been brokered by a number of Chinese-Americans with links to the CCP. It was later reported that $300,000 had been provided by the daughter of General Liu Huaqing, a vice chairman of China's Central Military Commission until 1997.[1]

The brokers were frequent visitors to the White House, often bringing Chinese associates. One organised a meeting between Bill Clinton and Wang Jun, head of the Hong Kong–based companies CITIC and China Poly Group, both of which have close links with the PLA. A Hong Kong insider said that 'the leadership of CITIC is known to harbour within its ranks a large number of secret agents' from military intelligence, and Poly Technologies (a Poly Group subsidiary) has been described as 'a haven for the Red Princes'.[2] Wang Jun, in other words, had ties to Chinese intelligence when he met the US president in the White House.

There is much more to the 'Chinagate' scandal, which was convoluted and had implications never fully exposed, in part because the Lewinsky scandal distracted attention. But it did reveal the ability of China's intelligence agencies to penetrate to the highest levels.[3]

Chinagate was a foretaste of something else. Beijing's espionage activities (stealing secrets and intellectual property) and its influence operations (shaping opinion and behaviour) frequently go hand in hand, and often involve the same people and organisations. But while united front operatives in the West can often be identified, not least because they are inclined to brag about their activities, intelligence agents operate under deep cover. This chapter explains how influence is leveraged to facilitate espionage, and how espionage is used to inform and enhance influence activities.

Historically, Western spy agencies have confined themselves to stealing government and military secrets, by recruiting agents, planting moles and intercepting communications. While the Chinese state engages in these traditional practices, it also crosses boundaries, sending intelligence agents into all kinds of other domains. Beijing devotes enormous resources to both industrial espionage, aimed at commercial secrets, and state espionage, aimed at government and military secrets. The assistant director of counter-intelligence at the FBI, Bill Priestap, observed in late 2018 that the bureau has handled 'thousands' of complaints about and investigations into non-traditional espionage activity, mostly concerning China. 'Every rock we turn over, every time we look for it, it is not only there—it is worse than anticipated,' he said.[4] The U.S. Department of Justice estimates that between 2011 and 2018 China was involved in 90 per cent of economic espionage cases.[5]

Industrial espionage has been practised by private companies for a long time, but China has taken the leap of deploying its diplomatic and intelligence services to facilitate the theft of intellectual property.[6] In addition, the united front apparatus and the intelligence agencies reach deeply into overseas Chinese communities where they recruit both agents of influence as well as informants and spies. While traditional forms of espionage rely on specialised training, China's diffuse program of intelligence gathering relies on thousands of amateur information collectors, what James To calls 'de-centralised micro-espionage'.[7] Professionals, businesspeople, students and even tourists are encouraged to provide information to handlers in embassies and consulates as part of the 'thousand grains of sand' strategy. In 2007 the head of the Canadian Security Intelligence Service observed, 'It's surprising, sometimes, the number of hyperactive tourists we get here and where they come from.'[8] The information may be about technology, trade negotiations, business pricing and strategies, or reports on the activities of members of the diaspora.[9]

Peter Mattis, among others, argues that, although there are indeed thousands of amateurs gathering information, much of the activity is conceived and directed by professionals in the intelligence services.[10] Mattis describes a 'layered approach to intelligence collection', from traditional operations by spy agencies down to amateurs working from their homes and offices.[11] Rather than waiting for what comes in, intelligence professionals target particular pieces of intellectual property, often working with factories and research labs in China, and then finding people who can acquire them.[12] With advice or training from their handlers, some amateur spies use 'tradecraft' methods such as encryption, covert communication, aliases and counter-surveillance practices. In November 2019 Xuehua Peng, a San Francisco tour guide and US citizen, was convicted on spying charges after being caught making 'dead drops'; to wit, hiding cash-filled envelopes in hotel rooms then returning to pick up memory cards containing classified security information, which he took to China and handed to agents at the Ministry of State Security.[13]

China's espionage agencies

Since the remit of China's intelligence agencies is much broader than those of Western nations, they need more resources, and Xi Jinping has made sure they receive them. As Roger Faligot has written, there has been a 'formidable increase in the authority of the Chinese intelligence apparatus, specifically since 2017'.[14] There are two primary spying organisations: the Ministry of State Security, and the Intelligence Bureau of the CMC Joint Staff Department (formerly 2PLA, the Second Department of the PLA General Staff Department).

Roughly speaking, the Ministry of State Security combines the functions of the CIA and the FBI, but with much more power and focused on the political security of the CCP. The MSS is responsible for both domestic and overseas intelligence and security operations. It can order Chinese organisations and individuals, including those abroad, to undertake intelligence activities. Much of the work is carried out by provincial and municipal offices. Peter Mattis and Matthew Brazil, authors of the most recent and authoritative account of China's spy agencies, identify eighteen MSS bureaus.[15] For our purposes, several are worth noting.

The 1st Bureau is responsible for agents in deep cover, with no links to the government, and the 2nd Bureau runs agents 'using diplomatic, journalistic, or other government-related covers'.[16] The 10th Bureau (Foreign Security and Reconnaissance) manages Chinese student organisations abroad, among others; the 11th, comprising the CICIR think tank, does open-source research and network-building abroad; the 12th (Social Affairs) handles 'MSS contributions to united front work'; and the 18th (U.S. Operations) carries out clandestine espionage in the United States. Most of the operations against the US are run by the Shanghai State Security Bureau.[17]

It was reported in 2005 that the FBI believed the MSS had set up around 3000 front companies to conceal its activities.[18] The MSS has various arms engaged in economic espionage and it has 'embedded itself deep in major financial and commercial organizations, particularly in Shanghai and Hong Kong'.[19] Not all economic espionage is state-directed. Chinese nationals are known to set up firms that take orders from companies in China to obtain and supply specific pieces of intellectual property from their competitors in the West, usually by identifying an employee willing to provide such secrets.[20]

The People's Liberation Army also undertakes extensive intelligence-gathering and espionage. The structure was overhauled in 2016 and much remains opaque, though Peter Mattis sets out the new structure as best as is known.[21]

The Intelligence Bureau of the CMC Joint Staff Department is responsible for military intelligence but also has a history of extensive activity in civilian domains. It draws on military attachés and signals intelligence to gather intelligence. The Joint Staff Department has its own think tanks—the China Institute for International Strategic

Studies, which focuses on research, and the China Foundation for International and Strategic Studies, which engages in academic and policy exchanges.[22] Its Institute of International Relations (now part of the National University of Defense Technology) trains military attachés and secret agents. In their 2016 book *China's Espionage Dynasty*, James Scott and Drew Spaniel estimated that 2PLA had 30,000–50,000 plants in organisations around the world, whose aim is to collect information, confidential and otherwise, to be sent back to China.[23]

The Central Military Commission's Political Work Department maintains the Party's control structures in the armed forces, including education, indoctrination and discipline. According to Mattis, its Liaison Department specialises in united front work, political warfare, and clandestine HUMINT (human intelligence).[24] It has maintained an extensive program of infiltrating or covertly taking over private companies, and of using state-owned companies as cover for intelligence activity. Many of these companies are based in Hong Kong. The Liaison Department operates the important front organisation, the China Association for International Friendly Contacts, described in chapter ten.

The PLA's powerful Strategic Support Force, formed in 2016, brings together 'most of the PLA's technical reconnaissance capabilities overhead, in cyberspace, and across the electromagnetic spectrum'.[25] With a focus on intelligence-gathering for military operations, the SSF is responsible for signals intelligence including monitoring telecommunications, as well as cyber intelligence, special operations, information warfare, and offensive cyber operations (tasks previously done by the General Staff Department's third and fourth departments).[26]

China's enormous appetite for other countries' technology—obtained legally or otherwise—is satisfied by a number of means. At the heart of defence-industry technology transfer is the State Administration for Science, Technology and Industry for National Defence, 'a veritable "intelligence vacuum cleaner"'.[27]

This central intelligence apparatus has parallel structures in State Security Bureaus in each province. Provinces and major cities also have their own talent and recruitment programs linked directly to the United Front Work Department.[28]

Recruitment methods

A review of China-linked espionage cases of all kinds in the US between 2000 and early 2019, carried out by the Center for Strategic and International Studies, tallied 137 reported instances. It found that 57 per cent of actors were 'Chinese military or government employees', 36 per cent were 'private Chinese citizens', and 7 per cent were 'non-Chinese actors (usually US persons)'.[29] (A study of all cases of *economic* espionage in the US between 2009 and 2015 found that 52 per cent of those charged were of Chinese heritage, a tripling of the percentage for the period 1997 to 2009.[30])

It's possible that the high proportion of Chinese-heritage spies is due to racial bias in the FBI and Department of Justice. But rather than a sharp rise of anti-Chinese racism in federal agencies, a more plausible explanation is that Beijing has stepped up its program of industrial espionage in the US and has recruited Chinese visitors to America, and Chinese-Americans, to commit the crimes.[31] Even so, the number of people of non-Chinese heritage induced to spy for China appears to be rising.

Ego, sex, ideology, patriotism, and especially money are all exploited by China's intelligence services to recruit spies. In 2017 an FBI employee, Kun Shan Chun (Joey Chun), was convicted of supplying information about the bureau's organisation and operations to Chinese agents, in exchange for free international travel and visits to prostitutes.[32] Among those who spy for China, ideology is a factor mainly for people of Chinese heritage (unlike during the Cold War, when Westerners spied for the USSR for ideological reasons). Beijing also deploys the threat of punishment of family members in China if a target refuses to cooperate.

Ideology appears to have been the motive for Russell Lowe, the alleged spy who worked for many years for Senator Dianne Feinstein, including the period when she chaired the Senate's intelligence committee, a role that gave her access to many of America's most closely guarded secrets.[33] Feinstein was informed by the FBI that she had a suspected spy in her office in 2013. Russell Lowe, a Chinese-American, had spent years as a pro-Beijing activist in the San Francisco Bay Area, providing political intelligence to the Chinese consulate. Among the organisations Lowe worked with was the Education for Social Justice Foundation, which exposes the sexual slavery of women, mostly Korean, by the Japanese Imperial Army during the Second World War. The comfort women atrocity is used by CCP agents to stir resentment and patriotic feelings among overseas Chinese, and to drive a wedge between Japan and its Western allies. Lowe is also linked to a group known as the End National Security Scapegoating coalition, which argues that the prosecution of Chinese-heritage spies is no more than racial profiling under the pretext of national security.[34]

Feinstein has been a China-booster from the early 1990s, often backing pro-Beijing legislation in the Senate. Her husband has strong business links in China, which she denies have had any influence on her. In 1997 she compared the Tiananmen Square massacre to the shooting of four students at Ohio's Kent State University in 1970, and called for a joint US–China commission on the two nations' human rights records.[35] Lowe left Feinstein's office after the FBI warned her about him.

China's intelligence agencies also target Westerners not of Chinese heritage for information-gathering. In 2017 a long-serving State Department employee, Candace Claiborne, was indicted for accepting money and gifts from Chinese agents in exchange for diplomatic and economic information.[36] She had been targeted by the MSS's Shanghai State Security Bureau after she asked a Chinese friend to find a job in China for a family member. Claiborne maintained secret contact with MSS agents for five years, supplying them with information in return for help with her 'financial woes'. She was sentenced to forty months in prison.

In the early 1990s Britain's MI5 wrote a protection manual for businesspeople visiting China; the advice remains relevant today: 'Be especially alert for flattery and over-generous hospitality ... [Westerners] are more likely to be the subject of long-term, low key cultivation, aimed at making "friends" ... The aim of these tactics is to create a debt of obligation on the part of the target, who will eventually find it difficult to refuse inevitable requests for favours in return.'[37]

China's civilian and military intelligence agents are trained in the art of cultivating 'friends'. Sinophiles, and newcomers with a fascination for the culture, are especially vulnerable. After grooming they may naively supply intelligence information believing they are contributing to mutual understanding and harmony.

Typically, Westerners are lured by money, sexual favours and the excitement of clandestine operations. Money appears to be the most common bait for those Westerners, judging by the cases that have become public. A target might be offered a modest sum for a short 'white paper' on, for example, US–China trade relations. Once payment for information has been normalised, larger payments and requests for confidential information are made, until the line has been crossed into illegality.

In the case of commercial secrets, the target, such as an engineer at a high-tech US company, might be offered a trip with expenses paid plus a stipend to give a lecture at a university in China. If the target is of Chinese heritage, they may also be leant on to help the motherland. No corporate secrets may be given away on this occasion, but as the relationship develops over time, the target betrays their employer.

One such instance is the case of Xu Yanjun, a senior officer with the Jiangsu office of the MSS, who was charged in 2018 with attempting to obtain 'highly sensitive information' from GE Aviation. Working with the Nanjing University of Aeronautics and Astronomics, Xu contacted American aerospace engineers and offered them educational exchanges.[38] Travel expenses were paid, along with a lecturing fee, and the desired relationships built gradually. In another case, Ji Chaoqin arrived in the United States in 2013 to study electrical engineering at the Illinois Institute of Technology. In September that year he was charged by the FBI for attempting to identify scientists and engineers as potential recruits for China. Ji had allegedly been recruited as a spotter by the Jiangsu office of the MSS.[39] He had enlisted in the U.S. Army Reserves.

When sex is the means of exploitation, there are three methods. The first is seduction that leads to the direct theft of secrets. For example, Ian Clement, deputy to the then mayor of London, Boris Johnson, was caught in a honey trap while in Beijing for the 2008 Olympics. He was approached by an attractive woman, agreed to have a couple of drinks, then invited her up to his hotel room.[40] There he passed out, apparently drugged, and woke to find his room ransacked for documents and the contents of his BlackBerry downloaded. A top aide to Prime Minister Gordon Brown fell for the same trap in the same year.[41]

The second method is seduction that leads to blackmail, using compromising photographs. This classic honey trap (*meiren ji*, literally 'beautiful person plan') was perfected by the Russians.[42] Though the method is not uncommon, cases rarely come to light.[43] In 2017 the former deputy head of MI6, Nigel Inkster, said that China's agencies were using honey traps more often.[44] In 2016 reports suggested that the Dutch ambassador to Beijing had been entrapped.[45]

The third method is the formation of a long-term relationship that causes the target to turn—that is, to see the world from a CCP point of view. In May 2018 two former agents of France's external intelligence service, Direction générale de la sécurité extérieure (DGSE), were arrested for spying for China.[46] One of them, Colonel Henri Manioc, had allegedly defected in 1998 after falling in love with a Chinese woman. He had been head of mission at the French embassy in Beijing.

In more recent times, China's intelligence agencies have exploited social media to approach potentially useful Westerners. In 2018 French authorities revealed that they had uncovered a program to approach thousands of experts using fake accounts on LinkedIn, the professional networking tool. Posing as think tank staff, entrepreneurs and consultants, the account operators told individuals that their expertise was of interest to a Chinese company, and offered them free trips to China. Those who accepted spent a few days being befriended through social activities and were then asked to provide information. It's believed that in some cases they were photographed in compromising situations, such as accepting payments, making them prone to blackmail.[47] The French exposé followed a similar one in Germany, where more than 10,000 experts and professionals were approached.[48] It's believed that several hundred expressed interest in the offers made to them. In 2016 a Chinese secret service agent posing as a businessman used LinkedIn to contact a member of the German Bundestag, offering to pay him €30,000 for confidential information on his parliamentary work. The MP, who has not been named, accepted.[49]

The CCP's activities have brought all people of Chinese heritage under more scrutiny, leading to accusations that American agencies have been engaged in racial profiling.[50] The evidence for this is scant, although there have been some unwarranted arrests, and the risk is that blame will be deflected away from the very active Chinese intelligence agencies and onto US law enforcement agencies, which have said they do not have the resources to keep up.[51]

Think tanks and research institutes

Various Chinese intelligence agencies have spent years cultivating relationships in Western universities and think tanks, partly with the aim of winning friends over to the CCP's point of view. Faligot notes that the 'Chinese secret services have frequently tried to infiltrate foreign institutes and China research centres'.[52]

One of the most important organisations for this work is the China Institutes of Contemporary International Relations.[53] It was reported to have 400 or so members in 2011, including PLA and intelligence officers, and is overseen by the MSS's 11th Bureau.[54] (CICIR's president from 1992–98 was Geng Huichang, who became Minister of State Security from 2007 until 2016, and a member of the CCP Central Committee.[55]) In addition to engaging in influence activities, CICIR trains future intelligence officers and prepares intelligence briefings for the Standing Committee of the Politburo. David Shambaugh has described CICIR as a 'Soviet-style intelligence organ'.[56]

Through exchange of personnel, CICIR has close links with the University of International Relations in Beijing, set up to train, among others, undercover intelligence officers for Xinhua News Agency.[57] Its influence derives not so much from recruiting informants as the cultivation of professional links across the globe. Its stock in trade is academic exchanges and conferences, described by Faligot as 'one of the tricks' CICIR uses to gain entry to 'the most closed circles of the host country'.[58]

CICIR holds an annual dialogue with the EU's Institute for Security Studies in Paris, and has met regularly with influential Washington D.C. think tank the Center for Strategic and International Studies to discuss cybersecurity.[59] These dialogues provide opportunities not only to create networks for intelligence gathering, but also shape the thinking of American and European experts, by, for example, presenting China as the victim of cyber intrusions and casting doubt on the US's ability to attribute hacking to China.[60]

In Italy CICIR has organised workshops with the Turin-based think tank Torino World Affairs Institute. TWAI's journal, *OrizzonteCina* (*China Skyline*) not only avoids criticism of the CCP but offers a generally admiring perspective on China under the CCP, including welcoming the extension of the BRI into Southern Europe.[61] TWAI has partnered with the University of Turin and the prestigious ESCP business school in Paris to create a China-centred 'knowledge hub'.

Since the early 2000s, CICIR has been arranging conferences with other Chinese organisations, including the China Institute for International and Strategic Studies, an arm of military intelligence, and the Chinese Academy of Social Sciences.[62] These conferences, too, are an opportunity to persuade foreigners to commit to regular exchanges.[63]

The Shanghai Academy of Social Sciences is a distinguished organisation with over 500 research staff, second in prestige only to the Chinese Academy of Social Sciences. Agents of the Shanghai bureau of the MSS are known to pose as researchers from the Shanghai academy, and academy staff are used by the Shanghai State Security Bureau as spotters for foreign spies and agents of influence.[64] The Chinese Academy of Social Sciences has been used for the same purpose. In July 2017 US journalist Nate Thayer wrote a detailed account of attempts by the Shanghai State Security Bureau to recruit him for espionage.[65]

In a 2017 affidavit, the FBI presented evidence that Kevin Mallory, who had previously worked for the Pentagon's Defense Intelligence Agency and had a 'top secret' security clearance, was recruited to spy for China by someone claiming to be from the Shanghai Academy of Social Sciences.[66] After being approached through his LinkedIn account, Mallory travelled to Shanghai where he was given a new phone and shown how to use an encrypted service for communicating and sending documents. He was asked to prepare white papers on US policy matters, which he agreed to do. According to the FBI, he also acquired secret and top-secret documents from defence-related firms and sent them to his contacts in Shanghai in exchange for thousands of dollars.

By contrast, US citizen Glenn Duffie Shriver fell in love with China on a summer study-program visit.[67] He moved to Shanghai and was recruited by the MSS after responding to a newspaper advertisement seeking someone to write a paper on trade relations. He was paid $120 for a short report. Over time, 'friendships' were built and Shriver was offered more money. Then he was encouraged to seek employment in the US State Department or the CIA and was paid large sums when he applied for positions. At his sentencing hearing he said things had spiralled out of control. He admitted being motivated by greed: 'I mean, you know, large stacks of money in front of me.'[68]

A thousand talents

The CCP's *qiaowu* activities among the diaspora are another means of recruiting spies.[69] MSS and PLA agents cultivate warm relationships through such things as dinners and events organised by embassies or cultural and professional associations. According to James To, the PLA and MSS also identify recruits before they leave China.[70] Carrots and sticks are deployed. The carrots are promises of good jobs and houses when targets return to China. The sticks include refusing visas and threats to harm families. Graduate students may become sleeper agents, only activated if they find themselves in jobs with access to desirable information. James To writes that clandestine and aggressive methods are used mainly on those overseas Chinese who can provide information of scientific, technological or military value.[71]

The Thousand Talents Plan aims to recruit highly qualified ethnic Chinese people to 'return' to China with the expertise and knowledge they've acquired abroad. Alternatively, those loyal to China can 'remain in place' to serve. The US Department of Energy, whose work includes nuclear weapons and advanced R&D on energy, has been heavily targeted to this end.[72] Around 35,000 foreign researchers are employed in the department's labs, 10,000 of them from China. Many of the latter return via the Thousand Talents or other programs. Other returnees take knowledge gained in top defence labs. According to one report, 'so many scientists from Los Alamos [science and technology labs] have returned to Chinese universities and research institutes that people have dubbed them the "Los Alamos club"'.[73]

Although the Thousand Talents Plan was only established in 2008, the systematic transfer of technology from the West has been under way for much longer. When China began to open up under Deng Xiaoping in the late 1970s and early 1980s, a program was developed to send technically talented young Chinese to the West. Many of the brightest students were sent to Germany and the United States to obtain PhDs in physics; some stayed on and achieved senior positions at top universities, from where they could send information to China.

In the United States it has been known for some years that scientists with access to advanced knowledge and valuable research data have been working for China.[74] But until recently very few have been willing to recognise the problem for what it is and to confront it. In March 2019 it was reported that the nation's largest funder of science, the Maryland-based National Institutes of Health, had written to hundreds of research universities asking about the links of certain researchers to foreign governments.[75] It expressed concern about the theft of intellectual property by researchers linked to the Chinese government or Chinese universities (Russia and Iran were also on the radar).

The following month a story broke about the prominent Houston cancer centre MD Anderson, which had fired three Chinese-American researchers named by the National Institutes of Health as suspected of stealing research and failing to disclose foreign ties.[76] The NIH partly funds the cancer centre. At least fifty-five other institutions were reported to have received similar letters from the National Institutes of Health.[77] Some of those named came under scrutiny because of their involvement in the Thousand Talents Plan. On 28 January 2020 one of Harvard's most senior faculty members, chemist and nanoscientist Dr Charles Lieber, was taken away in handcuffs when the FBI alleged that he had been recruited into the Thousand Talents Program. The Department of Justice alleges that between 2012 and 2017 he was paid $50,000 a month plus generous living expenses to set up a lab at Wuhan University of Technology and transfer his knowledge.[78] Lieber failed to disclose his China links to Harvard, even though the Wuhan centre was called the 'WUT-Harvard Joint Nano Key Laboratory'. His wooing had been going on for some years; in 2009 the Party had honoured him with a Friendship Award.[79] If the allegations are true, he appears to have been motived solely by greed.

The China Association for International Exchange of Personnel keeps a low profile and few people outside China have heard of it. Ostensibly dedicated to people-to-people exchanges, the CAIEP has offices in the US, Canada, Russia, Germany, the UK, Australia, Israel, Japan, Singapore and Hong Kong, and has agreements and collaborates with organisations in many more countries. In 1999 the US Congress's landmark Cox Committee report on Chinese nuclear spying described the CAIEP as 'one of several organisations set up by the PRC to illegally acquire technology through contacts with Western scientists and engineers'.[80] It controls 'a vast espionage operation that has combed the United States in search of sensitive weapons secrets'.[81]

Twenty years later, US law enforcement is still grappling with CAIEP's activities. In 2019 the Department of Justice arrested the head of its New York office on a charge of conspiracy to commit visa fraud.[82] The indictment gave an invaluable insight into CAIEP's recruitment of scientists, engineers, IT specialists and others to return to China with their workplaces' intellectual property. Building on united front work, the CAIEP works with ethnic Chinese professional associations, 'friends' in US universities, and Confucius Institutes, all in close collaboration with Chinese consulates.

The CAIEP is managed by the State Administration of Foreign Experts Affairs, which reports directly to the Ministry of Science and Technology (see the organisation chart on pages 124–5). Espionage experts Hannas, Mulvenon and Puglisi single out SAFEA (sometimes referred to as the Foreign Experts Bureau, a more direct translation of its official Chinese name) as the foremost PRC-based, technology-transfer organisation.[83] In practice 'there is no distinction to be made between cooperating with' CAIEP and with SAFEA.[84] The latter was caught red-handed in the US recruiting an engineer to supply to the PRC highly classified designs for US stealth missiles.[85] The engineer was sentenced to thirty-two years in prison. While the United States has been cracking down on illegal technology transfer, Canada has for years been actively facilitating the work of CAIEP and removing barriers for the 'exchange of talent'.[86]

SAFEA's objective of recruiting spies is hinted at on its website, where it states that its mission is to use 'many types of recruitment channels' and to do so by making 'full use of contacts with governments, exchanges with sister cities, international economic and trade negotiations, international conferences, and like opportunities' to recruit foreign experts.[87] One such channel is private companies. Triway Enterprises is a Virginia-based company set up under SAFEA's auspices, with branches in Beijing and Nanjing.[88] Its function is to link Chinese firms and local government offices with US experts who can supply intellectual property.

Professional associations

The Chinese Association for Science and Technology USA is probably the largest association for ethnic Chinese scientists and engineers in the US, with over 10,000 members.[89] It collaborates with Triway Enterprises and has tight links with China's government and universities, consistent with its mission to serve as a bridge between the US and China for scientific and technological cooperation.[90] Some of its office holders also hold positions at Chinese universities, and according to its national president in 2016, twenty presidents of its various chapters have returned to work in China.

The Washington D.C. chapter of CAST-USA has over 1000 members, drawn from Maryland and Virginia as well as D.C.[91] The CAST Network Society was founded in 2000 at the University of Maryland for Chinese-heritage experts in information technology.[92] In 2002 the University of Maryland agreed to host one of China's national innovation parks, the first of these facilities to be established abroad.[93]

CAST-USA is only one of an extensive network of similar associations in the US, and there are others elsewhere.[94] In Australia the peak body for such associations is the Federation of Chinese Scholars in Australia, whose office holders are professors and university administrators of Chinese heritage.[95] Its launch in October 2004 was celebrated by the *People's Daily*, which noted that the federation had begun 'with the energetic support and aid of the Chinese Embassy in Australia's education office'. China's ambassador to Australia at the time, Fu Ying, was reported as saying she 'hoped that the specialists and scholars would be able to transfer advanced technological achievements back to China'.[96] The founding president of FOCSA was Max Lu (Lu Gaoqing), at the time a nanotechnology expert at the University of Queensland. He has long maintained close connections with the Chinese state, including membership of an Expert Consultative Committee of the Chinese State Council.[97] In 2017 Lu became the vice chancellor of the University of Surrey in the UK.

Many of these professional associations have deep links with the Chinese state, collaborating closely with consulates and SAFEA offices. Professional associations are in some cases created at the suggestion of the Chinese state. Patriotic overtures are made, but so are promises of 'extremely high' salaries on top of legitimate salaries.[98] Hannas, Mulvenon and Puglisi write that Beijing 'courts these associations and steers their activities using a mix of psychological pressure, political control, and financial incentives'.[99]

There's a concentration of ethnic Chinese professional organisations in Silicon Valley, where around one in ten high-tech workers is from mainland China.[100] The Silicon Valley Chinese Engineers Association was created in 1989 for mainland Chinese experts living in the Bay Area. Its mission includes 'establishing channels to allow members to engage in China's rapid economic development'.[101] The dependence of China's growth on Western technology was disclosed, along with one of the methods of acquiring it, in an indiscreet 2013 interview by a senior IT engineer in Silicon Valley, Jack Peng. He also held office in the Silicon Valley Chinese Overseas Business Association, which links overseas Chinese experts with the PRC. According to Peng, 'China regards those of us living overseas as essential. It extends a hand to us to make the results of our research blossom on Chinese soil … Most of us serve as advisors to the Chinese government through the SCOBA organisation … Everyone has entered into a system of full-scale cooperation.'[102]

Canada has a similar network of PRC-linked professional associations. While these organisations provide social contact and career advancement, they also bring experts together in ways that can be manipulated, as directed by Chinese consulates.

In 2017 the head of the SAFEA, Zhang Jianguo, was in New York to celebrate CAIEP's thirty years of operation in the United States.[103] He expressed pleasure that it had maintained 'deep engagement with a host of US educational institutions, industrial associations and famous scholars', noting that it had arranged many academic visits and offered help to foreign experts working in China.[104]

The following year, a similar event was held in London to celebrate the UK's thirty-year anniversary of SAFEA/CAIEP activity. Those present were told by a British intellectual property lawyer that China was building a world-class system of IP protection and that most reports about Western companies having their technology ripped off could be explained by lax behaviour by the companies concerned.[105]

In 2019, as Chinese-American scientists with links to China came under greater federal scrutiny, some of them (backed by the Committee of 100, see chapter eleven) complained of a new McCarthyism, and of being forced 'to pick one side' (as if working for both sides were the norm).[106] Reporting the sacking of Chinese-American scientists suspected of giving IP to China, Bill Bishop of the respected *Sinocism* newsletter noted that some Chinese-American scientists of his acquaintance claimed the practice of secret 'double-dipping' had been going for many years and a crackdown was long overdue.[107] Bishop quotes one Chinese-American scientist saying that he and others like him are 'ashamed of the degree of pilfering they see around them'.

PLA scientists in Western universities

Western universities have been the target of intensive influence efforts by the CCP for some years, Their scientists have been invited to collaborate with Chinese universities, including the PLA's National University of Defence Technology, and Western universities have also invited Chinese scientists and engineers into their labs, to work on military-related research projects. As a result, universities in the West have been helping China to gain military superiority over the US through advanced weapons research.

Forensic research by Alex Joske has uncovered the extensive network of collaboration between researchers in Western universities and scientists linked to China's military.[108] He found that since 2007 the PLA has sent more than 2500 military scientists and engineers to study abroad, in the process developing research relationships with hundreds of top scientists across the globe. The highest number are to be found in the Five Eyes nations (the US, UK, Canada, Australia and New Zealand), along with Germany and Singapore. By 2017 Western scientists had written hundreds of scientific papers with Chinese military scientists.

In many cases, the PLA affiliation of Chinese military scientists working abroad has been obscured. Some claim to be from the Zhengzhou Information Science and Technology Institute, which, judging by the number of publications in which it's cited, is one of the world's leading centres of computer science and communications engineering. Joske discovered that its scientists have published, at times in collaboration with US researchers, over 900 papers in major science journals, including the prestigious *Physical Review Letters*, one of the world's top physics journals, and *The Computer Journal*, published by Oxford University.

Yet the Zhengzhou Information Science and Technology Institute does not actually exist. It has no website, no phone number and no buildings. It does have a post office box in Henan province's capital city, Zhengzhou, but that's about it. The name is in fact a cover for the university that trains China's military hackers and signals intelligence officers, the People's Liberation Army Information Engineering University, which is based in Zhengzhou.[109] Researchers from the University of Texas at Dallas, the State University of New York at Buffalo, Clemson University in South Carolina, Louisiana State University, and City University of New York have all collaborated with individuals who disguise their affiliation with this PLA university, which is in effect its cyberwarfare training school.[110]

The doors to PLA scientists appear to be most open in Australia. As Joske has shown, for some years a complex network of collaboration has been flourishing between Australian scientists and their counterparts in top PLA universities, helping to advance Xi Jinping's 'Strong Army Dream'.[111] Australian researchers have published hundreds of joint papers with researchers from the PLA's National University of Defense Technology, covering such areas as materials science, artificial intelligence and computer science. One collaborator is Professor Tao Dacheng, formerly at the University of Technology Sydney, now at the University of Sydney. His work on computer vision has applications in automatic target recognition, missile guidance, and battlefield assessment and prediction. Tao's research with NUDT scientists has been funded by Australia's national research funding agency.

Until recently the president of NUDT was Lieutenant General Yang Xuejun, who's now the president of the PLA's Academy of Military Science, China's leading military research centre. In 2017 Yang was appointed to the CCP's Central Committee.[112] One of his closer collaborators has been Xue Jingling, professor of computer science and engineering at the University of New South Wales and a 'Thousand Talents Scholar'.[113] Their work has focused on stream-processing technology, vital to the new-generation supercomputers that are used by the military for advanced aircraft design, combat simulation and testing nuclear missiles, among other things. Xue is also a professor at NUDT and has written at least thirty-six scientific papers with researchers there.

Scientists at Australian universities also have research collaborations with leading Chinese weapons and defence-systems manufacturers, such as the Aviation Industry Corporation of China, the major supplier of military aircraft to the PLA Air Force, and the China Electronics Technology Group Corporation, primarily a military research organisation, which once described itself as 'the national squad for military-industrial electronics'.[114] The CETC declares that its purpose is 'leveraging civilian electronics for the gain of the PLA'.[115]

In January 2011 a Massachusetts court jailed two PRC nationals for conspiring to steal and export military electronics components, and sensitive electronics used in military phased array radar, electronic warfare and missile systems.[116] The CETC was one of the organisations that was to be supplied with the stolen material. In October 2010 two PRC nationals were arrested in California on charges of conspiring to export restricted electronics technology to China without a licence and making false statements.[117] They were alleged to have entered into contracts with the 24th Research Institute of CETC to design and transfer technology for the development of two types of high-performance, analog-to-digital converters.

Western universities have displayed extraordinary naivety in their dealings with Chinese companies and universities, and are often unwilling to admit the risks even when confronted with the evidence. Funding bodies like the US National Science Foundation and the Australian Research Council have no due diligence procedures, and rely on universities to vet researchers and companies.[118] The universities often have a strong financial incentive to keep themselves in the dark while defending the traditional scientific culture of openness and transparency, even though this is being systematically exploited by Beijing.

Cyber attacks and influence ops

In what may be collaboration between China's influence apparatus and its cyber-hacking centres, large data banks containing personal information have been hacked by state actors in China. Even the EU, historically reluctant to wade into this topic, has taken note.[119] In Australia, in a massive and highly sophisticated hacking operation in 2018, large amounts of information on staff and students at the prestigious Australian National University were stolen, including names, addresses, phone numbers, passport numbers, tax file numbers and student academic records.[120] Many of this university's students go on to senior positions in the civil service, security agencies and politics. ANU also hosts large numbers of Chinese students.

Security agencies around the world have noticed an alarming spike in cyber attacks on medical records, with state-based actors in China the leading suspects. In August 2018 it was reported that 1.5 million medical records had been stolen from the Singapore government's health database, in an attack experts believe came from state-based hackers in China.[121] Prime Minister Lee Hsien Loong was among those targeted, leading him to tweet: 'Perhaps they were hunting for … something to embarrass me.'[122]

The Singapore theft followed a massive hack in the US in 2014 that sucked up the records of 4.5 million patients across 206 hospitals, and another in 2015 that saw up to 80 million records stolen from a health insurer.[123] In 2014–15 a state-sponsored Chinese agency known as Deep Panda hacked US healthcare providers, stealing the records of some eighty million patients, data that could be used to blackmail persons of interest.[124] The year 2014 also saw the theft of 4.5 million health records from a Tennessee-based hospital chain, in an attack again attributed by experts to state-backed hackers in China.[125] That same year, the medical records of an unspecified number of Australian soldiers, including special forces operating overseas, were sent to China by a health contractor that also has facilities in Guangdong.[126]

The medical records of current and future political, military and public service leaders are likely now in the hands of China's intelligence services and could be used to identify their weaknesses to be exploited for influence or for blackmail. Some may have medical conditions they don't want to become public. Data on medications would be enough. Publication of such sensitive information could wreck careers and make those who have been compromised open to coercion.[127]

The Huawei case

The story of Huawei, the world's biggest telecom equipment maker, is an excellent case study in how the PRC melds spying, intellectual property theft and influence operations. While the full story is too long to tell here, the key elements are instructive.

Suspicions about Huawei's links to China's intelligence services go back a long way. The company's founder, Ren Zhengfei, is believed by some to have been a director of the PLA's Information Engineering Academy, reportedly responsible for telecom research for the Chinese military and, according to industry analysts, associated with 3PLA, its signals intelligence division.[128] A 2005 RAND report noted that China's military is believed to be the company's political patron as well as an important customer from its earliest days.[129] According to a 2010 report, Huawei's chairwoman, Sun Yafang, was a former employee of the Ministry of State Security.[130]

In 2018 Huawei equipment was implicated in the theft of confidential information from the headquarters of the African Union in Addis Ababa. It appears very likely that every night for five years, this equipment was used to download masses of data and send it to servers in Shanghai.[131] It's widely believed among Huawei employees that the Chinese government places intelligence agents in Huawei's global network of offices.[132] As one employee in Shenzhen is reported to have said, 'The state wants to use Huawei, and it can use it if it wants.'[133] In Poland in January 2019, Huawei employee Wang Weijing was arrested on suspicion of spying for China.[134]

Huawei has been accused many times by its suppliers and competitors of stealing their intellectual property.[135] A U.S. Justice Department indictment alleged the launch in 2013 by Huawei headquarters of 'a formal policy instituting a bonus program to reward employees who stole confidential information from competitors'.[136] The company had circulated a schedule of payments, calibrated to the value of the stolen information, and provided an encrypted email service for especially sensitive information. Every six months, the three Huawei regional operations supplying the most valuable stolen information were to receive company awards.

However, framing the problem as one of law-breaking may obscure the larger danger posed by Huawei. As Elsa Kania put it, 'Huawei's global expansion, in and of itself, can serve as a vector for Beijing's influence.'[137] After all, if Huawei achieves its goal of becoming the dominant supplier and builder of the global communication network of the twenty-first century, that gives Beijing enormous influence around the world. Huawei is at the fulcrum of President Xi's two fusions, the Party–corporate fusion and the civilian–military fusion, to which might be added a third, the influence–espionage fusion.

Through a year of intense controversy, including President Trump placing Huawei on the 'entity list', which bars US companies from supplying Huawei without government approval, Huawei benefited from the public backing of friends of China.[138] As we have seen, John McCallum, Canada's ambassador to Beijing, took Huawei's side when Meng Wanzhou was arrested. Well-known US economist Jeffrey Sachs has loudly denounced the 'war on Huawei' (see chapter eleven). Peter Mandelson, president of the Great Britain-China Centre and fellow of the 48 Group Club, accused the US of 'fomenting hysteria' about Huawei, and argued that the criticisms of the company were driven by Trump's campaign against China—this despite the fact that criticisms had been made by a wide range of intelligence and industry sources in other countries, and before Trump became president.[139]

Huawei's presence in Britain had been built over some years. It made large donations to the Conservative and Liberal Democrats parties and gave £50,000 to the all-party Parliamentary Group on East Asian Business.[140] It paid for numerous trips by MPs to tour China's research facilities, and as early as 2012 it secured a meeting with Prime Minister David Cameron. It appointed to its 'international advisory board' (whose members are paid handsomely to do little other than give the company respectability) Lord Clement-Jones, former chair of the Liberal Democrats; Sir Andrew Cahn, former head of UK Trade & Investment, a government department; and Baroness Wheatcroft, a Tory peer.[141] Today, Huawei's UK board is chaired by the former CEO of BP, John Browne. It all paid off in January 2020 when, to the dismay of Five Eyes partners, the British government gave the green light for Huawei's participation in Britain's 5G network. It was a decisive victory for Beijing.

In Western countries, corporate boards of prominent people are an important part of Huawei's program of cultivating friends and building influence. Huawei's foreign board members often speak to the media, repeating the company's denial of connections to the Chinese government. They deny evidence of espionage and testify to the all-round good citizenship of Huawei. They have what two experts call a 'limited view of Huawei's inner workings'[142] but they provide an acceptable face for the company.

In Australia the chair of Huawei's board is a former rear admiral, John Lord. In Canada, in the midst of the crisis over Meng Wanzhou's arrest, Huawei appointed Alykhan Velshi, formerly a top adviser to Prime Minister Stephen Harper, to be its government adviser and public face.[143] In Germany Huawei is represented in more than twelve industry lobby groups.[144] In December 2018 Huawei sponsored the annual convention of the ruling party, the Christian Democratic Union, an opportunity for the company's executives to develop warm personal relations with Germany's leaders.[145]

In a move not available to Western companies wanting political influence, the CCP mobilised its united front organisations in Canada to defend Huawei during the 2019 crisis. The media conference at which John McCallum spoke out in support of Meng was organised by a prominent Toronto figure in the Chinese community, Tao (Thomas) Qu, who is well known for his participation in pro-Beijing community organisations, including events to 'protect the image of China', such as demonstrations against a visit by the Dalai Lama and against the raising of the Tibetan flag.[146]

Soon after Meng's apprehension, a Vancouver-based group held a press conference at which its two spokespersons denounced the arrest and parroted Beijing's talking points.[147] The ruse worked, with Canada's state broadcaster, CBC News, reporting that 'some members of Vancouver's Chinese-Canadian community are rallying in support of Meng Wanzhou'.[148] Tom Blackwell of the *Windsor Star* investigated the two women behind this group, the United Association of Women and Children of Canada. One, Hong Guo, migrated from China to Canada in 1993 and was now running a law firm in Richmond, a city with a high concentration of ethnic Chinese. She first attracted public attention in 2018 when she ran for mayor and claimed, in reply to a question from the media, that there were no human rights abuses in China. In fact, she said, 'China has lots of freedom of speech.'[149] Hong Guo has made donations to the Liberal Party, scoring a photo-op with Prime Minister Trudeau.

The second woman who spoke at the press conference was Han Dongmei. She had migrated to Canada five years earlier and now managed an investment fund, which she'd launched in the Great Hall of the People in Tiananmen Square. Her company donated C$100,000 to the Liberal Party. The United Association of Women and Children of Canada is clearly a front organisation that acts as a vehicle for Guo's and Han's influence work.

Huawei has done what many big corporations do to bolster their image—sponsor high-profile sporting events, such as the high-rating 'Hockey Night in Canada'. In New Zealand Huawei rolled out an advertising campaign comparing itself to the nation's iconic All Blacks rugby team. In Australia the Huawei logo is emblazoned on the jerseys of the Canberra Raiders rugby league club, whose board includes former top intelligence and security officials.[150] The company has made itself a substantial revenue source for New Zealand and Canadian media, even sponsoring New Zealand's premier journalism awards, at a time when news and opinion sites are heavily involved in debate over Huawei.[151]

In striving to gain access to elites, Huawei does not neglect high culture. In addition to promoting classical music concerts in Europe, it has used its artificial intelligence capability to complete the remaining movements of Franz Schubert's Symphony No. 8, the 'Unfinished Symphony', staging a high-society concert in London to perform the score.[152]

Huawei's campaign to win friends extends to universities. Its research budget in 2017 was an astonishing $13.3 billion, a large part of which it spends in scores of universities across the Western world.[153] It funds work at over 150 universities, including twenty-three research and development facilities in fourteen European countries.[154] In Canada it has built a dense network of research collaboration, often with the best IT people. This money buys a cohort of elite supporters, from professors to senior executives, who speak out on the benevolence of Huawei and its contribution to the nation.

But with understanding spreading of the risks of dealing with Huawei, prestigious universities have been cutting their ties. Oxford University, Stanford University, Massachusetts Institute of Technology, and the University of California, Berkeley have announced they will no longer accept funding from Huawei.[155]

Huawei has begun playing hardball. When French researcher Valerie Niquet told an interviewer that Huawei is 'directly' under the control of the Chinese state and the Party and has 'a real strategy of power', the company sued her for defamation.[156] Such a use of the law, whatever its legal basis, is likely to deter other critics of the company.

9
Media: 'Our surname is Party'

Media discourse

The CCP's massive push into the global media landscape is another element of its strategy for shifting the international discourse about the CCP, China, and China's place in the world. By discourse we mean the frames, themes and words used to talk about a certain topic, as well as the beliefs, attitudes and sentiments embedded in language. For some years, CCP leaders have maintained that China, in order to upend the balance of power in what they call the 'global public opinion environment', needs its own CNN—that is, a highly influential media organisation that is the first to report events and shape how people think about them.

In an important speech in 2016 Xi Jinping emphasised the need to create a Chinese 'flagship media with strong international influence'.[1] Enormous resources have been devoted to this, estimated by some to exceed $10 billion annually.[2] Earlier, in 2011, the then president of Xinhua News Agency, Li Congjun, wrote an op-ed that was published on the website of *The Wall Street Journal* calling for a 'new media world order'.[3]

If one were to focus only on the propaganda retailed by official Party media, it would be easy to dismiss Beijing's messaging as too clumsy and heavy-handed to be globally influential, especially in an environment that could hardly differ more from the closed space in which CCP media operate at home. But this underestimates the many subtle elements of the CCP's strategy to control the global discourse. Returning to Germany after many years in China and Hong Kong, Didi Kirsten Tatlow wrote of how radically discussion about China had changed, with enthusiasm for China evident everywhere.[4] China's media have the advantage of substantial financial backing from the state or state proxies, while media in the West are facing a severe financial squeeze. With a great deal of assistance from Western media specialists, China's media have not only expanded massively but also been shrewder with the content aimed at foreign audiences.

At the same that China's media has been expanding, the CCP has been strategically using foreign media to place its own content and also influencing coverage in Western media, through persuasion techniques, financial incentives, or threats to uncooperative outlets and foreign correspondents. The CCP has partnered with some foreign outlets to spread 'positive news' about China, including Xi Jinping's signature policy and prime vehicle for discourse control, the Belt and Road Initiative.

The Party's determination to shape global conversations, combined with the lack of funding many media face, also risks undermining the ethical rules that Western journalists are obliged to follow. Western media organisations can be judged against this code of ethics, and there are many serious media outlets that do their best to adhere to it. News organisations under Xi Jinping, as David Bandurski and Qian Gang at the invaluable *China Media Project* have explained, are instead expected to adhere to 'Marxist news values' and pledge their loyalty to the Party.[5] In the concept of journalism it promotes, the Party is the sole arbiter of truth.

The CCP continues to profit from a unidirectional flow of information across China's borders. While the Party spreads its message abroad through its own media, the Chinese market, tightly quarantined by the Great Firewall, remains largely closed to foreign media, with social media also blocked. Large Western media conglomerates can sell selected products in China, but as we will see, this may serve to increase the leverage Beijing's censors have over them.

Party above all

Media in China are an arm of the Party. They must serve the Party's purpose and spread 'positive energy'. The infamous Document No. 9 of

2013, which marked a decisive defeat for China's liberals, explicitly bans the promotion of 'the West's idea of journalism'.[6] Media, according to the document, 'should be infused with the spirit of the Party' and guided by a Marxist view of news; furthermore, those not complying can expect to be punished. In case Document No. 9 was not clear enough, Xi gave an 'important speech' in February 2016 in which he said that 'the media must be surnamed Party'. The Chinese term for surname, *xing*, implies more than the English translation conveys, and 'being surnamed party' means that the media are part of the patriarchal Party family headed by Xi Jinping.[7] Media organisations across the country subsequently held political study sessions to absorb the 'spirit' of Xi's speech.

The CCP's demands for media loyalty are not abstract pleas, but are enforced through an intricate system of control, before and after publication or broadcast. Propaganda departments regularly send orders to media in China regarding the topics that must be highlighted and those that must not be covered. On some topics, media are instructed to strictly follow the coverage of Xinhua, the official mouthpiece. Designated political editors closely inspect content for political mistakes. After news items have been aired or printed, they are checked again for deviations from the Party line. Any political mistake results in fines and demotions for those deemed responsible.[8] In 2015 four journalists were punished for a minor typo that resulted in a speech of Xi's being referred to as his resignation.[9] It was corrected after forty-five minutes but to no avail. New laws also punish 'fake news'. In 2015, during the Chinese stock-market crash, financial journalist Wang Xiaolu was arrested for 'fabricating news'. (He reported the facts.) Wang was paraded on television where he confessed that he should not have published his reports 'at such a sensitive time' and begged for leniency.[10]

Party media aimed at a foreign readership and published in languages other than Chinese, such as the *China Daily*, are subject to similar political restrictions. Their journalists must display 'high political literacy', and some positions require CCP membership.[11] As of 2019, journalists are required to study Xi Jinping Thought on Socialism with Chinese Characteristics for a New Era, and to pass a test proving their proficiency.[12]

In recent years, the Party has also been training journalists from developing countries.[13] According to Reporters Without Borders, tens of thousands have been so trained.[14] Since 2009, Xinhua has organised and funded the World Media Summit, which has attracted major Western players such as *The New York Times*, the BBC, Reuters, and Associated Press.[15] Another platform is the Media Cooperation Forum on Belt and Road, held by the *People's Daily* in cooperation with local governments since 2014.[16] Its 2018 forum was attended by officials from the Central Propaganda Department, as well as media from ninety countries.[17] When engaging with foreign journalists, CCP cadres don't highlight the need to be loyal to the Party, but instead promote a vision of the media as 'bridges' between countries, furthering harmonious relations and mutual understanding.[18]

A global media force

The idea of globally influential Chinese media is almost as old as the PRC itself. As early as 1955, Mao Zedong instructed Xinhua to 'manage the globe' and 'let the whole world hear [China's] voice'.[19] Under Mao, Xinhua was instructed to focus first on Asia and Africa, before trying to win over Europe and America.[20] And indeed, Louisa Lim and Julia Bergin argue persuasively that Africa has served as the 'testbed' for Chinese media expansion.[21]

The creation of 'international first-rate media' was accelerated in 2008 when the CCP began pouring money into global expansion. In January 2009 the *South China Morning Post* reported that China planned to invest 45 billion RMB (US$6.6 billion) in global media,[22] after the Party pledged to increase China's 'international communication capabilities' at the Third Plenary Session of the 17th Party Congress in late 2008.[23]

Since then, all the CCP's central media have expanded at a rapid pace. In March 2018 the CCP merged its national TV broadcaster China Central Television, its national radio network China National Radio, and its international radio service China Radio International into the China Media Group, also known as the Voice of China. Although this is formally placed under the State Council, it takes its orders from the Party's Central Propaganda Department.[24] The international arm of China Central Television was rebranded China Global Television Network in late 2016. It broadcasts in English, Spanish, French, Arabic and Russian.[25] Headquartered in Beijing, CGTN has production centres in Nairobi, Washington D.C. and London.[26] China Radio International has thirty-two correspondents' bureaus, and broadcasts in more than sixty languages.[27] It also distributes its programs through a global network of radio stations and cooperation agreements, on which more later.

Xinhua, or New China News Agency, has also been expanding rapidly since 2009.[28] It now has over 180 bureaus outside China, with regional headquarters in New York City, Brussels, Hong Kong, Moscow, Cairo, Nairobi, Vientiane and Mexico City.[29] It also has a 24-hour English-language news channel, CNC World, launched in 2010. Like China Radio International, it distributes its content through partnerships, and through stations that it owns.[30]

Another major player is the China Daily Group. Its flagship publication, *China Daily*, is China's oldest English-language daily, founded in 1981 with the assistance of Australian paper *The Age* and funding from the Australian government.[31] The China Daily Group takes its orders from the State Council Information Office, the name used by the CCP's Office of External Propaganda when interacting with the outside world.[32] It has forty bureaus overseas, including in the US, Canada, the UK, Germany, France, Belgium and Australia.[33] In 2018 it employed 921 people worldwide.[34]

The funding injection of 2009 also created a second English-language paper, the *Global Times*, whose Chinese edition was launched in 1993. The *Global Times* is a subsidiary of the People's Daily Group and serves as an outlet for the more jingoistic and hawkish positions that the CCP does not want to run in its more official media, a tactic that allows the latter to sound reasonable by comparison.[35] The editor-in-chief of the *Global Times*, Hu Xijin, is well known for his nationalistic outbursts.

While China's media are mostly Party-owned, they have been advised to 'appear with their commercial face', especially when working with foreign counterparts.[36] When the China Global Television Network registered in the United States, under the *Foreign Agents Registration Act,* it asserted its 'editorial independence from any state direction or control'.[37]

As CGTN is part of the China Media Group, which is led by the Central Propaganda Department, this claim is demonstrably false. It has also been disputed by current CGTN America employees, who confirm that Beijing calls the shots. Clips of Xi Jinping with messy hair cannot be aired, and images showing Taiwanese flags are cropped.[38]

A former employee of Xinhua has told of being asked to use his press credentials to spy on a media conference of the Dalai Lama in Canada in 2012. When it was confirmed that his observations would not be used in a public report he resigned.[39] Other Xinhua employees admit to having written reports intended for internal consumption by China's leaders only.[40] Xinhua has from the 1950s served as a source of low-level intelligence for Chinese officials.[41]

In order to better appeal to the tastes of its international audiences, China's state media have been pursuing a strategy of 'media localisation'—hiring foreigners, adjusting content, and launching more regional editions and programs.[42] The *China Daily* has a global edition as well as special daily editions for the United States and weekly editions for Europe and Asia. CGTN has been hiring local anchors, much like Russia Today has done. More importantly, the station has been able to attract journalists, reporters and producers who have previously worked for outlets like CNN, NBC and the BBC.[43] The Party believes that news reported by people with Western faces is more credible. By contrast, foreign media in China are not allowed to hire Chinese citizens except as assistants.[44]

CCP media have a strategy of letting foreigners speak on topics that China does not wish to comment on itself, and also to add legitimacy to its views on other topics. This strategy has a long tradition. In 1968, at the height of the Cultural Revolution, Mao Zedong warned Chinese media across the country that they had gone overboard in repeatedly declaring China 'the centre of world revolution'. That was, of course, precisely what Mao himself believed, but as it was unhelpful for China to be praising itself, he instructed media to instead quote foreigners making this point.[45]

Attacks on Western media's 'anti-China bias' are often outsourced to foreigners.[46] Foreigners are also brought out for issues the CCP cares about strongly, and to praise China's contributions to the world. After the Hague Tribunal's ruling on the South China Sea in 2016, Nirj Deva, director of the European Parliament's EU-China Friendship Group, mouthed the CCP's view that the Philippines should have resolved the issue through bilateral discussions.[47] British journalist and author Martin Jacques, who is frequently interviewed on CGTN, said in a 2017 interview that the West must learn from China, and that the shift to a China-led world is an 'unalloyed good thing' and 'one of the greatest periods of democratisation the world has ever seen'.[48] One scholar who appeared on a CGTN program was warned not to be too critical if she wanted to be invited back. She was given the name of another foreign interviewee and advised to be 'more like him'.[49] (As do some other media, CGTN offers money to foreign experts for interviews.)

Westerners finetune CCP propaganda

Western institutions have long helped the CCP's media to expand and improve their global coverage. When China Radio International went digital in the late 1990s, this was made possible in part by a loan from the Austrian government and equipment provided by Siemens Austria.[50] The Netherlands' national research institute for mathematics and computer science, Centrum Wiskunde & Informatica, is helping Xinhua to build an 'advanced user experience laboratory', exploring the use of sensors to measure audience attention levels, among other things.[51]

Propaganda cadres are also getting expert advice on how to navigate the Western media landscape. The China Media Centre at the University of Westminster in London has hosted three-week training courses for Chinese propaganda officials.[52] The centre was founded in 2005 by journalism professor Hugo de Burgh, and launched by Sun Yusheng, then vice president of China's state broadcaster CCTV, and Jeremy Paxman, sometimes described as Britain's most respected journalist.[53] Its training programs are targeted at Central Party School cadres and defence officials, employees of state-owned enterprises and official media.[54] The courses are partly funded by British taxpayers through the UK's foreign ministry. The centre's director, Hugo de Burgh, is an honorary fellow of the 48 Group Club, a former board member of the Great Britain-China Centre, and a professor at Tsinghua University.

This last position is under the Chinese Ministry of Education's 985 Program, which aims to bring international talent to China.[55] He is a strong advocate of closer ties between Britain and China.[56]

According to the CCP, the University of Westminster program has been very successful. The head of spokesperson development for the Central Office of External Propaganda wrote: 'Chinese officials' understanding of the functions of the media in Western countries and their ability to respond to and interact with the media has been much enhanced by the excellent intensive 3-week briefings designed and executed by the China Media Centre and provided to ministries, provinces and cities over the past 7 years.'[57]

As part of the 2018 training course, the China Media Centre organised a roundtable on 'China's international relations and economic strategies: Perceptions of the UK and China', with five senior cadres from the Central Propaganda Department.[58] The centre has brought many Party officials to Britain to mingle with the media and political elite, including five seminars at 11 Downing Street, at the invitation of the chancellor of the Exchequer.[59] Boris Johnson, whose first trip to China was joined by Hugo de Burgh, has participated in the centre's courses and has declared that he can think of no-one better than de Burgh to teach us about China's media.[60]

Those arguing in favour of these kinds of training courses maintain that they will help bring about a more open media in China. In fact the opposite is the case: they help the CCP finetune its propaganda and use it more effectively across the globe. The courses teach techniques used by Western journalists to extract answers, and also how government officials can handle adversarial questions in press conferences.[61] At a time when official Chinese spokespeople are regularly under fire for the Party's concentration camps in Xinjiang, and other human rights violations, teaching them how to 'handle' questions seems to be more in the CCP's interest than the British public's.

While there are serious Chinese journalists who want to do proper journalism, the space for them has shrunk dramatically over the past six years, and such journalists are not the ones sent on training programs abroad. The participants instead come from the Party, its agencies, and those TV shows and national newspapers notable for their compliance.[62]

Crossing the Great Firewall

Since the unrest in Xinjiang in July 2009, almost all Western social media have been blocked in China. A prominent exception, because it complies with censorship demands, is Microsoft-owned LinkedIn, which has over 40 million users in China.[63] In December 2018 LinkedIn blocked the account of dissident Fengsuo Zhou, informing him that 'while we strongly support freedom of expression, we recognised when we launched that we would need to adhere to the requirements of the Chinese government in order to operate in China'.[64] In the same month, LinkedIn also blocked the account of Briton Peter Humphrey, a corporate-fraud investigator imprisoned in China for what he said were false charges and who was forced to make a televised confession.[65]

Despite this domestic ban, all of China's media targeted at foreigners, such as Xinhua and the *Global Times*, have a vigorous presence on social media—on Facebook, Twitter and YouTube. On these platforms, CCP media offer content in many languages, some targeted at specific countries, though the most important languages are English and Chinese. According to reports in the *People's Daily*, in 2015 Xinhua established a team of over a hundred people to exclusively manage its presence on Western social media, a number that has likely ballooned since then.[66]

Western social media are another means for the CCP to spread misleading information. The Twitter account of the *People's Daily* claimed Taiwan's 2019 legalisation of gay marriage as a progressive success of the PRC, tweeting: 'Local lawmakers in Taiwan, China, have legalised same-sex marriage in a first for Asia.'[67] (LGBTQ rights have arguably deteriorated in China under Xi. Just a few months after Taiwan legalised gay marriage, the PRC explicitly ruled out doing the same.[68]) Also on Twitter, in 2019 the *China Daily* presented protesters against the Party's proposed extradition bill in Hong Kong as *supporters* of the plans, with headlines such as '800,000 say "yes" to extradition bill', and 'HK parents march against US meddling'.[69] In the same year, Xinhua used its Facebook page to label the Hong Kong protesters 'cockroaches'.[70] *China Daily*'s European bureau chief, who is very active on Twitter, referred to them as 'rats'.[71]

Paid ads are also used on Twitter to promote China's political system and the CCP's line on Xinjiang, Hong Kong, and other sensitive topics.[72] In August 2019, after CCP media paid for ads condemning the Hong Kong protests, Twitter announced it would no longer allow state media to place paid content, but only after a public outcry.[73]

On YouTube, Party-state media have posted clips in formats meant to appeal to younger watchers. One such clip presents China's political system as a meritocracy, in which the office of president is earned through hard work and experience, as opposed to the United States, where the candidate with the most money wins.[74] If the second half of this claim is partly true, the first is wholly false, unless merit is concentrated solely in the ruling families. While clips like this have been dismissed by the Western press, not much is known about who views them and how they're received.[75]

The fact that the CCP has been using these platforms while simultaneously blocking them in China is another example of how it exploits the openness of democracies. It has intensified the crackdown on 'unauthorised' (that is to say, private) Chinese users of Twitter, and also censors Chinese social media like WeChat, which has over one billion active users per month, including millions in the diaspora around the world. Politicians in the West keen to attract 'the Chinese vote' have set up WeChat accounts to appeal to them. As a result, the communications of political candidates in democratic countries are monitored and censored in Beijing.[76]

The CCP also mobilises a vast cohort of internet trolls on Western social media, known colloquially as the '50 cent army'. Many of these trolls are government employees masquerading as private citizens. The best estimate we have is that these 50-centers generate 450 million comments on social media each year (including Chinese social media).[77] Attacks on Taiwanese or Uyghur sites on Facebook, flooding them with pro-CCP comments, have become common.[78] When a group known in China as 'Diba' attacked a Uyghur activist site, the *Global Times* praised the action as 'patriotic'.[79] In 2019 Twitter took down 1000 accounts, and suspended an additional 200,000, which it linked to a state-organised disinformation campaign against Hong Kong.[80] A preliminary analysis of these accounts by the Australian Strategic Policy Institute showed that many of them had previously won followers by tweeting about unrelated topics in a number of different languages, before going dormant and then re-emerging in June 2019 to tweet in Chinese and English about the Hong Kong protests.[81]

While Facebook, Twitter and YouTube routinely claim to support free speech, they have an ambivalent relationship with Beijing. All have stakes in China and hope to get access to the Chinese market. Facebook's Mark Zuckerberg has tried to ingratiate himself with China's leadership by doing a 'smog jog' in Beijing, meeting with several top propaganda officials, and asking Xi Jinping to name his unborn daughter.[82] On Google-owned YouTube, clips produced by the *Hong Kong Free Press*, and an interview with pro-democracy activist Denise Ho produced by China Uncensored, have been demonetised, meaning the creators cannot earn money by allowing ads on their videos.[83] Similarly, on Twitter, images of the Hong Kong protests were frequently marked as 'sensitive content' and thereafter not displayed.[84] While this is likely a result of CCP-coordinated mass reporting by Beijing's trolls, it shows that these platforms are ill-equipped to deal with crowd-sourced, state-sponsored attacks on content.

Borrowing boats

The CCP's practice of using channels other than Party-state media to amplify its message is known as 'borrowing a boat to sail the sea'.[85] One example, often timed to coincide with an official visit, is publishing op-eds written by Chinese leaders in the host country's media.[86]

A bigger 'borrowed boat' is the international network used by the CCP's China Radio International to distribute content. This network consists of a number of local companies whose common denominators are that they work for CRI and, as researcher Jichang Lulu has pointed out, have the word 'global' in their Chinese names.[87] A 2015 Reuters report identified on the network at least thirty-three radio stations with covert Chinese government involvement.[88] In the United States, CRI is leasing local channels through the Los Angeles–based EDI Media Inc.[89] Its founder and president, James Su, is a vice president of the All-China Federation of Returned Overseas Chinese, a united front agency; Su is also a 'senior consulting member' of the Beijing municipal government.[90]

In Europe, CRI works primarily through the Finland-based company GBTimes (not to be confused with the *Global Times*), 'a bridge between China and the rest of the world'. Founded in 1994 by Chinese entrepreneur Zhao Yinong, it was rebranded several times before changing its name to GBTimes in 2014.[91] The company is a joint venture, 60 per cent owned by Guoguang Century Media Consultation Co., which is directly owned by CRI.[92] While Zhao claims that his company does not try to hide its ownership by CCP media, it certainly does not highlight the fact.[93] According to official Chinese media, the company has over 200 employees and provides services in twenty different languages.[94] In Australia, Melbourne-based CAMG Media fulfils a similar role for CRI.[95] Like GBTimes, it is 60 per cent owned by Guoguang Century Media. CAMG journalists have been criticised by foreign journalists in Beijing for asking 'soft-ball' questions of officials at China's National People's Congress.[96]

Another instance of boat-borrowing is *China Watch*, a supplement that has been produced by the *China Daily* since 2010 and is inserted in Western newspapers. Chinese analysts believe the 2008–09 global financial crisis was a boon for China, as all Western media were struggling to stay in the black. The list of papers that include *China Watch* reads like a who's who of the industry—*The New York Times*, *The Wall Street Journal*, *The Washington Post*, *The Daily Telegraph*, *The Sydney Morning Herald*, *The Age*, *Le Figaro*, *El País* and *Handelsblatt*, among others.[97] Some also publish *China Watch* content on their website. The annual budget has been revealed for only one paper—*The Daily Telegraph* in London receives £750,000 (US$1 million) per year to publish the insert and content.[98]

The relationship between *The Daily Telegraph* and Chinese authorities seems to go beyond carrying the *China Watch* insert. In 2019 the Chinese ambassador to the UK, Liu Xiaoming, praised the Telegraph Media Group for 'playing a positive role in enhancing the mutual understanding between China and western countries'.[99] The praise has been earned. Telegraph executives are happy to meet with Chinese officials.[100] Editor emeritus Ian MacGregor even participated in the April 2019 symposium, Xi Jinping Thought on Diplomacy, held by the Chinese embassy in the UK (discussed in chapter three).[101]

When *China Watch* content is featured on a website such as those of *The Telegraph* and *The Wall Street Journal*, it is marked as 'paid content'.

But when these articles are re-posted on social media, the distinction is lost, making them look like proper articles rather than paid content. Another reason why arrangements like *China Watch* are worrying is the incentive they create for newspapers to stay within the CCP's bounds in its main pages. However, as Peter Mattis argues, the biggest effect is that association with major papers around the world lends credibility to *China Watch*'s content.[102]

Cooperation agreements

CCP media are increasingly signing cooperation agreements with foreign media organisations. When the New York–based global news agency Associated Press signed an agreement with Xinhua in 2018 to expand 'mutually beneficial cooperation', it caused concern in the US, with members of congress demanding AP make the content of the agreement public.[103]

The AP–Xinhua agreement is not unique.[104] The London-based Reuters, a rival of AP's, has had a long relationship with Xinhua, signing its first agreement in 1957.[105] When Tom Glocer (a fellow of the 48 Group Club) was CEO of Reuters, its ties with China grew closer. In a meeting with then ambassador Fu Ying, Glocer promised to report China 'comprehensively and objectively ... [and] to carry forward the long-term friendly cooperation with China'.[106] In 2009 Reuters joined the Xinhua-organised World Media Summit. When Xi visited Britain in 2015 to inaugurate the 'Golden Era' of the Sino-UK relationship, he gave an exclusive interview to Reuters.[107]

In 2017 Xinhua's China Economic Information Service signed a deal with media outlets in Europe, including the German–Austrian financial-news agency DPA-AFX, Italy's Class Editori, the Polish News Agency, the Greek Athens News Agency, Belgium's *Le Soir*, and British Metro, to establish the Belt and Road Economic and Financial Information Partnership.[108] Portugal signed a media cooperation agreement as part of its BRI deal in 2019, which commits parties to 'organize mutual visits of news agencies, carry out joint media coverage [and] hold seminars as well as training for journalists'.[109] Xinhua also has cooperation agreements with Agence France Press (the third of the big three, along with AP and Reuters), German news agency DPA, the

Athens-Macedonian News Agency, Australian Associated Press, the Latvian state news agency LETA, and Italian news agency ANSA.[110] China Media Group and Italy's Class Editori also signed an agreement that, aside from content sharing, involves a new news column called 'Focus Cinitalia', joint television productions, and a joint work group to carry out the planned projects.[111]

While these arrangements are unlikely to result in uncritical reprinting of CCP talking points on highly political topics, in the words of the director of the National Endowment for Democracy, Chris Walker, 'engagement with Chinese state media can induce self-censorship on certain issues or the unwitting carrying of CCP propaganda lines'.[112]

Chinese-language media

As a result of concerted efforts by Beijing, nearly all Chinese-language media in Western countries are now directly or effectively under CCP control, with only a few noteworthy exceptions, such as Mingjing News, the Falun Gong–linked *Epoch Times*, and New Tang Dynasty TV.

Such control is vital to the Party. If it cannot (yet) convince the mainstream press in foreign countries, it can at least push its views through Chinese-language media. As we've seen, these media also help promote nationalistic responses, such as the 2016 demonstrations against The Hague Tribunal's ruling on the South China Sea, and the Chinese students' complaints about 'anti-China' comments.[113] Responsibility for media lies with the Propaganda Department of the CCP's Central Committee, and may also be shared with the United Front Work Department, which manages China's second official news agency, China News Service (see the organisation chart on pages 124–5).[114] CNS directly operates some media (in Australia, for example) and works with other overseas Chinese media.[115]

Over the past two decades, many independent media companies in the West have been taken over by pro-Beijing businesspeople.[116] Several Chinese-language papers in the United States are owned by the Asian Culture and Media Group, reportedly set up by the Overseas Chinese Affairs Office in 1990.[117] New media companies have also been set up by patriotic businesspeople. Criticism of CCP policies is excluded. John Fitzgerald reports that official Party media representatives have been present in Melbourne radio studios to instruct producers on when to cut off callers to talk shows who stray from a Beijing-friendly viewpoint.[118]

Residual independent outlets have come under intense pressure to toe the Party line. Companies that advertise in independent outlets are threatened with being shut off from the Chinese market, and their owners ostracised from the community. At times, consulates make threats to punish the families of media owners and journalists back in China.[119]

In Canada journalists have reported being pressured to temper their criticism of the Chinese government and to promote its view. The freelance writer Jonathan Fon has said that whereas he once got his opinion pieces published without difficulty, now they are routinely rejected.[120] In 2019 a radio talk-show host in Toronto was fired after doing a robust interview with a pro-Beijing community leader.[121] The host, Kenneth Yau, said that after expressing support for Hong Kong protesters he received threats to kill his family and rape his daughter. In response, the radio station's manager, Louisa Lam, said that 'protecting freedom of speech has been one of our company's objectives', but presumably it wasn't the most important one.[122]

Overseas Chinese media liaise through various CCP-directed global and regional organisations. One is the World Association of Chinese Mass Media, founded in Toronto in 1998, which now has over 160 members. In addition to conferences outside China, overseas Chinese media are often invited by official united front bodies to events in China, where they receive 'guidance' and make speeches demonstrating their loyalty to the motherland.[123]

The equivalent for Europe, the Association of Overseas Chinese Media in Europe, was founded in 1997 and has a membership of over sixty Chinese-language media organisations.[124] It is based at the Paris office of *Nouvelles d'Europe* (the *Europe Times*), the flagship publication of the pro-CCP Guanghua Culture and Media Group. In 2011 *Nouvelles d'Europe* began a major expansion across the continent, with editions now produced in London, Vienna, Frankfurt, Rome, Istanbul and Madrid. It is also engaged in non-media activities through its subsidiaries, like the Chinese culture centres in the same cities.[125] Guanghua cooperates with all major CCP media, but also lists *Le Figaro*, Agence France Presse, *The Daily Telegraph*, *Die Welt* and *Frankfurter Allgemeine Zeitung* as media partners. In addition, it formally cooperates with Chinese embassies in France, Britain, Germany, Austria, Italy and Spain.[126]

The websites and online communities owned by Guanghua are operated in accordance with Chinese law. The terms of service of its website (oushinet.com) state that in addition to respecting the laws of the country in which the user is based, users may not 'engage in activity that endangers national security or divulges national secrets or harms the legitimate rights and interests of the country [meaning China], society, the collective or citizens'.[127] Guanghua is not an exception in this regard. The website of the Italy-based EZ TV even provides links for readers to report content to China's online police, just as any PRC-based news site would.[128]

The *Nordic Chinese Times*, founded in 2009 and based in Stockholm, is run by the Nordic Chinese Chamber of Commerce (Nordic Chinese Ekonomisk Förening). It has a strategic partnership with China News Service, which targets overseas Chinese. Its president, He Ru, has participated in several sessions of the Guangxi Committee of the Chinese People's Political Consultative Conference, and facilitated cooperation agreements between Chinese and Nordic media.[129] The *Nordic Chinese Times* has also received 'professional guidance' from various Chinese media officials on how to better convey China's voice and tell China's story well.

The Ouhua Group in Spain is a good example of how Chinese media abroad are tied into larger united front networks. Its honorary chairman is Marco Wang, an influential Spanish-Chinese businessman who is also the executive chairman of the Spanish-Chinese Chamber of Commerce.[130] The CCP's trust in him is manifested by his service as an overseas Chinese representative to the CPPCC.[131] Ouhua partners with Xinhua, China News Service and other CCP media, but also with provincial branches of the former Overseas Chinese Affairs Office.[132]

Buying boats

After the 2008 global financial crisis, Chinese officials and analysts evaluated the possibility of buying cash-strapped media in the West, a strategy known as 'buying a boat to sail the sea'.[133] According to a 2018 Bloomberg report, Chinese investors have spent almost US$3 billion buying media shares and ads in Europe since 2008.[134] The Macau-based Chinese fund KNG, for example, owns 30 per cent of the Global Media Group, which in turn owns the Portuguese newspaper *Diário de Notícias*.[135] Some media companies have been bought outright. London-based Propeller TV, launched in 1993 with British government funding and broadcast by BSkyB, was bought by the Chinese Xijing Group in 2009. The station operates under the motto 'Bringing the World to China and China to the World'.[136]

While not a major broadcaster, Propeller TV has helped to organise high-level events, such as the China UK Film and TV Conference, which was attended by government representatives from both China and the UK and aimed at promoting partnerships with Chinese media companies. In the same year, Propeller TV organised the China-UK Media Roundtable, attended by the deputy head of the CCP's Propaganda Department, to celebrate the beginning of 'a golden age of the Chinese and British media'.[137]

In 2014 the influential American business magazine *Forbes* was bought by a Hong Kong–based investment consortium known as Integrated Whale Media, which is owned by Yam Tak-cheung and Taiwanese businessman Wayne Hsieh.[138] In 2017 a regular column in *Forbes* by Anders Corr was terminated after he wrote an article about the influence of tycoon Ronnie Chan in the Asia Society's Hong Kong branch. This society, co-chaired by Chan, had cancelled a talk by democracy activist Joshua Wong. According to emails sent to Corr, Chan personally contacted *Forbes*.[139]

The first major takeover of an English-language newspaper by a private Chinese company came in late 2015, when the Alibaba Group acquired Hong Kong's venerable *South China Morning Post*. It was revealed in 2018 that Alibaba's CEO, Jack Ma, a revered figure in China, was a longstanding member of the CCP.[140] Alibaba took down the paywall on the *Post*, making it more accessible around the world. Unnoticed in the Western press, they also took down the paper's popular Chinese-language website.[141] While the *South China Morning Post* still contains some good-quality journalism, it is also giving a platform to a growing number of pro-CCP voices. Democracy advocates in Hong Kong lament the passing of the once independent newspaper.

The *SCMP* was heavily criticised in 2018 for accepting an 'exclusive interview', arranged by China's Ministry of Public Security, with Gui Minhai, the kidnapped Swedish citizen and Hong Kong bookseller. Gui was critical of the Swedish government and declared that if Sweden didn't stop 'causing trouble' he might renounce his citizenship.[142] While arguably not as bad as the forced confessions co-produced by CCTV and Chinese authorities, 'interviewing' a person under these circumstances would appear to be a violation of journalistic ethics.

Self-censorship by foreign media

The CCP uses rewards and punishments to control how foreign media report on China. As more and more Western media become invested in the Chinese market, there are added incentives to lean on correspondents, so as to not jeopardise their access. Thus the CCP's leverage will grow.

A number of Western media organisations have tried to circumvent restrictions on reporting in China by creating Chinese-language websites. Despite early difficulties, some are still developing their Chinese web presence. Others try to profit from the Chinese market by offering to mainland customers subscription-based products and services (such as Bloomberg Boxes, specialised computer terminals for delivering financial information). Increased reliance on the Chinese market is perhaps the biggest threat to the editorial independence of these media, as Beijing can block their online content in China and cancel subscriptions to their services.

PEN America has noted that news outlets appear to omit stories from their Chinese-language websites that could anger Chinese authorities.[143] According to online magazine *Slate*, Bloomberg News has used a code to prevent sensitive news from showing up on platforms targeting mainland audiences.[144]

In a case of flagrant censorship in 2013, Bloomberg News toned down an investigative piece by Michael Forsythe on the wealth of Xi Jinping and his family. It then refused to publish another piece because executives were afraid the story would jeopardise the company's substantial business interests, mainly the sale of Bloomberg Boxes.[145] The episode became a public scandal only because Forsythe decided to take the story, and the story of the story, to *The New York Times*.

The CCP regularly organises tours for foreign correspondents based in China and for foreign journalists outside the country. The itineraries are carefully put together, often in conjunction with the All-China Journalists Association, a Party organisation committed to 'Marxist news values', and the tours themselves are also organised by front groups. Tung Chee-hwa's China U.S. Exchange Foundation, discussed earlier, has organised visits for US journalists. One arranged for a delegation from *The Philadelphia Inquirer*, the *Chicago Tribune*, National Public Radio, Vox and *Forbes* to China in October 2018, to visit various government departments and research institutions, so they could 'better understand the political and economic relations between China and the United States' in the time of the trade war.[146]

Journalists like to flatter themselves that their views cannot be influenced this way, but these highly choreographed tours often have the desired effect. In 2016 a number of Australia's most seasoned journalists travelled to China on one such tour and returned to write glowing reports about how in the New China 'people seem taller, more animated, healthier, louder and happier', and that there is no 'sense of an Orwellian 1984' emerging. One of the group urged Australia not to say anything to upset Beijing. Soon after they left China, an article by the All-China Journalists Association was published through Xinhua. Titled 'Why Australian journalists were moved to say their "expectations were exceeded"', it crowed that the reporters had informed their readers about 'the historical opportunity that China's economic development gives to Australia, and impartially conveyed "China's voice"'.[147] The idea for the trip had come from Bob Carr, Australia's former foreign minister, who became an enthusiastic China-booster after being picked by a Chinese billionaire to head a think tank he funded at an Australian university. (The billionaire has now had his Australian visa cancelled because of his links to the CCP.)

The granting or denial of visas is a powerful instrument of control for the CCP. When correspondents apply for visas, Chinese officials frequently tell them that they want to see more positive or 'balanced' coverage from them. And it's not only journalists who are pressured in this way. Swedish China expert Ola Wong recounted how a Swedish businessman in the PR industry, when applying for a visa, was called in for a meeting at the Chinese embassy in Stockholm. His Chinese interlocutors asked him whether he wanted to use his position in the Swedish mediasphere to change how China was being portrayed.[148]

Once in the country, journalists are often threatened with denial of future visas. Al Jazeera's Melissa Chan, French journalist Ursula Gauthier, Buzzfeed's Megha Rajagopala, ABC correspondent Matthew Carney, and *The Wall Street Journal*'s Chun Han Wong, among others, have all been effectively expelled through the authorities' refusal to renew their visas.[149] Bethany Allen-Ebrahimian was appointed Agence France Press's China correspondent but could not take up the job because she could not obtain a visa. After *Le Monde* covered a scandal about China's spying at the African Union, the newspaper was told by angry Chinese embassy officials in Paris that its journalists need not apply for visas.[150] The practice has also spread to Hong Kong, with Victor Mallet, a *Financial Times* journalist and vice president of the Foreign Correspondents Club, denied a visa after the club hosted a talk by independence activist Andy Chan Ho-tin.[151] It only takes a few refusals for the message to be received by all foreign correspondents in China—don't cross the red line.

Although visas have so far been refused only in respect of issues the CCP considers particularly sensitive, officials also pressure foreign media over smaller issues. The *Financial Times* was contacted by China's Ministry of Foreign Affairs after it referred to Xi Jinping as the 'core' of the CCP. This expression had been used by Chinese media in the past but had come to be associated with Xi's cult of personality. Pressure to change terminology has also been applied to several other news organisations.[152]

In 2019 the Ministry of Foreign Affairs sent a letter to more than thirty foreign media outlets, including the BBC, NBC, Bloomberg and *Asahi Shimbun*, asking for 'neutral, objective, impartial and comprehensive' coverage of the Hong Kong protests.[153] This is code for sticking closer to the CCP's narratives, and is a common request when Chinese officials meet with media representatives.[154]

When renewing his visa in 2017, veteran China correspondent Kai Strittmatter, who reports for the German daily *Süddeutsche Zeitung*, expected the usual threats of having his visa denied or delayed if he did not start reporting more positively about China. Instead, the official told him, 'I have to warn you; it can be dangerous.' He elaborated that 'ordinary Chinese people' could be very emotional, even 'violent' at times, and indicated that if they were to react with violence to his reporting, there was not a lot the Chinese authorities could do to protect him. Strittmatter left China in September 2018.[155] Other journalists, including Bloomberg's Michael Forsythe and *The New York Times*'s David Barboza, among others, have received death threats via anonymous letters, or relayed through third parties in response to stories the CCP did not like.[156]

The pressures facing foreign journalists pale in comparison to those experienced by Chinese journalists, many of whom have been fired, arrested, forced into confessions, or disappeared for reporting independently. The situation has become much worse under Xi Jinping. The 2019 Press Freedom Index prepared by Reporters Without Borders ranked China 177th out of the 180 countries it assessed. More than sixty bloggers and journalists, according to the index, are 'currently detained in conditions that pose a threat to their lives'. The CCP is now exporting a 'new world media order' that seeks to make this kind of assault on press freedom and freedom of expression acceptable.

10
Culture as battleground

Political culture

Culture, too, has always been political for the CCP. In the turbulent 1960s and 1970s, it attacked almost every element of traditional culture as feudal, bourgeois or otherwise oppressive, and discouraged or banned its practice. Yet with the waning of Maoist ideology in the 1980s and 1990s and the opening of the economy, the Party needed a less revolutionary justification for its rule. It chose a nationalism built around the uniqueness of China and its people, and their mission to overcome historical humiliation by the colonial powers and to take their rightful place as a great nation on the world's stage. As Janette Jiawen Ai argues in her study of the political use of China's heritage, 'China's traditions are deemed by the party-state to fill the void in the ideological system left by a decline in the official political doctrine in general, and to combat the influence of Western liberalism on Chinese politics and society in particular.'[1]

But the Party, especially under Xi Jinping, was not content to allow traditional culture to be disinterred without making itself the legitimate custodian of culture. The *Party* would decide what is authentic Chinese culture so that there could be no culture outside politics.

The CCP's 'Culture Going Global' strategy, set out in documents emerging from Party congresses starting in 2011 and ramped up under Xi

Jinping, is designed to export not Chinese culture, but 'red culture'; in other words, CCP values. As the *People's Daily* put it, 'Building leadership power over culture is one of the CCP's cultural missions.'[2] In a 2017 article, Liu Runwei—former deputy editor-in-chief of *Qiushi*, the flagship journal of the CCP's Central Committee—made a distinction between 'traditional Chinese culture' and revolutionary 'socialist advanced culture'. Liu, also president of the Chinese Red Culture Research Association, wrote that the former must succumb to the latter. 'The traditional Chinese culture, once it has gone through the party's innovative transformation, will change into "red culture", too.'[3] Red culture is at the centre of realising the great rejuvenation of the Chinese people.

A 2017 article in *Qiushi* titled 'Use cultural identification to achieve the greatest united front mobilisation', written by Yang Lin of the Central Institute of Socialism, stressed 'the strategic role of cultural identification' in united front work.[4] Two years later, a theorist affiliated with the Central Institute of Socialism, Lin Jian, described how the Party uses cultural diplomacy to deepen its influence abroad: 'Its goal is to build our country's image, raise our country's status and to increase our influence globally.' Cultural exchanges are an element of 'big united front', using 'shared values in bringing people's hearts together' to enhance China's influence overseas.[5]

Poly Culture

In recent years, the company Poly Culture has become known in the high culture scene of Western capitals. In 2005 it organised a tour by the China Philharmonic Orchestra to the United States, Canada and Europe.[6] In subsequent years it sponsored performances by the London Philharmonic Orchestra, the Berlin Philharmonic Orchestra, and the Vienna Johann Strauss Orchestra. In 2017 it co-produced an opera with the San Francisco Opera Company.[7] When it sponsored the 2018 London Design Biennale as a 'headline and medal ceremony partner', Poly Culture's executives and friends attended a 'prestigious reception' at the Foreign and Commonwealth Office, followed by an 'exclusive VIP after-party at The Groucho Club'.[8] All of this would be unremarkable if not for the fact that Poly Culture is inseparable from China's military intelligence apparatus.

Poly Culture is a subsidiary of China Poly Group, an opaque conglomerate ranked on the Fortune 500 list. It had assets in 2018 of almost $140 billion.[9] China Poly Group began life in 1984 as Poly Technologies Co. Ltd., a state-owned weapons-making company linked to China International Trust and Investment Corporation, another state-owned investment company and one that had a strong presence in Canada, among other places. Like CITIC, Poly Technologies was a front company for the PLA's General Staff Department (now the Central Military Commission's Joint Staff Department), a role it continues to serve.[10] Poly Technologies became a subsidiary of the larger China Poly Group in 1992.[11] The conglomerate has interests ranging from arms manufacturing to trade to real estate, and, in more recent years, all aspects of high culture.[12] Poly Culture was founded in 2000 and listed on the Hong Kong Stock Exchange in 2014.[13] (It was advised by the London-based global law firm Clifford Chance, which also does work for Huawei.[14])

From the outset, the top echelons of China Poly Group have been dominated by princelings, cementing the group's Party connections but also giving it a degree of independence within the Party. While it's a state-owned company, the red aristocracy has financial interests in it.[15] China Poly Group's first CEO, now honorary chairman, was He Ping.[16] The son of a veteran PLA commander, he served as an attaché (intelligence officer) in the Washington embassy and rose through the ranks to become a major general in the PLA. He is married to Deng Rong, daughter of paramount leader Deng Xiaoping, for two decades the most powerful man in China. (Deng Rong also worked in the Washington embassy, from 1979 to 1983.[17])

The current chairman of both China Poly Group and Poly Culture is Xu Niansha, a former navy captain and real estate developer. He's a top Party cadre, serving as a senior member of the national committee of the Chinese People's Political Consultative Conference and its foreign affairs committee.[18] (Curiously, in 2017 the Italian government bestowed on Xu the Order of the Star for his 'contribution in promoting the exchange and cooperation between China and Italy'.[19]) The general manager of Poly Culture, and chairman of several of its subsidiaries, Jiang Yingchun, is also a representative of the Beijing People's Congress, the city's equivalent of China's rubber-stamp parliament, the National People's Congress.[20]

As well as making money for China Poly Group, Poly Culture's role includes befriending and co-opting elites and raising China's global profile in cultural affairs. Poly Culture can be seen as part of the Culture Going Global arm of the Belt and Road Initiative, working with artistic groups in BRI countries to stage 500 performances each year.[21] Poly Culture has also cooperated with renowned institutions like Columbia University, the Lincoln Center, Yale University, and the Metropolitan Museum of Art.[22] In 2017 a youth orchestra belonging to Poly Culture held a 'China-Germany Friendship Concert' in Cologne Cathedral, hosted by the chairwoman of the German Overseas Chinese Federation, Li Aiping. The orchestra also visited the United Nations headquarters in Vienna.[23]

Poly Culture owns over a hundred subsidiaries, including an art auction business, Poly Auction, now the third-largest in the world; a theatre management business; and a subsidiary that owns cinemas.[24] Another subsidiary, Poly Art, is devoted to 'providing professional corporate art solutions for corporations'. Its strategic art planning helps 'corporate culture building, business performance promotion, and social responsibility expression'.[25] Poly Art aims to 'nurture and amass high-net-worth customers'. Its museum in Beijing specialises in Chinese art retrieved from abroad.

In 2015 Poly Culture established its North American headquarters in Vancouver, where it also opened an art gallery. The company was reportedly lured to Vancouver by strong lobbying from the province's trade minister, Hong Kong–born Teresa Wat.[26] A base there was also likely to attract less scrutiny than one in the United States, given the company's PLA links and the fact that Poly Technologies, the China Poly subsidiary, was sanctioned by Washington in 2013 for selling arms to Iran, North Korea, Syria, or possibly all of them (the US did not specify).[27] Poly Culture North America set up its office on the same floor in the same building as Wat's constituency office.[28] The company's CEO is Yi Chen, whose background is obscure.

At the Vancouver launch, Poly Culture and China Poly Group executives mixed with the political and business elite of British Columbia.

In 2017 the Vancouver Symphony Society signed a memorandum of understanding with Poly Culture North America to work together on co-presentations and promote Chinese performers and artists. The orchestra's board is packed with Vancouver's business elite.[29]

With its large Chinese-heritage population, initially dominated by migrants from Hong Kong but more recently by mainlanders, Vancouver has been a hotbed of united front activity, not least in the cultural sphere. In July 2019, in the presence of CCP propaganda officials, various British Columbian politicians launched a new united front group, the Vancouver Association for Promotion of Chinese Culture.[30] The PRC's consul general Kong Weiwei, vice consul Wang Chengjun, and the consulate's UFWD team were there to oversee proceedings. Federal Canadian politicians included Jenny Kwan and Joe Peschisolido (the latter under fire in newspapers for alleged links to Chinese organised crime), and from the provincial legislature there was Teresa Wat.[31]

When the city of Vancouver and the province of British Columbia decided to establish a Chinese Canadian Museum with the help of Simon Fraser University, united front forces could not keep their hands off. The project is headed by George Chow, Minister of State for Trade in the BC government.[32] Chow is a past president of Vancouver's Chinese Benevolent Association, a well-known united front organisation that in 2019 organised over 200 Chinese community groups to take out advertisements in newspapers condemning Hong Kong 'radicals' and supporting the Beijing-backed Hong Kong government.[33] In September 2019 the association hosted a gala event in Chinatown to celebrate the PRC's seventieth birthday. Chow was in attendance, as was Canada's defence minister, Harjit Sajjan, who was heavily criticised for celebrating the anniversary while Michael Kovrig and Michael Spavor, the Canadians detained in response to the Huawei crisis, were rotting in China's jails.[34]

In December 2018 Chow had reportedly gone to Guangzhou to discuss plans for the new museum with CCP officials.[35] When the museum set up a timeline of the important events in the history of Chinese immigrants in Canada, some events that most affected local Chinese people, such as the Tiananmen massacre and the handover of Hong Kong to China, were missing.[36] The timeline focused instead on events important to the CCP's narrative, highlighting racist measures like the head tax and other forms of colonial humiliation. Chinese-Canadians from Hong Kong took it upon themselves to fill in some of the gaps.[37]

The China Arts Foundation

The foreign influence function of Poly Culture is indicated by its links to the China Association for International Friendly Contact, which as we saw in chapter four is a front organisation for the International Liaison Bureau of the Political Work Department of the Central Military Commission. The Liaison Bureau engages in intelligence work, but also, in the words of CCP expert Geoff Wade, 'develops links with global elites and aims at influencing the policies and behaviour of countries, institutions and groups beyond China'.[38] The powerful Deng Rong is a vice president of CAIFC and her husband He Ping serves as a consultant, along with various Party heavyweights.[39]

CAIFC has set up a number of front organisations.[40] It is behind the Sanya Dialogue, the Nishan Forum on World Civilizations, and the Centre for Peace and Development Studies, and has close relations with the China-U.S. Exchange Foundation (see chapters three and five).[41] Many of its office holders are double-hatted senior PLA officers, although their military positions are generally obscured, leading Wade to observe: 'This intense engagement by senior members of the PLA in CAIFC activities clearly shows the degree to which it is a covert arm of the PLA, engaged in intelligence and propaganda work.'[42] CAIFC and its front groups invite members of Western elites to a broad range of activities. The First China Philanthropy Forum in November 2012, for example, was attended by Bill Gates and Tony Blair, along with some forty CAIFC consultants and directors.[43] In the same year, it joined with the China Arts Foundation to invite Bill Clinton to give a speech. Clinton pulled out when the State Department baulked at it.[44]

The China Arts Foundation was set up in 2006 by Deng Rong, with the backing of CAIFC, ostensibly to 'create awareness about Chinese culture, history and politics through music'.[45] The foundation 'acts as a magnet for China's elite'.[46] In 2010 it brought together the New York Philharmonic and the Shanghai Symphony Orchestra for a concert in

Central Park, which featured superstar Chinese pianist Lang Lang.[47] (The following year, at a White House state dinner for visiting President Hu Jintao, Lang Lang played a well-known anti-American propaganda song.[48]) The director of the Shanghai Symphony, Yu Long, is a member of China Arts Foundation's board.[49] Before the Central Park concert, the foundation hosted a private VIP reception that included author Ron Chernow, high-society interior designer Geoffrey Bradfield, and billionaire investor and philanthropist Theodore Forstmann.[50] The following year, the two orchestras signed an agreement to host touring exchanges and to collaborate on a new orchestral training institute in Shanghai.[51]

In 2014 the China Arts Foundation established a New York branch, known as the China Arts Foundation International, to promote cross-cultural artistic events.[52] CAFI's president is Angela Chen. Chen attended Harvard Business School and made her name in the US finance industry, first at Merrill Lynch, then as vice president at Prudential, America's largest insurance company.[53] She also runs Global Alliance, 'a boutique business relationship consultancy for US companies seeking to establish a presence in mainland China'.[54]

Global Alliance and the China Arts Foundation both operate out of an apartment at 502 Park Avenue in New York, that is, Trump Park Avenue. After living for some years in a less opulent condominium in the tower, in early 2017 Angela Chen paid president-elect Donald Trump $15.8 million for a penthouse.[55] An investigation by *Mother Jones* noted that both her jobs entail connecting elites in the US to elites in China.[56] Chen uses CAFI to build *guanxi*; real estate mogul Larry Silverstein and fashion guru Giorgio Armani have featured at CAFI events.[57] In 2014 Chen was appointed co-chair of the international advisory board of the New York Philharmonic.[58] In that same year, CAFI's Chinese New Year Gala welcomed philanthropist and banker Steven Rockefeller, and Stephen Schwarzman of the Blackstone Group, a Trump confidant and Beijing favourite.[59] CAFI has also held a reception in conjunction with Tiffany's to welcome the National Ballet of China.[60] (In October 2019 Tiffany's expunged an ad featuring a model posed with her right hand covering her eye, which ultra-nationalist Chinese netizens interpreted as a reference to a young women who was wounded in the eye by a beanbag round fired by Hong Kong police.) CAFI's Chinese New Year

Gala for 2015 brought together former US ambassador to China Jon Huntsman, former president of the Asia Society Nicholas Platt, and the previous managing editor of *Fortune*, Andrew Serwer. Platt and Serwer are members of CAFI's board.[61]

So CAFI, an affiliate of China's military intelligence service, has built an exceptionally rich network among America's corporate, political and cultural elites. Along with the US members, CAFI's board includes Wang Boming, editor-in-chief of *Caijing*, the influential finance journal, who is said to be close to Wang Qishan, one of seven members of the supreme Standing Committee of the Politburo and Xi Jinping's right-hand man.[62]

Cultural monopolisation

During his 2017 visit to Italy, the boss of the CCP's Overseas Chinese Affairs Office, Qiu Yuanping, urged overseas Chinese to contribute to the Belt and Road Initiative by participating in the work of the Huaxing Arts Troupe.[63] This project is one of eight launched by the OCAO in 2014 to 'help Overseas Chinese'.[64] By 2019 there were forty-two Huaxing Arts Troupes in twenty-five countries, performing various 'red concerts' and 'songs and dances in praise of the heroic journey of Communism in China'.[65] The Frankfurt Huaxing Arts Troupe's 2018 Spring Festival gala was planned by the OCAO and supported by the consulate.[66] In February 2018 the Chicago Bulls basketball team hosted a performance by the city's Huaxing Arts Troupe as part of the Chinese New Year festivities directed by the local consulate.[67]

In Australia, Melbourne's Huaxing Arts Troupe is also officially endorsed by the OCAO and holds many extravagant 'red' cultural events. It appears to be involved in low-level intelligence gathering. In 2018 it prepared a 'work report', sent to Huaxing headquarters in China, in which it boasted of having 'established a database that contains contact information of important political figures, important Chinese community groups, celebrities, and artists'.[68] Events hosted or co-hosted by the troupe attract a range of politicians, including state premiers and federal parliamentarians, as well as officials from the Chinese consulate. The Melbourne Huaxing troupe is headed by Tom Zhou (Zhou Jiuming or 'Mr Chinatown'), a businessman and casino-junket operator, who in

2019 emerged as a central figure in a money-laundering scandal at the city's Crown Casino.[69]

Most governments use their national culture for the purpose of public diplomacy, but the Chinese government uses it covertly to exert influence, including over the diaspora. In 2008 a Party website explained the goal as being to 'fully utilise the function of traditional festivals—Chinese New Year, Qingming tomb sweeping festival, Dragon Boat festival, Mid Autumn festival and Chongyang Festival—that can stimulate patriotic feelings for China and channel ethnic sentiment'.[70] Lunar New Year, for decades celebrated by people of Chinese heritage around the world, has in recent times been appropriated by Party sympathisers and used to impress on political leaders the views of 'the Chinese community'.

No expression of China's culture, even the most innocuous, escapes the Party's determination to monopolise it. The *qipao* (or *cheongsam*) is an elegant, close-fitting dress regarded as traditionally Chinese. In fact it is neither Chinese nor traditional, but owes its origins to the Manchus and was first worn by women in China some years after the fall of the Qing dynasty in 1911.[71] The *qipao* was vilified as bourgeois during the Cultural Revolution and was not worn, but in recent years it's made a comeback and is popular among middle-class women.[72]

Societies to celebrate the *qipao* have sprung up all over the world. In 2015 *China Daily* reported that about 150,000 *qipao* enthusiasts had gathered at events around the world 'as a demonstration of traditional Chinese art'.[73] The president of the China Qipao Association, Swiss-Chinese businessman Wang Quan, said he wanted to 'impress the world with exquisite Chinese traditional dress'.[74]

However, the *qipao* movement has been turned into a global propaganda weapon. The Ministry of Culture has a committee to oversee it.[75] When Qi Quansheng, deputy director of the All-China Federation of Returned Overseas Chinese (part of the United Front structure), hosted a propaganda seminar in Tianjin in 2018, the influence of *qipao* culture was one of the topics for discussion.[76] Later that year, Jinan University ran a *qipao*/tai chi training class for overseas Chinese community groups; it was attended by a phalanx of Party officials, including a top official from the 10th Bureau of the UFWD, who reminded those present of

Xi Jinping's injunction to use traditional culture to spread his Chinese Dream.[77] In the same year, the Wuhan office of the UFWD reported a promise made by the vice chairman of the China Qipao Society Global Alliance, Li Ye, that his organisation would 'closely unite around the Party'.[78]

It therefore comes as no surprise that the chairman of the China Qipao Society, Wang Quan, is an overseas representative of the Chinese People's Political Consultative Conference.[79] The society he chairs receives the full backing of the Ministry of Culture, and its activities are being integrated into the Belt and Road Initiative.

The German branch of the World Qipao United Association, established in 2018 in Neuss near Düsseldorf, is one of the most important local hubs for overseas Chinese in Germany.[80] Its inauguration ceremony had the support of the Chinese consulate in Düsseldorf.[81] It is presided over by Jiang Haiying, who is also president of the Chinese Women's Association of Germany, which reports to the Chinese embassy.[82] As a reward for her loyalty, Jiang Haiying was invited to attend the PRC's seventieth anniversary celebrations in Beijing.[83] In 2015 Jiang was elected an executive vice president of the Qingtian Hometown Association of Germany, whose 'special advisors' include senior Chinese United Front officials.[84]

In Australia, a senior office holder in a 'peaceful reunification' group is also president of the Qipao Society of Australia, leading to its politicisation. In 2016 the society signed a declaration supporting Beijing's defiance of The Hague Tribunal's ruling that China had no basis for its claim over the South China Sea.[85]

So the Party exploits the *qipao* movement to carry out united front work 'in a more friendly way and relaxed cultural atmosphere'.[86] The glamour of the *qipao* attracts foreign audiences, raises the profile of united front groups and legitimises them as 'cultural ambassadors', in the process enabling access to elites in fashion, business and politics. All this points to the Party's determination to present itself as the legitimate custodian of Chinese heritage and to mobilise its notion of Chineseness to win loyalty among ethnic Chinese at home and abroad. The tragedy is that it makes it difficult for overseas Chinese who do not support the CCP to share in the revival of *qipao*.

Crushing cultural deviance

While promoting those expressions of Chinese culture that it controls, the Party also tries to suppress those it does not control. When Beijing attempted to brush up China's image with some cosmopolitan glamour by hosting the Miss World contest in 2015, the case of Anastasia Lin injected a sour note. A Chinese-Canadian actress and activist for human rights in China, Anastasia Lin had won Miss World Canada and was due to compete for the Miss World title, to be held on Hainan Island. But she was declared *persona non grata* and denied a visa to travel to the competition venue. The *Global Times* explained that the decision was taken because Lin had been 'misguided by her values'. She was not evil-minded, it wrote, but simply 'lacks reasonable understanding of the country where she was born'.[87] Prejudiced Westerners, the paper believed, were likely to be swayed when 'a 25-year pretty girl grumbles'.

For Miss World contestants, speaking about their commitment to a social cause—girls' education or world poverty—is usually a *sine qua non* for success, but Lin picked the wrong one. (It didn't help that she was a practitioner of Falun Gong, which she described as 'fancy yoga'.[88]) Because of her advocacy, her father in Hunan has been harassed by MSS agents, and now on their phone calls 'he always mentions how great the Chinese president is'.[89]

Petty censorship on behalf of Beijing has been taken up by officials in the Western mainstream. At a dragon-boat festival in Ottawa, the organiser ordered a man to take off a T-shirt promoting Falun Gong.[90] The Chinese embassy was one of the festival's sponsors. Another Falun Gong practitioner outside the venue, in a public park, was threatened with removal. He expressed the view of many when he said, 'Canadians should not be taking directions from the Chinese embassy.'

In early 2019 an arts centre in Cary, North Carolina, which was about to stage an exhibition of works by US-based Chinese artist Weng Bing, decided not to wait for an objection from Beijing and pre-emptively excluded three paintings it deemed 'political'.[91] Two of the paintings depicted Xi Jinping unflatteringly. Lyman Collins, cultural arts manager of Cary, told the artist that he personally liked the paintings and wanted to protect free speech, but he wanted to 'take all views into account', presumably including those of the CCP. Weng said she had been inspired to paint the works after watching Dong Yaoqiong, a Chinese artist in Shanghai, livestream herself splashing ink on a poster of Xi at a protest against 'tyranny'. In a chilling reminder of the Soviet practice of defining political opposition as a psychiatric disorder, Dong Yaoqiong was sent for 'compulsory treatment' to the psychiatric ward of Hunan's Zhuzhou No. 3 Hospital. Weng said that after watching the video she 'couldn't stay silent any longer', but, like Dong's, her protest was also muzzled by officials.[92]

Film and theatre censors

As a city that has attracted a large number of Chinese dissidents, Berlin receives disproportionate attention from Beijing's cultural police, and with some success. The organisers of the 2019 Berlin International Film Festival announced that two Chinese films, including one by famous director Zhang Yimou set in the politically sensitive period of the Cultural Revolution, had to be pulled for 'technical reasons'.[93] 'Technical reasons' has become the default excuse when managers of venues and theatres give way to political arm-twisting.

One theory is that the films may have failed to garner approval, and thus an exit permit, from China's state censors, particularly given that in 2018 the CCP, in a bureaucratic restructuring, had taken more direct control over the entertainment sector.[94] Another possibility is that the festival organisers may have been pressured by German car-maker Audi, the festival's principal sponsor.[95] Audi's sales had just reached record levels in China, its biggest market. The company had sponsored a new Confucius Institute in Ingolstadt in 2016.[96]

At the same time, news broke that a segment made by dissident artist Ai Weiwei had been cut from the film *Berlin, I Love You* under pressure from distributors, who said they would not buy the film with the segment included.[97] Ai, who helped design Beijing's famous 'Bird's Nest' Olympic stadium, earned the ire of authorities when he criticised the cover-up of the 2008 Sichuan earthquake, which killed thousands of children. In 2018 one of his Beijing studios was demolished without notice. One of the producers of *Berlin, I Love You*, Emmanuel Benbihy, claimed that Ai's segment was removed for 'artistic reasons'. However, two other producers told *The New York Times* they had fought to keep the segment in, but were forced to remove it due to pressure from distributors.[98] Ai, who had not been informed of the excision of his segment, believes it was a pre-emptive buckle: 'Most of this censorship actually originated with Western organizations. They are engaged in self-censorship so as to comply with China's censorship regime. This is internalized political pressure, not necessarily something that the Chinese government has told them directly.'[99]

Ai's identification of Western cowardice was confirmed by Edda Reiser, another of the film's producers, who was privy to the backroom dealing. She admitted, 'We underestimated not the influence of China, but the fear. The fear of China in the free world.'[100]

Film festivals in Copenhagen and Melbourne have come under similar pressure. In the past, Beijing's attempts to exclude certain people or films in the West were seen as clumsy, and gave inadvertent publicity for the film. Not anymore; now a growing number of organisations are willing to comply with Chinese government requests and to blame 'technical difficulties' for their timidity.

The incorporation of culture into the Belt and Road Initiative is deepening Beijing's political influence.[101] The Ministry of Culture formalised it in the One Belt and One Road Cultural Development Action Plan (2016–20).[102] By the end of 2016, over sixty countries along the Silk Road route had signed cultural exchange and cooperation agreements with Beijing.[103]

The CCP's tightening grip on culture also means the Party controls the construct of 'Chineseness'; it is replacing a multiplicity of voices and styles with an increasingly monolithic one. British-Chinese artists, for example, have complained that 'international' Chinese artists—that is, those sent from China and with the blessing of Beijing—have increasingly marginalised the art of British-Chinese.[104]

In London, the Southbank Centre's 'China Changing Festival', run over three years from 2016, has been accused of putting artists from mainland China centre-stage and keeping those from Britain in the wings.[105] The Southbank Centre is one of a handful of Western cultural institutions to sign on to the Silk Road International League of Theatres, approved by the Ministry of Culture as part of its Belt and Road Cultural Development Action Plan.[106] Reporting on the league, the *People's Daily* quoted a former vice chancellor of the Central Party School saying that the BRI aims to build not just 'the bond of interest' through the economy and trade, but also 'the bond of the human heart' through cultural ties.[107] In addition to theatres, the action plan has established international alliances of libraries, museums, art museums, art festivals and art colleges.[108]

A number of theatres in Russia, Japan, Eastern Europe and the global South have signed agreements. The French National Theatre Union (Association des Scènes Nationales) signed a memorandum of understanding with the Silk Road International League of Theatres in 2016, as did the Minneapolis-based Arts Midwest.[109] Another Western institution to join the league is the Royal Theatre in Madrid, the venue for one of the most blatant, Beijing-inspired acts of cultural censorship seen to date. It's a story worth telling as it's an increasingly common one. First, some backstory.

Some of the Falun Gong practitioners who fled China after the 2001 crackdown created the Shen Yun dance troupe to perform 'classical Chinese dance' and to promote Falun Gong's principles and draw attention to its persecution by the CCP.[110] The Chinese government has been determined in its efforts to prevent performances by Shen Yun everywhere. By early 2019 over sixty attempts had been documented worldwide, including in Europe and North America.[111]

A first wave occurred in 2008 but largely failed. Then, in 2010, pressure from Chinese authorities saw shows in Romania, Greece, Moldova and Ukraine cancelled. In 2011 the Chinese consul general in Auckland, New Zealand wrote to city councillors telling them not to attend a forthcoming Shen Yun performance. 'This consul general has no right to tell me not to go to a production in Auckland,' said one indignant council member. 'How dare they.'[112]

In 2012 Chinese authorities failed to stop a Shen Yun show at the London Coliseum, and in 2014 the consulate in Barcelona tried unsuccessfully to block a performance by pressuring the National Theatre of Catalonia and Spain's Foreign Ministry. The consulate threatened repercussions for relations between Spain and China if Shen Yun were allowed to perform.[113] In the same year, the Chinese embassy in Brussels demanded that a Shen Yun performance, due to take place during

Xi Jinping's visit to the city, be cancelled. The Belgian National Theatre refused to comply. In Berlin in 2014 the Chinese cultural attaché visited Jörg Seefeld, the marketing and sales manager of the Stage Theatre, which was due to host a Shen Yun event, and told him that unless he cancelled the performance Chinese theatre troupes would not use the theatre, and that if he ever wanted to visit China he would be denied a visa. Seefeld, who had been imprisoned in East Germany, was unmoved by the threats.[114]

In March 2015 the director of the Chinese-language program at the Utah State Office of Education, Stacy Lyon, emailed principals of Utah's language-immersion schools urging them, in effect, to reject approaches by the Shen Yun dance troupe to stage performances in their schools. Lyon wrote that funds awarded to schools for Confucius Classrooms were not to be used to support Shen Yun events.[115]

As China's power kept growing, its censorship attempts had more success. In 2017 the Chinese embassy in Copenhagen successfully pressured the Royal Danish Theatre to refuse to host Shen Yun.[116]

Which brings us back to Madrid. The Royal Theatre had joined the Silk Road International League of Theatres in 2016, after which visits and exchanges began to occur. In November 2018 President Xi's wife, Peng Liyuan, paid a visit to the theatre, accompanied by the Queen of Spain.[117] In January 2019 China's diplomats were upset that the theatre had scheduled performances by the Shen Yun troupe, and began pressuring the general manager to cancel them. The ambassador is a member of the theatre's 'Diplomatic Circle'.

The Royal Theatre cancelled the shows, even though 900 tickets had been sold. Management cited 'technical difficulties'. The Falun Gong–aligned *Epoch Times* reported that someone posing as a high-level Chinese government official phoned the Chinese ambassador in Madrid a few days after the cancellation.[118] The ambassador bragged about having personally put pressure on the theatre's general manager, suggesting that if the performances went ahead the theatre would lose access to China's market. The ambassador reminded this alleged official of the Royal Theatre's agreement with the Silk Road International League of Theatres. The general manager, who had just returned from a trip to China, was initially worried about reputational damage, according to the ambassador, but gave way, agreeing to use the ambassador's suggested excuse of technical difficulties.

Two months after the cancellation, the theatre's managing director, Ignacio Garcia-Belenguer, signed a cooperation agreement with China's National Center for the Performing Arts.[119] He said it was 'another step towards greater collaboration between the two institutions which have enjoyed a close relationship for several years'. He noted that the relationship had been boosted as a result of the visit to the theatre of Peng Liyuan in November 2018.

'The Marxist view of art and culture'

It's often observed that China has little cultural soft power to deploy. This is not because China's cultural traditions do not have great appeal but because China's culture has been thoroughly distorted by the Communist Party, overlaid by a thick coating of propaganda. Soft power grows organically from civil society and typically loses its authenticity when governments become too involved, all the more so when they attempt to manipulate it to serve political ends.

If the CCP has been unable to benefit much from China's soft power, Beijing has been highly effective at regulating America's chief source of cultural influence: Hollywood. The self-censorship by Hollywood film producers in order to ensure access to the huge Chinese market has often been reported in newspapers, but we'll give just one illustration: '... when the creators of "Pixels" wanted to show aliens blasting a hole in the Great Wall of China, Sony executives worried that the scene might prevent the 2015 movie's release in China, leaked studio emails show. They blew up the Taj Mahal instead.'[120]

Indian sensitivities don't rate, it seems. Zhang Xun, a top movie regulator, made China's position clear to American producers: 'We have a huge market, and we want to share it with you ... We want to see positive Chinese images.'[121] Now, when American films are being planned, funds sought and scripts written, Beijing's censors are always at the front of the minds of producers, directors and scriptwriters.

And even costumers. In the 2019 sequel to *Top Gun*, the patches on the back of Maverick's leather jacket were subtly changed to remove the Japanese and Taiwanese flags.[122] Adding to the pressure to self-censor in this case, one of the movie's producers was a film company owned by the Chinese internet giant Tencent.

The same thing is happening in Bollywood, because Indian films also attract large audiences in China. The actor Aamir Khan has made millions from Chinese viewers and has become a strong advocate of friendly relations between India and China.[123]

In July 2019 Xi Jinping sent a congratulatory letter to the China Writers Association and the China Federation of Literary and Art Circles, honouring the seventieth anniversary of their formation. Read out by the head of the CCP's Propaganda Department to writers gathered at a symposium, the letter expressed Xi's view that the 'development of literature and art is an important cause of the Party and the people, and the literary and art front is a vital front of the Party and the people'.[124] Five years earlier, Xi had been plainer: 'Art and culture will emit the greatest positive energy when the Marxist view of art and culture is firmly established and the people are their focus.'[125]

The China Writers Association is a state organisation whose first duty is to 'organize writers to study Marxism-Leninism, Mao Zedong Thought, and Deng Xiaoping Theory, and to study the guiding policies of the party'.[126] In more liberal times, some writers wanted to use the association to foster greater creative freedom, and in 2016 two vice presidents of the Suzhou branch resigned in what was seen as a protest against tightening control.[127]

When, in the spirit of cross-cultural exchange, Western writers festivals and writers organisations team up with the China Writers Association—as did the University of Waterloo in 2014 and the Melbourne Writers' Festival in 2015, and as the International Writing Program at the University of Iowa does on a regular basis—they are teaming up with writers guided by the CCP, authors approved by the Party who will not risk deviating from Party ideology.[128] Dissident Chinese writers are not allowed to participate in these events, and any who arrive craving open exchanges with their foreign counterparts find they are closely chaperoned by Party minders. Chinese writers drawn from the diaspora are excluded or marginalised, unless they are members of a local Chinese Writers Association, under United Front guidance. For all their good intentions, these festivals are not free exchanges.

The 'Chinese culture' that Westerners hear about at them is a version circumscribed by the Party.

Many Westerners are by now familiar with the CCP's crackdown on religious worship in China, which includes the use of CCTV cameras in churches and mosques and forcing believers to practise in approved ways. The 11th and 12th Bureaus of the United Front Work Department devote extensive efforts to this repression, setting up 'representative organisations' for each religion.[129] It was reported in 2019 that Tibetan nomads had been told they would continue to receive state subsidies only if they 'replaced their altars devoted to Buddhist deities with images of Chinese political leaders'.[130] Christians have been pressured to replace images of Jesus with photos of Xi Jinping. In a move that resonated with its position in the 1930s, the Vatican reached an agreement with Beijing to allow the Party to choose Catholic bishops.[131]

Even more surprising are the Party's efforts to spy on, infiltrate, guide or control religious groups of Chinese people in the West. Space limitations preclude a full discussion, but we note reports of Chinese Christian churches being monitored and infiltrated. Pastors believe that among their congregations are spies for the local consulates, who report on any criticism of the Party.[132]

The CCP has made even more extensive efforts to control Buddhism in the West, including the formation of tame Buddhist associations.[133] In 2018 Shi Xuecheng, secretary-general of the Buddhist Association of China and a member of the CPPCC, arrived in Sydney to oversee the launch of the Australia China Buddhist Council. He was flanked by diplomats and top united front figures, among them Huang Xiangmo, a wealthy political donor soon to be banned from the country because of his Party links.[134] The Party-endorsed Master Shi agrees with the CCP's ambition to 'Sinicise' religion. (However, Beijing lost a useful functionary when Shi Xuecheng was forced to step down after he was accused of molesting nuns.)[135]

Among the 'red Buddhists' sheltering beneath the umbrella of the Australia China Buddhist Council is Wang Xinde, head of a wealthy 'Holy Tantra' Buddhist sect based in Tasmania that has a worldwide following, especially in Canada. Wang also serves as president of the Tasmanian branch of the Australian Council for the Promotion of

Peaceful Reunification of China, the foremost united front body.[136] Wang is frequently pictured with local politicians, and his website is unabashed about his desire to promote Xi Jinping's 'China Dream' and to 'tell a good China story, propagate Chinese voice'. He has said, 'We will hold the latest policies enacted by the motherland as guidance for everything we do.'[137] In 2019 he re-posted an article calling for pro-democracy protesters in Hong Kong to be killed.[138]

Of course, the Party has also worked hard to take control of Tibetan Buddhism. When the Panchen Lama, whose spiritual authority is traditionally second only to that of the Dalai Lama, met Xi Jinping in 2015 he proclaimed that 'under the leadership of the Party Central Committee with Comrade Xi Jinping as its core, our future is bright, and our tomorrow is glorious'.[139] When the previous Panchen Lama died, the successor nominated by the Dalai Lama in 1995, Gedhun Choekyi Nyima, aged six, was kidnapped and disappeared. The Party installed its own boy.

Perhaps the most intriguing example of the Party's determination to control China's culture is the story of Xu Xiaodong, which is brilliantly told by Lauren Teixera in an article titled 'He never intended to become a political dissident, but then he started beating up tai chi masters'.[140] Xu is an expert in mixed martial arts (MMA originated in Japan and Brazil and became enormously popular in the US in the 1990s). He owned a gym in Beijing and over the years he'd built a following on social media. But he also earned the ire of authorities for ridiculing practitioners of traditional Chinese martial arts, especially revered tai chi masters, as 'fakes'. They can do tricks, he'd say, including amazing feats on popular TV shows, but they can't fight. When more than a hundred outraged masters challenged him to fight, he picked the best seventeen and sought them out. It would be MMA versus tai chi. YouTube clips show him defeating all seventeen, often in very short, brutal fights.

Xi Jinping's direction to use culture as part of the great rejuvenation of the Chinese nation includes heavy promotion of tai chi and traditional Chinese medicine. When Xu exposed so many tai chi masters as 'fakes' with his foreign fighting techniques, he embarrassed the Party. 'The Chinese government would really like for him to stop his war against tai chi', wrote Teixera, and it has taken all kinds of measures to stop him, putting him on a social credit backlist. Banned from flying and taking fast trains, Xu had to take a 36-hour slow train to Xinjiang to fight a famous kung fu 'pressure point' master. (He pummelled him into submission in less than a minute.)

When the American MMA promoter Ultimate Fighting Championship decided to extend its reach into China, it was happy to build on Xu's years of hard work in building a large fan base for this martial art. But when it stages fights in China, Xu Xiaodong is not on the invitation list.

11
Think tanks and thought leaders

'Eating the CCP's food'

Because of the political and business leaders linked to them, think tanks are an ideal target for both short- and long-term influence operations. Winning them over is vital to the CCP's intention to 'change the debate without having to directly inject their own voice'.[1] It is no exaggeration to say that whenever an influential think tank works on China-related topics, the CCP will take a keen interest.

The think tank world is closely linked to philanthropy, making it difficult to disentangle the manifold interests that shape an institution. Many of those in the United States working on China issues are sponsored by business elites close to China. While some funding also flows directly from the Chinese government and Chinese companies, endowments from 'friends of China', like Goldman Sachs and Tung Chee-hwa, play a bigger role.

Think tanks always insist on their independence. Like political parties that accept corporate donations, they cannot do otherwise. But the reality is closer to the adage of not biting the hand that feeds you, or in Xi Jinping's words, 'We must not allow the eating of the CCP's food by those who smash the CCP's cauldron.'[2] Giving money creates obligation: you made me happy, so I am obliged to make you happy, or at least not unhappy. Some researchers are unswayed by expectations that they won't smash the cauldron, but few can resist pressure from their employers, even in universities. That's not to say all think tanks will turn into propaganda organs churning out nothing but the Party's message; far from it. Yet investment in research typically pays off in one way or another, which is why the Party's International Liaison Department emphasises interacting with think tanks. The Silk Road Think Tank Association has over a hundred Chinese and foreign members.[3]

So it is a problem that many think tanks in the West accept funds from wealthy 'friends of China' or companies whose bottom line depends on good relations with the CCP. This colours the work emanating from them, including from some of the most authoritative and influential. Several Western think tanks have opened branches or representative offices in China, giving the CCP additional leverage over the content produced. The result is a picture of China that is on the whole arguably more positive than it would be without financial ties. Again, a comprehensive review is beyond this book's scope, but some illustrations make the point.

The Brookings Institution is one of the largest and most renowned think tanks in the United States. It describes itself as nonpartisan, and people across the political spectrum rely on its work. But funding for its China research comes from a well-known 'friend of China', John L. Thornton, a former president of Goldman Sachs. Thornton, who endowed the eponymous China Center at Brookings, is so important to the institution that he chaired Brookings's board of trustees until late 2018 and remains on it.

In 2008 Thornton received the highest honour bestowed on foreigners by China's government, the Friendship Award.[4] He is chairman of the board of the Silk Road Finance Corporation, a Hong Kong–based investment firm that facilitates Chinese investment in Belt and Road countries.[5] Its CEO, Li Shan, is a member of the CPPCC.[6] Thornton is a friend of Wang Qishan, a member of the Standing Committee of the Politburo and Xi Jinping's enforcer and firefighter.[7]

Thornton also holds a professorship at Tsinghua University, where he is director of its Global Leadership Program, which he founded after retiring from Goldman Sachs in 2003.[8] The Brookings Institution itself is in partnership with Tsinghua: the Brookings-Tsinghua Center for Public Policy was opened in 2006.[9] To coincide with Xi Jinping's visit to the US in 2015, the think tank launched its Brookings China Council, straddling its Washington D.C. Thornton Center and the Brookings-Tsinghua Center in Beijing, with Thornton co-chairing with the president of Tsinghua University, Qiu Yong.[10] Xi Jinping's nephew reportedly interned at Brookings.[11]

Brookings has accepted sponsorship from Huawei. Between July 2016 and June 2018 it received at least $300,000 from the company's US-based subsidiary, Futurewei Technologies. Huawei also paid for Brookings's research on safe city technology; the resulting report failed to disclose that some of the technology it commended is made by Huawei. In the words of Isaac Stone-Fish, who broke the story in *The Washington Post*, 'Brookings praised Huawei's technology in a report sponsored by Huawei.'[12]

A similar entanglement of elites exists at the UK's most renowned think tank, Chatham House. It accepts money from a broad range of sources, including the Chinese government and Chinese companies such as the China International Capital Corporation and Huawei.[13] While the financial contributions from China are relatively minor, Chatham House has received praise from China's ambassador to the UK, Liu Xiaoming, for its 'positive contribution ... enhancing mutual understanding and cooperation between China and the UK'.[14]

Liu is not wrong that Chatham House has been good for the CCP. In 2019 its director, Robin Niblett, urged new prime minister Boris Johnson to draw Britain closer to China, building on the work of the May government and David Cameron's 'Golden Era' of Sino-British relations.[15] Niblett backs the City of London's project of making London the finance hub for the BRI. Chatham House's go-to expert on China, Yu Jie, has urged the UK government to stop sending mixed signals on China, to nurture the relationship between the two countries, and to get over its security concerns and realise that 'China is an indispensable partner if a post-Brexit "Global Britain" is to succeed'.[16]

The Party's biggest asset at Chatham House may be its chair, Jim O'Neill, former chief economist at Goldman Sachs. O'Neill has urged Britain to create 'more and more win-win situations between Britain and China' and for Britain to become a 'great trusted partner of China'.[17]

He has spoken alongside ambassador Liu Xiaoming and friendly British journalist Martin Jacques at Vision China, an event hosted by the *China Daily*, where he praised the BRI as 'possibly the most important thing for the future of world trade'.[18] O'Neill is also a welcome guest on China's Party-state media, where he waxes enthusiastically about China's economy.[19] He has joined the 48 Group Club's Stephen Perry to heap praise on Xi Jinping Thought.[20] In keeping with the overall tone that a chair like Jim O'Neill sets for the think tank, Lord Browne of Madingley, the chairman of Huawei Technologies (UK), is on Chatham House's Panel of Senior Advisors.[21]

Chatham House also joined hands with top Chinese think tank the China Centre for International Economic Exchanges to co-author an upbeat, pro-BRI report called 'EU–China Economic Relations to 2025: Building a common future', a title that genuflects to Xi's terminology. Aside from the questionable decision to partner with a think tank led by the CCP (more on which below), the funding for Chatham House's contribution came from Huawei.[22] Chatham House has also partnered with the Institute of World Economics and Politics, a Chinese government think tank, and the Chinese Academy of Social Sciences to research the use of the renminbi to finance BRI projects.[23] The report talked up the role of London as the global renminbi hub and centre of BRI financing.

The Chicago-based Paulson Institute is another prime example of China-friendly business elites sponsoring research on China. Founded in 2011 by Henry Paulson, former secretary of the US Treasury, and the former chairman and CEO of Goldman Sachs, the institute is 'dedicated to fostering a US-China relationship that serves to maintain global order in a rapidly evolving world'.[24] One way it has done this is by helping Beijing to incorporate green investment principles into the BRI (with the cooperation of the City of London).[25] Its MacroPolo economics blog argues for continued economic cooperation and has a tendency to emphasise the stability of the Chinese economy and the consistency of its reforms.[26]

Like Thornton, Paulson is very well connected to the CCP leadership, dating from his time at Goldman Sachs. In April 2019 he met with Politburo Standing Committee member Han Zheng to discuss bilateral ties between China and the US.[27] A report published on the Beijing municipal government's website referred to Paulson as an 'old friend' of Beijing mayor Chen Jining.[28] The Paulson Institute has also signed a memorandum of understanding with the Beijing government.[29] The institute's representative office in Beijing, along with the World Economic Forum (a Party favourite), were among the first batch of foreign NGOs to register under China's new foreign NGO law, allowing each to continue operating in China.[30]

Perhaps the most shamelessly pro-Beijing think tank is the Los Angeles–based Berggruen Institute, founded in 2010 by German American billionaire Nicolas Berggruen. From its earliest days, the Berggruen Institute has expressed sympathy for the CCP's authoritarian ideals and has enjoyed good relations with China's elite. China Central Television has featured Berggruen opining that the Party and the Chinese government aim to do one thing, 'serve the citizens'.[31] His colleague, Nathan Gardels, has praised the one-party state as the best form of government and said that democracy is unsuited to Hong Kong.[32] Articles written by Berggruen-affiliated analysts often promote or defend China's political model. For instance, a Berggruen take on China's political system asserted that the legitimacy of the CCP in China 'flows from prosperity and competence'.[33] Through the Understanding China conference series, organised by the former acting head of the CCP's Central Propaganda Department, Zheng Bijian, members of the Berggruen Institute have met with Xi Jinping and other top leaders.[34] (Zheng has also met with Berggruen's leadership on other occasions.[35]) The conference has attracted high-level participants, such as former UK prime minister Gordon Brown, former Danish prime minister Helle Thorning-Schmidt, and *Huffington Post* founder Arianna Huffington.[36] In December 2018 the institute collaborated with Peking University to found the Berggruen Research Center, based at the university.

The Berggruen Institute has partnered with *The Washington Post* to publish *The WorldPost*, edited by Nathan Gardels, with op-eds and feature articles from 'contributors around the world'.[37] A similar partnership appears to exist with *The Huffington Post*.[38] One such article in *The WorldPost* contends that Western companies need to adjust to Chinese people's 'different understanding' of privacy—that is, no 'privacy from government'—so as to arrive at truly 'global privacy norms, even if they look different from what we are used to'.[39] Another article, written by Song Bing—a former Goldman Sachs executive, now vice president of the Berggruen Institute and director of its China Center—describes how the West has misunderstood China's social credit system.[40]

Song Bing is married to Daniel Bell, who is director of the Philosophy and Culture Center of the Berggruen Institute, which collaborates with prestigious universities to promote 'cross-cultural' work on governance and other questions.[41] A most enthusiastic CCP apologist, Bell is best known for his book *The China Model: Political meritocracy and the limits of democracy*, which heaps high praise on the CCP.[42] Bell argues that the West should learn from the CCP's 'meritocratic rule' and he interprets Xi Jinping's rise as a product of that meritocracy.[43] Daniel Bell also has a position as chair professor of the Schwarzman Scholar Program at Tsinghua University in Beijing.

The *China Daily* also claims to have a partnership with the Berggruen Institute, with the goal, according to an article published on the website of China's Cyberspace Administration, to assemble a team of overseas commentators 'to let China's positive energy "go out"'.[44] Through the partnership, which the *China Daily* also reports it has with several other think tanks, the paper has published 300 signed opinion pieces on its website, from almost 200 overseas think tank experts, to 'influence more audiences abroad and explain China's story well'.[45]

The Hong Kong connection

CCP-linked money has been finding its way into the coffers of influential think tanks via the China-United States Exchange Foundation, which also funds the United States Heartland China Association, and the Sanya Initiative (see chapter three). CUSEF was founded in Hong Kong in 2008, and its chair is shipping magnate Tung Chee-hwa. Tung was Hong Kong's first chief executive (1997–2005) and is also a major funder of CUSEF.[46] The foundation has links to China's military and also cooperates with the PLA front organisation the China Association for International Friendly Contact (see chapters three and ten).[47]

Tung Chee-hwa is also vice chairman of the Chinese People's Political Consultative Conference, and in 2019 he accused the US and Taiwan of 'orchestrating' the protests in Hong Kong.[48] CUSEF's vice chairman is Victor Fung, Group Chairman of Li & Fung, a supply-chain manager for US and EU companies, and another important united front figure in Hong Kong. Fung, too, is a member of the Chinese People's Political Consultative Conference, and an adviser to the mayor of Beijing and the Nanjing municipal government.[49] His Fung Foundation funds China research.[50]

CUSEF's special representative in the United States is Fred Teng. Teng is president of the America China Public Affairs Institute, whose mission is to 'increase knowledge, understanding, and more accurate perceptions about China within the US government and among key policy and opinion leaders'.[51] It works closely with the CCP and the Chinese government to organise delegations of US leaders to China, and advocates a bilateral free trade agreement and a security partnership between China and the US, covering anti-terrorism, cybersecurity and law enforcement.[52]

CUSEF's New York PR company is BLJ Worldwide (whose website states: 'we develop sophisticated and intelligent communications campaigns'). It is registered as a foreign agent under the *Foreign Agent Registration Act*.[53] To influence Congress on China issues, it has hired lobbying firms, including the Podesta Group,[54] which in 2016 and 2017 also lobbied on behalf of Chinese telecom-equipment maker ZTE.[55] One of the Podesta Group's former principals was John Podesta, a powerful player in Democratic Party politics. After leaving the group in the hands of his brother, John Podesta became chief of staff to President Bill Clinton, and later, in 2016, chairman of Hillary Clinton's presidential campaign. From 2003 to 2011 Podesta was president of the Center for American Progress, a Washington think tank sometimes regarded as a parking lot for senior Democrat staffers during Republican presidencies. As such, it's an excellent target for CCP influence, and its staff have had a high-level visit to Beijing brokered by CUSEF. The two organisations have had a partnership since 2011, occasionally working with the Shanghai Institute for International Studies,[56] which is attached to the Ministry of Foreign Affairs.[57] In 2015 the Center for American Progress and CUSEF jointly organised a high-level dialogue in Beijing.[58]

In addition to providing funds to the Brookings Institution, the Atlantic Council, the Carter Center, and the Carnegie Endowment for International Peace,[59] CUSEF has endowed a chair in China Studies at the Johns Hopkins School of Advanced International Studies, one of America's foremost international-relations schools. Together with the Kissinger Institute, CUSEF also jointly runs the Pacific Community Initiative at Johns Hopkins SAIS. Bethany Allen-Ebrahimian notes that graduates of SAIS 'feed into a variety of government agencies, from the State Department to the CIA, and the military'.

Party-linked money in Brussels

The Chinese Mission to the European Union has emerged as a major donor to think tanks working on China or on topics of interest to the CCP. As François Godement and Abigaël Vasselier write in their assessment of China's power in Europe, 'a list of conferences and seminars in Brussels will immediately reveal that almost all think-tanks dealing with international relations and economics or Asia receive Chinese sponsorship'.[60]

The Madariaga – College of Europe Foundation was one Brussels-based think tank partly funded by China's government. It later merged with the Bruges-based College of Europe—according to one observer, the 'Harvard for Europe's elites'.[61] The foundation was set up by Pierre Defraigne, former director of the European Commission's trade department. According to him, Madariaga 'developed a constructive and balanced working relationship with the Chinese Mission', facilitating visits between high-ranking Party leaders and their counterparts in the European Parliament, the European Commission, and the EU's foreign and defence ministry.[62] In 2014 the foundation received 20 per cent of its budget from the Chinese Mission to the EU. More importantly, 40 per cent of its budget came from a company called Beijing Peace Tour Cultural Exchange Center.[63] The Chairman of Peace Tour, Shao Changchun, had to leave Belgium after Belgian state security investigated his organisation and reportedly found evidence of interference and espionage.[64] Shao also runs several other foundations, including the China-Europe Culture and Education Foundation, and the Silk Road Peace Prize Foundation.[65] Even Defraigne eventually grew wary of Peace

Tour's funding, admitting that he 'put an end to it as I realised that we could have been used as a lobby for special interests'.[66]

Madariaga closed shop in Brussels, but the College of Europe, which absorbed it, and the college's EU-China Research Center, founded in 2014, continue to work closely with the Chinese Mission to the EU, accepting financial sponsorship and jointly organising seminars and conferences on the BRI and Sino-European relations.[67] The College of Europe also hosts the Europe-China Seminar on Human Rights, founded by the China Society for Human Rights Studies. This society, which is linked to the CCP's Office of External Propaganda, was set up in 1993 to defuse criticism of China's human rights record by shifting the global debate away from individual and political rights (see chapter thirteen).[68]

Shortly before the EU–China summit of June 2017, the Brussels-based European media network Euractiv published a report titled 'EU-China: Mending differences'.[69] It was sponsored by the Chinese Mission and featured an interview with China lobbyist Luigi Gambardella, in which he praised the BRI and said that 'China has been insisting on mutually benefitting policies'.[70] In 2015 Gambardella founded ChinaEU, whose official mission is to promote cooperation between the EU and China in the digital economy.[71] Dubbed by *Politico* 'Europe's Mr. China' and Brussels's 'most visible lobbyist',[72] Gambardella meets with members of the European Parliament to push for more cooperation between China and the EU.[73] Like other 'friends of China', he frequently writes for and is cited in Party-state media, and has become a regular at China's annual World Internet Conference in Wuzhen.[74]

Together with the Chinese Mission, the Brussels-based think tank Friends of Europe organises the Europe-China Forum, as well as the Europe-China Policy and Practice Roundtable.[75] In March 2019 Friends of Europe, the Chinese Mission, and the CPPCC's China Public Diplomacy Association jointly organised a high-level EU–China event called 'Can cooperation trump competition?'[76] The think tank's director of policy, Shada Islam, is frequently cited in Party-state media.[77]

The picture for other Brussels-based think tanks working on Asia is similar. The EU-Asia Centre, for instance, accepts money from the Chinese Mission and works closely with Beijing authorities.[78]

Its founder and director, Fraser Cameron, is a former British diplomat and EU official, whose opinions are promoted by the *China Daily*. In the paper he declared the EU to be a 'strong supporter of the Belt and Road Initiative'.[79] In 2015 the European Institute for Asian Studies rejected a proposal to host a talk on Tibet by Australian expert Gabriel Lafitte, claiming 'a public seminar on Tibet is not possibility [*sic*] for EIAS'. Yet weeks later it organised a talk on economic development in Tibet by a senior CCP official and military officer.[80]

In Switzerland, Beijing has a friend in the World Economic Forum, which it has used to create a tight network of connections with the global business elite. In a paid advertisement in *The New York Times*, the *China Daily* announced that the forum's founder and chairman, Klaus Schwab, was one of only ten foreign experts to receive the prestigious China Reform Friendship Medal—for backing 'China's efforts to re-engineer the global economic order'.[81] Schwab, who praised Xi's 'open and collaborative spirit', said the forum will continue to help China 'realize the shared dream of world peace, happiness, justice, equality and love triumphing over poverty'.[82]

Beijing appears to have neutralised or captured substantial parts of think tanks across Europe, cultivating sympathetic voices and muting critical ones, including those studying its interference activities in Europe.

Other forms of pressure

Money is not the only leverage Beijing has over think tanks in the West. In 2019 Isaac Stone-Fish reported that the Chinese embassy in the United States was working on a 'white list' of persons to receive preferential visa treatment.[83] Staff in think tanks working on China-related issues are as prone to this form of pressure as journalists (and academics, as we shall see in the next chapter), and even without Chinese financing or other ties to the CCP they feel the heat. Researchers interviewed for a Hoover Institution report said they had been informed by visa agents that listing their think tanks as their place of employment could make it more difficult to obtain a visa, even impossible.[84]

In a different move, in 2019 Huawei sent a letter to the sponsors of the Australian Strategic Policy Institute, which include Boeing and

Google, accusing the think tank of having 'an unhealthy fixation' on the company. Huawei, according to the letter, was 'extremely disappointed in the way ASPI has conducted itself'. It had 'become the "go to" organisation for all things anti-China', and the letter insinuated it would be bad for sponsors to be associated with such an institution.[85]

Europe's only think tank devoted exclusively to China, the Mercator Institute for China Studies in Berlin, has also faced pressure. In 2017 the CCP's nationalistic *Global Times* published a series of articles railing against the institute for nurturing 'misguided academics' and for its 'politicised' research. The paper ran a personal campaign against MERICS's then director, Sebastian Heilmann. Beijing was especially unhappy in early 2018 when MERICS, jointly with the Global Public Policy Institute, released a report critical of the CCP's growing influence activities in Europe. The report, 'Authoritarian Advance' (of which Mareike Ohlberg was a co-author), called on Europe's leaders to take measures to resist Beijing's push into Europe. When Heilmann left MERICS soon after, the *Global Times* claimed credit for his departure, suggesting that its criticisms of the institute had 'put pressure on' its funding foundation, the Mercator Stiftung.[86]

While there is no basis for this claim, Heilmann's replacement as director, Dutch Sinologist Frank Pieke, has voiced a number of positions that are considerably more friendly to the CCP. He has said, for instance, that Huawei has been demonised, and described concerns about the company as 'paranoia'.[87] In 2019 Pieke argued that China had 'enormously underestimated the violent nature and intolerance to genuine competition of Western civilization'; further, whereas previously 'Beijing thought the West would accept a much bigger Chinese role in the world', it has had a rude awakening so that now, Beijing's diplomacy 'is no longer driven by the assumption that people are fully rational'.[88] The root of the problem, Pieke claims, is not the rise of an increasingly aggressive authoritarian power, but 'Western attitudes to communist China'. Western anxiety, he says, is a *projection*, one that 'says more about the West's fears about its own future than about what's happening in China'.

This rosy picture of the CCP as a naive global actor, full of good intentions and taken by surprise by irrational Western hostility, ignores thirty years of Party writings that illustrate how, even when relations with the West were at their best, the CCP never abandoned its Cold War thinking.

After his appointment as the new director of MERICS, but before he had taken up his new position, Pieke criticised the 'Authoritarian Advance' report in an interview with Chinese media.[89] After a series of comments about erroneous Western views of China, he said the report had mistakenly made China into an enemy and was based on weak evidence. It was clear from the interview that a report like this one would not emerge from MERICS under his watch. However, despite Pieke's stance, some of his statements, and MERICS itself, continue to attract the 'ire of the Chinese authorities'.[90] In January 2020 the think tank announced that Pieke had resigned from his position 'due to differences in opinion about the strategic development of MERICS'.[91]

Opinion-makers

Those Western intellectuals and opinion-makers who express views that buttress the legitimacy and global ambitions of the CCP do so in ways both blatant and subtle. In an example of the former, Tom Plate, vice president of the Pacific Century Institute, argues that the best ideas for solving the world's problems come from professors at Beijing's Central Party School, along with the ideas of Singapore author Kishore Mahbubani and Australian strategic thinker Hugh White.[92] China's ambassador to Canada agrees: after denouncing Western critics of the CCP, he urges us to listen to 'level-headed statesmen' like Jimmy Carter and to read Mahbubani's new book, which describes Xi Jinping as an exemplar of 'rational good governance'.[93]

When Huawei's Meng Wanzhou was arrested in Canada, Jeffrey Sachs, Columbia University's eminent economics professor, wrote an opinion piece titled 'The war on Huawei' in which he characterised the action as 'almost a US declaration of war on China's business community', and an instance of 'Trump's gangster tactics'.[94] Sachs declared that 'today's greatest threat to the international rule of law' is not the CCP regime in China, but the United States.

Sachs's attack on US hypocrisy—he pointed out that the US government has not arrested the CEOs of American companies that violated the same laws—would have carried more weight if he did not have such close ties to Huawei, as Twitter users quickly pointed out.[95] In November 2018 Sachs endorsed 'Huawei's vision of our shared digital future [as] powerful, exciting, and uniquely well informed'.[96] These were the opening words in a page of platitudes from Sachs praising Huawei as the company leading us to the future.[97]

According to Chinese state media, Sachs has extolled Xi Jinping's grand Belt and Road Initiative as 'one of the most important economic development initiatives in the history of contemporary economics'. It's visionary and 'full of wisdom', he said, 'a building for a humanised platform to promote peace and cooperation between Europe and Asia'.[98]

The cultivation of Jeffrey Sachs appears to have taken place over some years, via his links to a number of Chinese state bodies as well as the private energy corporation CEFC, at whose functions he has spoken.[99] (The top leaders of CEFC have since been charged with corruption.) On CNN he reprised his criticism of the arrest of Meng Wanzhou. On Canada's CBC he praised Huawei and defended China's incarceration of two Canadian citizens in retaliation. Echoing Beijing's propaganda tropes, he said that Meng's arrest reflected the 'US Cold War mentality', for which he was featured on China's state television channel.[100]

After Sachs was roundly criticised for defending Huawei, and his links to Beijing exposed, the *Global Times* leapt to his defence, insisting on his right to free speech.[101] Sachs closed his Twitter account after his mauling, but he was soon earning nods of approval in Beijing, appearing there in March 2019 at a Chinese government jamboree, where he attacked Donald Trump for the 'economic illiteracy' of the trade war.[102]

The CCP's legitimacy is also bolstered by the voices of the rich and influential Chinese-Americans who make up the Committee of 100. According to C100's website, the idea for the group was conceived in 1988, when co-founder I.M. Pei and Henry Kissinger discussed 'organizing an influential group of Chinese-Americans to address issues of international concern between the United States and China'.[103] The committee was then set up in 1990, a time when the CCP suffered international isolation after the Tiananmen Square massacre, 'with a sense of urgency to build bridges between China and the United States'.[104] Today its official mission is twofold: 'promoting the full participation of all Chinese-Americans in American society' and 'advancing constructive dialogue and relationships between the peoples and leaders of the United States and Greater China'.[105] In theory, this could allow a broad range of activities; it could allow the C100 to support reciprocity in US–China trade relations, and the rights of minorities in China; it could allow the C100 to speak out on behalf of Chinese-Americans who've been trapped in China under exit bans.[106]

However, any analysis of C100's public statements shows that its focus is much narrower, and often aligned with the interests of the CCP. It appropriately defends any ethnic Chinese person whose rights have been violated in the United States but is silent on the gross violation of human rights in China. As Mark Simon puts it, 'In their discussions about the US-China relationship it is difficult to find any significant objection to the actions of the CCP.'[107]

Several of C100's more prominent members have extensive business and personal links with the CCP leadership and its united front apparatus. Founding member C.B. Sung was an adviser of the Shanghai Federation of Returned Overseas Chinese.[108] Also a member is the co-founder of HNA Group, the conglomerate linked to red aristocrats, as is the president of Baidu, the giant internet company involved in the CCP's censorship regime. C100 delegations and leaders frequently meet with high-ranking CCP officials from the United Front Work Department and the Overseas Chinese Affairs Office.[109] In a 2007 meeting with then head of the UFWD, Liu Yandong, the former chair of C100, John Fugh, assured her that 'the Committee of 100 will continue working towards Chinese modernization, China's peaceful reunification and good Sino-US relations'.[110]

Former C100 vice president the late Charles Sie advised high-ranking United Front officials visiting Los Angeles on how to make propaganda on Tibet more effective. One suggestion was to bring former Tibetan 'serfs' to LA to meet Hollywood stars, so the latter could learn about the progress the CCP had achieved in Tibet.[111]

Victor Fung, whose Fung Foundation funds think tanks, is a member of C100, as is another Hong Kong businessman, Ronnie Chan, who holds positions in think tanks in both China and America. Chan is chairman of the strategic advisory board of the CCP-aligned Center for China and Globalization, and an adviser to the State Council's China Development Research Foundation. In the US he is a director of the China-friendly Peterson Institute, a senior associate in CUSEF, and co-chair of the advisory board of the joint-publication project of Yale University and the CCP's Foreign Languages Bureau, among other positions.[112] Ronnie Chan also chairs the board of trustees of the Asia Society's outpost in Hong Kong, which refused to allow student activist Joshua Wong to speak at a book launch in 2017.[113] Chan donated US$350 million to Harvard University in 2014.[114]

While it's possible that there are some C100 members who disagree with the pro-Beijing leaning of its leaders, it's hard to avoid the conclusion that the committee is uncomfortably close to the CCP, and as a result much less representative of the concerns of Chinese-Americans than it could be.

The Party's domestic think tank expansion

Under Xi Jinping China has redoubled its efforts to build up think tanks in China that can lend support to the Party. China's Thirteenth Five-Year Plan, published in 2015, outlined plans to establish between fifty and a hundred 'high-end think tanks' in the humanities and social sciences, to enhance the credibility of China's political and economic system.[115] From the outset, the aim was to amplify China's voice internationally. A central document on 'new types of think tanks with Chinese characteristics' explained their importance to the promotion of Chinese values in the world, to building new 'discourse systems' and to increasing China's international influence.[116] In March 2019 Huang Kunming, director of the Propaganda Department, reminded China's top think tanks of their responsibility to expand international exchange and cooperation in order to 'tell China's story well' and to 'disseminate China's point of view'.[117] The creation of these think tanks thus serves the CCP's goal of changing global perceptions—and it's working.

While some think tanks are overtly attached to government or Party departments, many founded in the last decade are framed as 'independent' and 'non-governmental'. The Charhar Institute, for example, describes itself as a 'non-governmental and non-partisan think-tank'.[118] But its founder, Han Fangming, is vice chairman of the Foreign Affairs

Committee of the CPPCC. He also holds appointments in the united front body the Chinese People's Association for Friendship with Foreign Countries (see the organisation chart on pages 124–5), and at a research centre at the Central Party School.[119]

Charhar's claims of independence are misleading not only because of personal ties to the Party apparatus, but because CCP control of think tanks is enshrined in policy documents. These make it clear that *all* think tanks must 'uphold Party leadership' and 'uphold the Party managing think tanks'.[120] National guidelines stipulate that think tanks 'should carry out activities for the purpose of serving the Party and government decision-making'.[121] Think tanks that strive for independence come under intense pressure. Foremost among them recently was the Unirule Institute of Economics, which closed down in 2019 after being harassed and impeded by authorities for several years.[122]

Despite this Party mandate, Western think tanks have been eager to join high-level meetings with China's think tanks and to partner with them. One prominent example is the Beijing-based Center for China and Globalization, which as we saw in chapter six is tightly linked into the Party structure. It was founded in 2008 by Wang Huiyao (also known as Henry Wang), a united front person who holds a number of positions in governments and CCP departments. Since 2008, Wang has been on the Central Committee of the Jiusan Society, one of China's eight recognised 'democratic parties', and he is deputy director of a special committee of the All-China Federation of Returned Overseas Chinese (see the organisation chart on pages 124–5).[123]

The CCG is active in its outreach. Wang Huiyao has spoken at the Committee of 100's yearly meeting in China. He was a panellist at the 2019 Munich Security Conference,[124] at which CCG organised its first side event on the BRI.[125] Wang is also a member of the steering committee of the Paris Peace Forum, Emmanuel Macron's 'Davos for democracy', where he rubs shoulders with Pascal Lamy and world leaders, from Angela Merkel to Vladimir Putin.[126] When Wang was scheduled to speak at a conference on foreign influence, organised by the Wilson Center's Kissinger Institute, the organisers were called out by Senator Marco Rubio for failing to disclose Wang's political affiliations. Wang pulled out.

Another important Chinese think tank is the China Center for International Economic Exchanges, established in 2009 'following the instructions of Premier Wen Jiabao. Its role is to be 'the highest-level think tank established in China'.[127] The centre is supervised by China's central planning and macroeconomic agency, the National Development and Reform Commission, and headed by former vice-premier Zeng Peiyan.[128] The CCIEE's personnel office doubles as the office of its Party committee's Discipline Inspection Committee.[129] Experts working at CCIEE are de facto government officials with little latitude to think outside the Party's parameters.[130]

CCIEE is well funded and an active participant in global economic debate. It partnered with Bloomberg to plan a major international conference aimed at making the national goals of China and the United States compatible, in the words of its advisory board chair, the ubiquitous Henry Kissinger.[131] In addition to Kissinger, the conference's board is stacked with other friends of China, including former US treasury secretary Henry Paulson, former White House chief economic adviser Gary Cohn, former Australian prime minister Kevin Rudd, and Tung Chee-hwa, the Hong Kong billionaire who funds the China-U.S. Exchange Foundation.[132]

In 2016 CCIEE partnered with the East Asian Bureau of Economic Research at the Australian National University to write a report on the future of the economic relationship between the two nations.[133] The report was touted as 'the first major independent study' of the relationship, and it called for it to be 'turbocharged' through larger flows of Chinese 'tourists, students, investors and migrants' into Australia. But instead of calling on China to open up its markets, Professor Peter Drysdale, the report's lead author, wrote that Australia's 'sheltered industries' needed more Chinese competition, even though Australia has one of the most open economies in the world. Australia's problem—and the report is replete with Australia's problems—is that the public 'does not grasp the benefits of foreign investment' from China and is often motivated by xenophobia. The report recommends the abolition of Australian restrictions on Chinese investment, including those pertaining to critical infrastructure. The problem, the report suggests, is not that in China important business decisions are often intimately tied to the interests and strategic aspirations of the Party-state, but that the Australian public is ignorant. The 'joint report' reads like a Beijing wish list, but at ANU the Party was pushing on an open door.

In 2017 CCIEE did a similar joint report with Bruegel (a Brussels-based economic think tank), Chatham House, and the Chinese University of Hong Kong. Partly funded by Huawei and titled 'EU–China Economic Relations to 2025: Building a common future', the report calls for free-trade and investment agreements between the EU and China, embracing of the BRI, and greater cooperation in science, technology and innovation. The senior advisory group for the report included Peter Mandelson of the 48 Group Club; Huang Ping, director of China's first Europe-based think tank, the China-CEE Institute in Budapest; CUSEF founder Tung Chee-hwa; and CPPCC member Victor Fung.[134]

The Taihe Institute is another Party-linked think tank masquerading as independent. Founded in 2013 in Beijing, it claims to have research centres in Europe and the United States. In Germany the director of the Taihe Institute's Europe Centre is Thorsten Jelinek, formerly associate director at the World Economic Forum. Nothing is officially known about who is responsible for the Taihe Institute in the Party hierarchy, but it employs a large number of researchers from the China Institutes of Contemporary International Relations, a large think tank at the Ministry of State Security.[135] Taihe's highest-profile event is the Taihe Civilizations Forum, the first of which was held in 2017. Among the speakers that year were former Czech prime minister Jan Fischer; the Brookings Institute's Cheng Li; the president of the National Committee on U.S.-China Relations, Steve Orlins; and the Wilson Center's Robert Daly.

In her study of BRI-themed influence operations, Nadège Rolland describes the Silk Road Think Tank Association, the Silk Road Think Tank Network and the Belt and Road Studies Network (the last mentioned is run by Xinhua).[136] The Silk Road Think Tank Association operates under the auspices of the International Liaison Department of the CCP, and is coordinated by the department's in-house think tank, the China Center for Contemporary World Studies.[137] The Silk

Road Think Tank Network's secretariat is located in the Development Research Center of the State Council. Renowned European institutions have joined the Silk Road Think Tank Network, including Chatham House, the Elcano Royal Institute in Madrid, the German Development Institute, and the OECD Development Centre. These think tanks declared their allegiance (*biaotai*) when they endorsed the following joint declaration, complete with CCP slogans:

> In 2015, based on the common understanding that the Belt and Road Initiative is an important endeavor to promote world economic growth, deepen regional cooperation and improve the wellbeing of people around the world, adhering to the Silk Road spirit of 'peace and cooperation, openness and inclusiveness, mutual learning and mutual benefit', and adhering to the principles of 'extensive consultation, joint contribution and shared benefits', we jointly launched the Silk Road Think Tank Network (SiLKS).[138]

Beijing has also set up its own think tank in Washington D.C.[139] The Institute for Chinese-American Studies was established in 2015 as an outpost of the Chinese government's National Institute for South China Sea Studies. It aims primarily at 'sending a clear message' about Beijing's claims on the South China Sea.[140] Henry Kissinger, ever ready to lend his authority to CCP-backed initiatives, sent a video message welcoming the initiative. Kissinger is a revered figure in CCP circles.[141] It's said that at the Central Party School in Beijing there is only one picture of a foreigner adorning the walls, that of Kissinger.

There's a widespread view in D.C. that the Institute for China-America Studies has proved ineffective.[142] Its profile has been low and it seems to have produced no policy papers, nor done any lobbying. But there's more than one way to skin a cat. ICAS is a means of organising, encouraging and rewarding its friends. Among its board members is Myron Nordquist, associate director of the Center for Oceans Law and Policy at the University of Virginia School of Law. An expert in the law of the sea, Nordquist wrote a detailed dissection of The Hague Tribunal's ruling that China's occupation of islands in the South China Sea had no basis in law. He concluded that the tribunal erred in its interpretation of the law and was motivated by political factors. This provided Beijing with ammunition to defend its actions.[143]

Another ICAS board member is Sam Bateman, a former Australian navy officer and now a visiting fellow in ocean security at the University of Wollongong in New South Wales.[144] He is a regular apologist for China's expansionism, arguing, for example, that US Vice President Pence's 2018 speech calling out Beijing took Sinophobia to new heights.[145] Bateman also argues that tensions in the Asia-Pacific are due to American aggression, and has produced a series of specious arguments about why The Hague Tribunal's ruling on the South China Sea was unimportant and not in Australia's interests. Echoing the CCP's position, he wrote that Australia should instead aim 'to help promote cooperation and build trust'.[146]

A third ICAS board member is Gordon Houlden, a former diplomat who spent many years in China and is now director of the China Institute at the University of Alberta. He has been more independent than Nordquist and Bateman, writing soon after The Hague decision that 'Canada has an abiding interest in negotiation and arbitration within the ambit of international law', and urging the Canadian government to make a statement 'reaffirming our commitment to rule-based governance of maritime issues'.[147] ICAS has also found supporters in Michael Swaine and Susan Thornton, two of the principal drafters of the 'China is not the enemy' letter mentioned in chapter three. They have spoken at a number of events organised by the institute.[148]

In Budapest, the China-CEE Institute is headed by Huang Ping, who is also the director general of the Institute of European Studies at the Chinese Academy of Social Sciences. Even though the China-CEE Institute is registered in Hungary as a non-profit corporation, it's embedded in the Chinese bureaucracy, with its website stating that it is organised and managed by CASS.[149] The system of 'organising units' and 'managing units' in China ensures political compliance and loyalty to the CCP by establishing a chain of responsibility. The China-CEE Institute is noteworthy primarily for the fact that it is the first branch of CASS in Europe. It has held a number of high-profile conferences on the BRI, and celebrates the good relations and cooperation between China and Central and Eastern European nations.[150]

We might finally mention the World Forum on China Studies. The forum is organised by the Shanghai Academy of Social Sciences. Sponsored by the CCP's Office of External Propaganda, and the Shanghai municipal government, the forum has been held in Shanghai every two years since 2004.[151] In recent times it has expanded abroad—in 2015 it held events at the Asia Society in New York City and at the Carter Center in Atlanta.[152] In 2017 the forum organised an event in Berlin titled 'China and Globalization: New Era, New Challenges'. Its co-hosts for this were the prestigious German Institute of Global and Area Studies, and the Bertelsmann Foundation (Bertelsmann Stiftung).[153] Not bad for an event sponsored by the CCP's top external propaganda body.

12
Thought management: CCP influence in Western academia

Universities as a political battlefield

While Confucius Institutes are often reported by Western media as channels for the Party-state to exert influence at foreign universities, the CCP's global 'thought management' project is much more ambitious and is pursued through many channels. In this chapter we examine the CCP's engagement in the disciplines of social sciences and humanities in Western universities (having considered scientific and technological research in chapter eight).

Pressure on universities to conform to the CCP's view of the world is intensifying, and is applied not only through Confucius Institutes, but also by direct lobbying by Chinese embassies and consulates; by encouraging Chinese students to report on university activities and to organise protests; by threats to choke the flow of Chinese students to those universities that depend on their fees; and by threats to cancel joint programs and executive training classes. Along with these forms of coercion, researchers are kept wondering whether their Chinese visas will be denied.

The CCP systematically pushes its official 'China narratives' and other academic ideas through its 'Chinese scholarship going global' strategy. As countries around the world try to close their knowledge gap on China, cash-strapped university administrators have structural incentives to seek out cooperation agreements with Chinese institutions. But they do so knowing very little about the CCP's objectives and methods. The Party frames the understanding of 'Chinese perspectives' as an important part of academic exchange, and of making international academia more equitable and less Western-centric. The problem is that 'Chinese perspectives' are really the CCP's perspectives. While there's nothing wrong with presenting the Party perspective per se—after all, the CCP has some 90 million members and is a global force to be reckoned with—conflating this with the Chinese perspective without a disclaimer about the underlying agenda (to create a 'global discourse system with Chinese characteristics' in order to secure the Party's continued rule) is at best misleading. Worse, it results in the exclusion of alternative voices, including those of ethnic Chinese scholars critical of the CCP.

The CCP believes that ideas are central to the contest for political power, and academia therefore has a vital role to play in the ideological struggle. Universities in China have become much more tightly controlled by the Party under Xi. In order to understand what the Party is trying to achieve globally, it will help to take a brief look at its project of building 'systemic confidence' through academic research at home. As in other arenas, changing the international academic landscape is an extension of this domestic project. Here too, the goal is to mute criticism of the Party, export its censorship norms, and promote research that boosts the 'Chinese path', the 'Chinese system' and 'Chinese theories'.[1]

For many decades, the CCP has been obsessed with the potential for Western academic ideas to weaken belief in the Party and cause instability in China. According to a volume on Deng Xiaoping's thoughts on propaganda, published shortly after the suppression in 1989 of the democracy movement, Western 'cultural infiltration' has two levels.[2] The first is the distribution of hostile political views by foreign media, which can be fairly easily monitored and countered. The second is ideological and academic infiltration, whereby 'hostile forces' deploy modern, social-science theory and values to win over Chinese intellectuals. This kind of infiltration, the author argued, is much harder to defend against.[3]

Almost thirty years later, an opinion piece in the *People's Daily* echoed the point: 'Clearly explaining the China path is both a very important political responsibility and a very serious academic research task for Chinese academics'.[4] The task is not left to the inclinations and initiative of scholars; ideological research is coordinated through the National Office for Philosophy and Social Sciences, which takes orders from the Leading Small Group for Philosophy and Social Sciences, as well as from the Central Propaganda Department.[5] Xi Jinping has highlighted the importance of the humanities and social sciences for increasing China's international influence.[6]

Recently updated foreign-language curricula for Chinese secondary schools now include classes designed to 'inoculate' students against infection by Western ideas and strengthen confidence in the Chinese system. Students learn to compare the two systems in order to 'independently' arrive at the conclusion that the Chinese system is superior.[7]

The seven 'false ideological trends' forbidden to Party cadres, as outlined in Document No. 9 (see chapter two), apply also to academics. Students have been encouraged to report on their professors. In Wuhan a professor was fired after her students denounced her for making 'incorrect' comments about the lifting of presidential term limits.[8] Others have been fired or suspended for criticising China's leaders, or for lesser 'thought crimes', including remarks made in chat groups.[9]

Confucius Institutes

Confucius Institutes were conceived under the Hu-Wen (Hu Jintao/ Wen Jiabao) administration and initiated in 2004 as an innocuous way to spread the Party narrative while simultaneously gaining entry to foreign universities. They are a product of the CCP's fascination with 'cultural soft power'.

Although the institutes are ostensibly devoted to teaching Chinese language and promoting Chinese culture, they are, as former propaganda chief Li Changchun put it, 'an important part of China's overseas propaganda set-up'.[10] The institutes are managed by the Office of Chinese Language Council International, known as the Hanban, in the Ministry of Education. However, the prominent US Sinologist David Shambaugh has claimed that the funds are actually provided by the CCP's Propaganda Department and are 'laundered' through the Ministry of Education.[11]

In the Western world, the largest number of Confucius Institutes is to be found in English-speaking countries. As of July 2109 the United States had about ninety, although there has been a wave of closures.[12] Great Britain has about thirty and Canada thirteen.[13] In Europe the majority are in France, Germany and Italy. The countries of Central and Eastern European, often seen as the primary target of CCP influence in Europe, each host one to four Confucius Institutes, though the overall number has been growing as institutes in Western Europe close.

Unlike Goethe Institutes and British Councils, Confucius Institutes are mostly located within foreign universities.[14] This gives them leverage over the host institutions. The selection of staff for the institutes, and their curricula, are decided in Beijing, leading China scholar John Fitzgerald to observe: 'Universities that accept [Confucius Institutes] on Beijing's terms, with all the compromises they entail, signal they are willing to set aside academic principles to build good relations with China [and] indicate normal due diligence does not apply to relations with Chinese universities and firms.'[15]

In the United States, the conservative National Association of Scholars commissioned a thorough review of Confucius Institutes in 2017.[16] It reported that many professors associated with the institutes felt 'immense pressure to stay on the good side of Confucius Institute directors and university administrators affiliated with the Confucius Institute'.[17] The boards of the institutes often include people with close links to United Front organisations.[18] Articles published on the UFWD's website have discussed how Confucius Institutes can be used to carry out united front work.[19] The NAS report called for them to be shut down. There are also been credible reports that some institutes facilitate spying.[20]

Interference by Confucius Institutes in academic freedom, freedom of expression, and other personal rights has been documented in a large number of countries. One of the most egregious instances occurred at the 2014 annual conference of the European Association of China Studies, in Portugal. The conference was sponsored by the Hanban and the Taiwanese Chiang Chingkuo Foundation. Unhappy with the mention of the foundation and other Taiwanese organisations in the conference program, Hanban director general Xu Lin ordered that all conference programs be confiscated and the offending page torn out.[21]

While the incident caused shock among conference participants, there were no repercussions for the Hanban or Confucius Institutes in Europe.

Censorship is not unknown in other works sponsored by the institutes. Topics like the 'three Ts'—Taiwan, Tibet and Tiananmen—are excluded from discussion at most Confucius Institutes.[22] Journalist Isabel Hilton noticed that a section in an article she'd written for a volume sponsored by a Confucius Institute had been deleted; the offending text concerned a Chinese environmental activist.[23]

The institutes have been involved in behind-the-scenes lobbying to cancel events. In Melbourne in 2018 the screening of a documentary critical of Confucius Institutes was cancelled by Victoria University, which had hired out one of its theatres for the purpose.[24] The university was warned of an impending problem by the director of the campus's Confucius Institute, Professor Colin Clark, and the university caved in when the Chinese consulate applied pressure. When it was contacted by the film's promoter, the university lied, claiming that the theatre had been double-booked and no other was available. On the scheduled day, a number of suitable rooms were empty. The irony was not lost: a documentary arguing that Confucius Institutes have political leverage over their hosts was banned because of the political leverage of a Confucius Institute over its host. Victoria University's code of conduct declares the university to be 'a place of independent learning and thought, where ideas may be put forward and reasoned opinion expressed freely while maintaining respect for others'.[25]

In 2013 the prestigious University of Sydney was accused of cancelling a visit by the Dalai Lama to avoid damaging its ties with China, including the funding it received for its Confucius Institute.[26] When the event was pushed off-campus, and use of the university's logo forbidden, vice chancellor Michael Spence said it was 'in the best interests of researchers across the university'.[27] Some five years later Spence said that government statements and media reports about CCP influence in Australia were no more than 'Sinophobic blathering', following this up the next year by accusing those expressing concern about CCP influence of wanting a return to the 'White Australia Policy'.[28]

The banning of any discussion of Chinese politics, including topics like the three Ts, has led to the bizarre situation where universities in

Australia have registered their American studies centres (partly funded by Washington) under the new foreign-influence transparency scheme, but do not see the need to register their Confucius Institutes because 'they do not discuss politics'—even though they host seminars extolling the benefits of the Belt and Road Initiative, and the 'culture' they teach is shaped by the Party's ideology.[29]

Some Confucius Institute contracts have been found to contain clauses that are illegal in their host countries or clash with the values of their host universities. For instance, they often stipulate that the institutes may not engage in any activities that break Chinese law, which can be interpreted to include vague, catch-all laws against 'endangering national unity' and 'endangering national security'.[30] The Confucius Institute at McMaster University in Canada explicitly forbade its employees from practising Falun Gong, a form of discrimination that is illegal in Western democracies. When McMaster University failed to have the clause removed, it closed down the institute. Understanding how widespread this problem is can be difficult, as terms of agreement are typically secret. The University of Edinburgh refused a request for information on potentially discriminatory clauses in its contract, citing confidentiality.[31]

Confucius Institutes vary in their transparency and in how much they interfere in their host universities. Bigger and more influential universities have more bargaining power than smaller or less prestigious ones. When the Chinese side was negotiating an agreement for a Confucius Institute at Stanford University, it tried to exclude all discussion of sensitive issues like Tibet. When Stanford refused, the Hanban backed down.[32] Prestigious universities that agree to host Confucius Institutes should understand that they lend legitimacy to an arrangement that may be used to exert pressure on smaller players.

Direct pressure

Chinese embassies and consulates frequently attempt direct interference in Western universities. In 2018 the University of Salamanca in Spain cancelled its Taiwan Cultural Week after the Chinese embassy complained that the representative of Taiwan had been referred to as 'ambassador'. The embassy made it clear that China did not 'consent' to the event.[33] In Hungary, the University of Debrecen was pressured by the Chinese embassy to exclude Taiwanese students from participating in the university's international food day, just a few hours before the start of the event.[34] And when in April 2019 the Chinese studies department at the Vrije Universiteit Brussels organised an event with a Kazakh national who had been detained in one of Xinjiang's infamous 're-education camps', the Chinese embassy sent letters to the organisers and prospective attendees asking them not to go. The event went ahead as planned, but with heightened security.[35]

Sometimes, events are rejected under what look like pretexts. In 2014 a faculty member at an Ivy League university had a suggestion for an event on Hong Kong's Umbrella Movement rejected on the grounds that it was not 'substantively academic enough', even though the institution often hosted activists.[36] The administrator hoped that the faculty member understood 'the complexity' of the university's East Asian engagement.

Chinese students are another pressure point on campuses. At the seminal 2015 United Front Work Conference, Xi Jinping described Chinese students studying abroad as one of the 'three new focuses' of united front work.[37] Anxious to prevent them being 'infected' with Western ideas, the CCP makes extensive efforts to keep them in line. Many students are loosely organised through Chinese Students and Scholars Associations (see the organisation chart on pages 124–25). Some CSSAs state on their websites that they are recognised by, registered with or even subsidised by the local Chinese embassy or consulate. The CSSA UK describes itself as an official organisation 'under the guidance of the Education Department of the Chinese Embassy to the UK'.[38] The CSSA of Boston University states that it's registered with the Chinese consulate in New York, and the CSSA at Vanderbilt University in Nashville claims to receive 'subsidies and support' from the Chinese embassy.[39] Chinese students in the US and the UK have even established Party cells at some universities.[40]

There has been heated debate about the extent to which CSSAs are controlled by Beijing. Much of the activity of the associations revolves around social events and student support, but the CSSAs do have ties to the Party and the Chinese government. Some receive funding from Chinese embassies.[41] Their office holders typically owe allegiance to the CCP and liaise regularly with the local embassy or consulate. It is through the CSSAs that Chinese students on campuses can be mobilised to demonstrate 'patriotic support' during visits of China's leaders, or to counter activities that the CCP considers hostile. In 2016 the Chinese government pressured Chinese students and scholars in the Netherlands to demonstrate in support of China's position on the South China Sea.[42] In 2019 pro-Beijing Chinese students in Canada, Australia and Britain confronted, at times in aggressive and intimidating ways, students engaged in public support for Hong Kong democracy protesters. At the University of Queensland, one pro-Hong Kong student was assaulted. The next day, the Chinese consul general issued a statement praising the patriotic actions of the Chinese students, drawing a rebuke from Australia's foreign minister.[43]

When students at the University of Toronto elected Tibetan-Canadian Chemi Lhamo as president of the student union, she was severely harassed, receiving threats of death and rape from Chinese students on campus, possibly prompted by Chinese diplomats.[44] An online petition on Change.org labelled her pro-Tibet activism as 'clearly against Chinese history, Chinese laws and Chinese students' rights', arguing that China's Anti-Secession Law of 2005 obliged all Chinese citizens to protest against Chemi Lhamo's actions.[45]

While some activities like this may be organised independently by students, in other cases they are clearly initiated by or coordinated with Chinese embassies and consulates. Students at McMaster University contacted the Chinese embassy to report a planned talk by Uyghur activist Rukiye Turdush, and later sent photos of the talk to the embassy. *The Washington Post*, which reviewed some of the WeChat messages concerning this incident, called it a 'vivid example of how Chinese students have grown into a vocal and coordinated force on Western campuses'.[46] McMaster University subsequently stripped the CSSA of its status as a student club.[47]

While the Chinese students at McMaster had been tasked by embassy officials to check if any Chinese students were involved in organising the talk,[48] a more general concern is when PRC students surveil each other, including in class, of their own accord. In recent studies, several professors across the US reported that they assumed their Chinese students were reporting on each other. Some said that Chinese students had approached them directly with concerns about being denounced.[49] European academics interviewed for a study by the Leiden Asia Center shared similar concerns.[50] At the Australian National University, a comment made in class by a Chinese student was reported to the embassy, and her parents in China received a visit from the Ministry of State Security, warning them about their daughter's behaviour. The MSS visit came two hours after she made the comment.[51]

Self-censorship

A much-cited 2002 article by Perry Link (who has for many years been blocked from entering China) likened the CCP to 'the anaconda in the chandelier': 'Normally the great snake doesn't move. It doesn't have to. It feels no need to be clear about its prohibitions. Its constant silent message is "You yourself decide", after which, more often than not, everyone in its shadow makes his or her large and small adjustments—all quite "naturally".'[52]

While Link was primarily talking about the effect of the great snake on Chinese academics, he argued that the effect was beginning to be felt abroad as well. These days it is apparent that the anaconda is hovering over China scholars in the West and many are 'naturally' adjusting what they write and say. Some just want to protect their access to China to do research; others consider it politeness towards their Chinese partners, or they want to protect their contacts and sources.[53] According to a 2018 academic study, 68 per cent of 500 interviewees agreed that self-censorship is a problem among China scholars.[54]

The topic is a sensitive one that arouses passionate responses. Western scholars tend to wear their intellectual independence proudly and few admit to engaging in self-censorship, although many claim to see it in others. A study by Anastasya Lloyd-Damnjanovic on Beijing's political influence on US campuses observed:

> It is telling that in a few cases, faculty agreed only to be interviewed off the record, i.e., on the condition that the information conveyed could not go down on paper. In one case, a faculty member insisted the interview be conducted at a time when she could access

> a hotel landline because she feared her cell phone was monitored. Many faculty expressed anxiety about being publicly identified in this study for fear that the PRC government might retaliate or that some social progressives in the United States might perceive criticisms of the PRC as 'racist'. This was true even among respondents who claimed they do not self-censor.[55]

As Perry Link noted, if we were to omit all issues that are sensitive to the CCP—Tibet, Tiananmen, Taiwan, Xinjiang, the wealth amassed by the families of top leaders—'we are left with a picture of China that is not only smaller than the whole but crucially different in nature'.[56] This picture is particularly distorting in places where there are few or no alternative sources of knowledge about China.

As with journalists, visas are one of the most effective means of keeping researchers in line, especially those who rely on access to China for their living.[57] Scholars who have spent decades building their expertise can have their careers stymied if access is denied. Young academics without tenure and those with family ties in China are particularly vulnerable to CCP pressure.[58]

More common than denying a visa is to let the application hang. Applicants must list the date of their flight to China on the visa form, and consular officials will simply not respond to the application before that date.[59] In addition to the few who have been explicitly blacklisted, a much larger pool of researchers live in constant uncertainty, not fully welcome but not obviously banned. The problem is compounded by the fact that few people like to talk about the denial of a visa, making it difficult to gauge the full extent of the practice.

As the debate over CCP influence and interference in Australia reached a high point in early 2018, some seventy China scholars signed an open letter stating that the discussion was 'sensationalist', and just another manifestation of the nation's long history of anti-Chinese racism.[60] The scholars claimed to 'see no evidence' of Beijing interfering in Australia, despite widely reported incidents to the contrary. As in the case of the group of US scholars cited in chapter three, the Australian scholars shifted the blame from the CCP to their own nation's moral faults. While those faults certainly exist, ignoring the agency of the CCP betrays the commitment to the truth that the Western academy is meant to stand for. The *Global Times* warmly welcomed the Australian scholars' letter as proof that the debate over CCP influence should be ended, as it is only 'fanning the flames' of racial animosity.[61]

Financial dependence

The Western tradition of free intellectual inquiry, of following the truth wherever it leads, has always faced corruption by money; in recent times, some of that corruption has followed Chinese money. One problem is what Christopher Hughes of the London School of Economics calls the 'enterprise university' model.[62] If a university runs research projects with Chinese counterparts for profit, or depends on tuition fees from PRC students, this creates structural incentives to stay on China's good side. Where decision-making is centralised, individual researchers can't push back against attempts at interference, nor can they shut down ethically dubious cooperation with Chinese institutions.[63] As Hughes puts it, 'If you are someone who raises questions or works on something sensitive ... you will not make yourself very popular with the people whose job it is to get the balance sheets right ... I am speaking from direct experience of myself and colleagues who have spoken out, who have been marginalised, or taken aside for cups of tea and told, "Stop stirring things up."'[64]

For many universities, enrolments from China have proven highly lucrative, especially when governments cut back education funding. More than 360,000 Chinese students were studying at US universities in 2018,[65] and Canada had over 140,000.[66] In the United Kingdom, with over 100,000 enrolled, Chinese students easily make up the largest group of foreign students.[67] Australia, with over 150,000 Chinese students enrolled in 2018,[68] has proportionally the highest dependence on fees from China, by a wide margin.

As a rule, Chinese parents want to send their children to the most highly ranked universities abroad and are avid readers of university league tables. When prestigious Western universities become dependent on Chinese fees, they are more sensitive to pressure from the embassy or consulates. The threat of being cut off from this money stream has been used frequently by the Chinese government to try to bring Western universities into line. Few such threats ever make it into the public domain. By publicising them, university administrators would cause a severe loss of face. By acceding to them, they open themselves to stern criticism for abandoning their principles. But some cases have surfaced. After the Dalai Lama visited the University of California, San Diego in 2017, the Chinese government informed the university it would refuse to fund Chinese scholars who wished to study there.[69]

Research partnerships, academic exchange agreements and training programs in China are also used as bargaining chips. Some universities have scores of such arrangements, and developing a deep network of institutional and personal links with China has become a mark of professional success. Executive training programs have become lucrative business for Western universities. The University of Cambridge hosts the China Executive Leadership Program, which is co-sponsored by the CCP's powerful Organization Department and the State Council's China Development Research Foundation. The program trains senior executives from large state-owned corporations selected by the Party to spend three weeks at Cambridge. Such programs can become another Beijing pressure point. An executive training program at the University of Maryland was reportedly suspended after a speech by the Dalai Lama on campus in 2013, and again after Yang Shuping's 2017 graduation speech (see chapter five).[70]

Many university leaders in the West have shown by their actions that they are not committed to academic freedom, and often do not understand what it is. There are many instances of university executives buckling to Beijing's pressure and using phrases like 'we understand the concern, but the situation is complex', or 'the university must balance the freedom of our academics against the other goals of the university'. The principle of academic freedom is worth nothing if universities are not willing to protect it actively.

Reshaping Chinese studies

In the CCP's campaign to reshape global debate, an essential target is the field of China studies itself. As we've seen, Confucius Institutes are one channel for this, as is the World Forum on China Studies, launched in 2004 by propaganda authorities to foster a community of foreign researchers sympathetic to the Party.[71]

Another is the three-week Visiting Program for Young Sinologists, run by China's Ministry of Culture and Tourism and advertised through *China Watch* on *The Telegraph* website.[72] In June 2019 the program was hosted by the Shanghai Academy of Social Sciences, to 'let foreign scholars tell China's story well'.[73] The Chinese government also provides special scholarships for students from Central and Eastern Europe.[74] The goal is not to reap immediate benefits, but to make sure that the next generation of China experts in these countries is positively disposed towards the CCP.

It's not unknown for China to pay Sinologists to promote China. The American political scientist Edward Friedman reported that in the early 2000s he was offered $25,000 by officials from the Ministry of Foreign Affairs to write a book on how China was succeeding in its foreign relations.[75] He declined. Today, there is an official 'Foreigners Writing on China Programme', which provides funding for 'foreign sinologists, writers, media professionals, scholars and other notable public figures' to write books on China, at the invitation of domestic Chinese publishers, to 'spread the voice of China'.[76]

Around 2011 Wen Ruchun, the daughter of former Chinese premier Wen Jiabao, donated £3.7 million to endow a professorship at The University of Cambridge through her mysterious Chong Hua foundation. The first Chong Hua professor, Peter Nolan, had previously taught Wen Ruchun and co-authored a book with her husband.[77] The university apparently did not go through a formal process of appointment to fill the chair. A former Cambridge academic, Tarak Barkawi, wrote: 'Nolan has very close links with the Chinese government and appears to have played a central role in organising the donation.'[78] Nolan no longer holds the chair, but remains at Cambridge as director of the Centre of Development Studies, and director of the university's China Executive Leadership Program.[79] He is a fellow of the 48 Group Club.

In 2017 the School of Advanced International Studies at Johns Hopkins University announced the newly created C.H. Tung professorship, named after former Hong Kong chief executive Tung Chee-hwa. The new professor would also be director of a research program called the Pacific Community Initiative. The professorship and the research program are partly funded by the China-United States Exchange Foundation, the Hong Kong–based organisation founded by Tung in 2008.[80] Tung, as we've seen, is a vice chairman of the Chinese People's Political Consultative Conference, one of the Party's important influencing bodies and a prominent Party activist. In 2018 the University of Texas at Austin turned down a proposed donation from CUSEF to fund its China Public Policy Center because of the foundation's links with the CCP, although some faculty members supported the proposal.[81]

In 2019 the *Financial Times* reported that the London School of Economics had planned to establish a new China program with funding from Eric X. Li, a venture capitalist and staunch supporter of the CCP. The program would have been overseen by an advisory group from China, but it was cancelled after a backlash from academics.[82]

University cooperation

Opening campuses in China has become a popular way for Western universities to internationalise themselves while at the same time generating new sources of revenue. One of the earliest joint initiatives, well before the current wave, was the Hopkins-Nanjing Center, founded in 1986 by Johns Hopkins University and Nanjing University. After the Chinese government began encouraging cooperation in education in 1995, several Western universities established joint institutes. These are based at and function like colleges of Chinese universities.[83] Since 2003, foreign universities have been able to open full universities in China by forming a joint venture with a Chinese university in which the Chinese side owns 51 per cent.[84] This makes them Chinese legal entities subject to Chinese law, with all that this entails for academic freedom.[85]

Several renowned universities have accepted this arrangement, including New York University (establishing NYU Shanghai), Duke (Duke Kunshan), the University of Nottingham (Nottingham Ningbo), the University of Liverpool (Jiaotong-Liverpool University), and the University of California, Berkeley (Tsinghua-Berkeley Shenzhen Institute). Others, like the University of Cambridge, are still negotiating.[86] Occasionally, wholly American-owned universities have been allowed to operate in China. Sias University, which was originally founded as a joint project by Fort Hayes State University and Zhengzhou University in 1998, is an example.[87] Over 2000 university partnerships of various forms currently operate in China.[88]

Foreign-owned and partially foreign-owned universities have been presented as rare zones of academic freedom in China by their supporters, but they come with a host of problems, including limitations on academic freedom. In 2010, when an American student tried to launch the first academic journal at the Hopkins-Nanjing Center, administrators prevented its circulation outside campus, on the grounds that academic freedom was to be limited to the classroom. Most Chinese students involved in the journal asked to have their names removed, and one was pressured to withdraw an article.[89]

In 2018 the University of Nottingham Ningbo removed Stephen Morgan from his role as associate provost after he wrote an article criticising the outcomes of the 19th Party Congress in 2017.[90] In 2019, when classes resumed for the fall semester at NYU Shanghai, one topic that could not be addressed on campus was the Hong Kong protests. 'Most of us are on guard about what we say even when we talk about the weather,' a faculty member was quoted as saying.[91] Professor Rebecca Karl, who teaches at NYU's home campus in New York, has been blacklisted from the Shanghai campus. She said she had 'faced pressure from multiple fellow professors in New York not to organise a panel on the Hong Kong protests this semester out of concern that it would "hurt the feelings of my colleagues in Shangahi".' Karl said she did not trust her university to stand up for academic freedom in Shanghai: 'They have too much at stake.'[92]

In fact, by establishing campuses in China, Western university executives knowingly agree to sacrifice the principle of academic freedom. In 2011 NYU president John Sexton reportedly told Bloomberg News that 'students and faculty at the new [Shanghai] campus shouldn't assume they can criticise government leaders or policies without repercussions.' He added, 'I have no trouble distinguishing between rights of academic freedom and rights of political expression.'[93]

In a move that reflects the overall tightening of ideological screws on Chinese campuses, new regulations introduced in 2017 require joint-venture universities to set up a Party committee and appoint a

Party secretary.[94] According to the *Financial Times*, university administrators are not given a written copy of these new regulations but receive only an oral briefing on them.[95] In 2018 the University of Groningen in the Netherlands cancelled an agreement (the signing of which had been attended by Xi Jinping and the Dutch king) to offer full degrees at a campus in Yantai after the Chinese government announced that a CCP official must sit on the board of all foreign-funded universities. Large parts of the campus had already been built.[96]

Groningen's reaction distinguishes it from the capitulation of other Western universities. While nearly all joint ventures list the Party secretary on their foreign websites as well as their Chinese-language sites, only the latter provide information on 'Party building' activities and 'Party mass relations'. These activities include 'theory study sessions' on Xi Jinping Thought, CCP discipline, and the latest Party documents and slogans.[97] At the Chinese campus of Leeds University, Party-building includes training Chinese staff to 'do ideological work well'.[98] Even wholly American-owned public universities like Sias (the China branch of Fort Hayes State University) are not exempt from Party-building activities; there, on the occasion of the ninety-eighth anniversary of the CCP, Chinese staff renewed their oath to the Party.[99] And it's not only staff and Party members who are affected. Chinese students at NYU Shanghai, for example, also have to take classes on Mao Zedong Thought and other mandatory 'political studies' courses.[100]

Some joint-venture universities employ their faculty locally, meaning foreign faculty are no longer employed by foreign universities but by the Chinese government. NYU Shanghai and Duke Kunshan reportedly quietly switched to this model several years ago.[101] (According to Duke's mission statement, it will 'promote an intellectual environment built on a commitment to free and open inquiry'.[102]) At Kean State, an American public university in New Jersey, a plan to switch to local employment at its China campus in Wenzhou caused a backlash when the university's union became aware of it.[103] The Wenzhou-Kean campus had previously posted job advertisements stating that applicants who were CCP members would be given preference.[104] Like all joint ventures, Wenzhou-Kean University has a Party secretary, who is also chairperson of the board of directors overseeing the university.[105] CCP policy initiatives like the BRI are openly promoted at some joint education institutions. In 2018 the French EMLYON Business School, together with the East China Normal University, founded the Asia Europe Business School in Shanghai. According to its website, its mission is to create 'Belt and Road entrepreneurs'.[106] The French government has rejected participation in the BRI, while EMLYON Business School is helping create BRI champions to send back to France.

Once cooperation agreements are in place, it is very rare for Western universities to terminate them. One exception occurred in 2018, when the School of Industrial and Labor Relations at Cornell University ended its cooperation with Renmin University's School of Labor and Human Resources, and with its Business School. The decision was prompted by the kidnapping of Chinese students who had engaged in activism at Renmin University, but it followed mounting concerns about the deteriorating academic environment in China. In the words of Eli Friedman, director of Cornell's School of Industrial and Labor Relations, who personally made the decision to terminate the exchange, 'Foreign institutions have long hoped that engagement and quiet diplomacy in China would eventually lead to an expansion in academic, and possibly political, freedoms. It is increasingly clear that precisely the opposite has happened ... The actions we took at Cornell ILR may or may not turn out to be effective, but doing nothing was not an option.'[107]

The setting-up of campuses abroad has also gone in the other direction. In 2013 Fudan University established the Fudan-European Centre for China Studies at the University of Copenhagen, as 'a strategic initiative of Fudan University to meet the growing demand for a more nuanced and balanced understanding of China's development'. Some of its key events have served to promote Beijing's positions, including such insights as 'the recent worsening of cross-strait relations are due to the [2016] election of Tsai Ing-wen in Taiwan', and 'without intervention from the US, there would be no Taiwan Issue'.[108] (In 2016 the University of Copenhagen joined the US-based Scholars at Risk organisation, which helps protect any scholars facing threats and imprisonment around the world. The university has not yet provided sanctuary to any Chinese scholars.)

Another European-based institution is the Brussels Academy for China-European Studies, opened in 2014 as a cooperative venture between Renmin University of China, Sichuan University, Fudan University, and Vrije Universiteit Brussels. It works closely with the Confucius Institute at Vrije Universiteit Brussels.[109] In October 2019 the director of this Confucius Institute, Song Xinning, was barred for eight years from entering the European Union because of his alleged espionage activities. VUB had reportedly ignored previous warnings from Belgium's intelligence service. Song had built up an excellent network of contacts with thinks tanks across Europe, including the College of Europe, 'the Bruges elite school for Eurocrats'.[110]

In 2018 Peking University opened a campus of its HSBC Business School near Oxford, initially backed by British bank HSBC. At the inauguration, Chinese ambassador Liu Xiaoming stressed that the campus should become a platform 'to tell the China story'.[111] And later that year the University of Coimbra in Portugal announced it would host a Chinese Academy of Social Sciences Chinese Studies Center.[112]

Academic publishing

Translations of Chinese academic work are centrally planned and subsidised through a number of programs. In 2010 the National Social Science Fund of China set up a translation program in order to 'raise the international influence of Chinese humanities and social sciences'. To give the translated works legitimacy, they are published through 'authoritative publishing institutions' and 'enter mainstream distribution channels' abroad.[113] This means that Chinese publishers are encouraged to seek out partnerships with renowned international publishers, something they have done quite successfully.

In 2017 Cambridge University Press decided to exclude several journals containing articles critical of CCP positions from the package it offers universities in China. This caused outrage among scholars, and the press eventually backed down. But other publishers have managed to fly under the radar and continue to censor material that is to be used in China. The big Stuttgart-based academic publisher Springer Nature (publisher of *Scientific American* and *Nature*, among many other titles) allowed Chinese authorities to decide which articles would be unavailable on its online platform in China, justifying its censorship by saying it affected just one per cent of its content in China (the one per cent the CCP did not like).[114] Apart from a few news reports, Springer Nature received limited backlash, although a petition calling for a peer-review boycott of all humanities and social science journals published by Springer Nature and its subsidiary Palgrave Macmillan received 1200 signatures.[115] The editors of the journal *Transcultural Research* at the University of Heidelberg terminated their relationship with Springer Nature in protest over its decision, calling it an 'unacceptable breach of trust'.[116]

The CCP took a slightly different approach with Taylor & Francis, owner of the publisher Routledge. Rather than censoring individual articles, Chinese import agencies simply excluded eighty-three of the 1466 journals in the publishing group's package for libraries.[117]

Exactly how many publishers and journals are subjected to CCP censorship is unknown. An argument commonly used to justify such censorship is that it only affects publications distributed in China, not global offerings. Publishers defend themselves by saying they have to abide by local laws. Individual authors who have accepted censorship in the Chinese translation of their work have argued that the loss in content is outweighed by the benefit of making *most* of their work available to Chinese readers.[118]

Leaving aside this dubious justification for acceding to censorship, some authors with an eye on sales in China are tempted to circumscribe what they write. And publishers may accept and reject manuscripts based on their acceptability to Party censors. PEN International, which defends the free speech of writers, has expressed concern that the promise of large advances for Chinese translations may steer authors away from potentially controversial topics.[119]

However, there may be an even more fundamental problem. In 2019 an agent for Chinese printing companies handed Australian publishing houses a list of words and topics that could not appear in any books that were to be printed in China.[120] The list contained the names of Chinese dissidents and also political figures, including Xi Jinping. Publishers in New Zealand face the same prohibitions.[121] Most Western publishers print a large share of their titles, particularly illustrated books and those with high print-runs, in China, which has the most advanced and cheapest printing processes. These publishers must now either censor their books or pay more for having them printed elsewhere. It's important to note that this ban applies not to books for the Chinese market, but to those sold in any other market. When Australian publisher Allen & Unwin cancelled the publication of a book critical of the CCP in 2017, one of its concerns was that it might be banned from all access to Chinese printers.[122] While the censorship guidelines have been in place for some time, they were not enforced until 2019, according to Chinese printing companies.[123] In deciding whether to offer a book contract to an author, publishers must now take this factor into account.

The Party also uses publishing collaborations to spread its voice. Yale University collaborates with the Foreign Languages Bureau of the CCP, which interacts with the outside world under the nameplate China International Publishing Group. When the project was launched at the Great Hall of the People in 2006, Yale University's leaders appeared alongside high-ranking officials from the CCP's Propaganda Department.[124] And in 2017 the China Social Sciences Press established a branch at the Institute of Political Studies in Bordeaux (Sciences Po Bordeaux), to facilitate long-term, institutionalised partnerships with foreign publishers and to 'raise China's academic influence in Europe's main countries and international society'.[125]

In the UK, the dual-language Global Century Press, a subsidiary of the UK-based Global China Academy, has been publishing titles like *China's Role in a Shared Human Future: Towards theory* [*sic*] *for global leadership* (2018) by British sociologist Martin Albrow,[126] and *Walk for Peace: Transcultural experiences in China* (2016) by Lord Michael Bates and his wife Lady Xuelin Bates (whom we met in chapter seven).[127] Both books are instances of influential people in the UK lending their names to key CCP talking points and terminology.

Most large Western publishing houses have cooperation agreements with Party-state institutions to distribute English-language translations of Chinese academic research (both actual research and Party talking points). This includes books and journals paid for by Chinese institutions, such as the Chinese Academy of Sciences and the Chinese Academy of Social Sciences, or co-published with Chinese publishing houses. Springer Nature publishes dozens of journals in this way, including *China International Strategy Review*, produced by the Institute of International and Strategic Studies at Peking University; *Frontiers of Education in China*, co-published with the Higher Education Press; and the *Journal of Chinese Sociology*, which is under the auspices of the Chinese Academy of Social Sciences and is 'mainland China's first English journal in sociology'. Springer Nature and its subsidiary Palgrave Macmillan also launched the *Belt and Road Initiative*, a bundle of works on the BRI by authors from various disciplines; many of these works are the product of highly politicised and tightly controlled environments at Chinese universities.[128] Routledge recently published the *Routledge Handbook of the Belt and Road* (2019), consisting of articles translated from Chinese and co-edited by the vice president of CASS, Cai Fang, and Cambridge professor Peter Nolan.[129] The Dutch company Elsevier publishes journals supervised by the Chinese Academy of Sciences.[130]

Making available Chinese research in the humanities and social sciences, much of which is high quality, is generally a valuable contribution. But few readers are likely to be aware that most publishing collaborations are not initiated by individual Chinese institutes or Western publishers, but by the Party-state, with the explicit aim of spreading concepts and theories 'with Chinese characteristics'. The series *Key Concepts in Chinese Thought and Culture*, published by Palgrave Macmillan in partnership with Beijing Foreign Language Teaching and Research Press, is part of a top-down 'translation and communication' project run by China's State Council.[131]

As the boundaries between Chinese and international publishing continue to blur, Chinese censorship becomes increasingly normalised. Foreign readers see the name of a renowned publishing house on a book about China and are unaware that the content accords with Beijing's line.

In another instance of non-capitulation, however, Dutch publisher Brill terminated an agreement to publish four journals in cooperation with a publisher owned by China's education department.[132] Though the reason was not stated, this happened shortly after an article in one of the journals was removed at the request of censors. The article in question, 'Subversive writing' by Jin Liu, an associate professor at Georgia Tech, was for a special issue of the journal *Frontiers of Literary Studies in China*, and had been peer-reviewed and accepted before being removed. The journal's editors, who had not been consulted, only found out when they were reviewing the proofs; moreover, their introduction had been edited to delete reference to the censored article.

When the editors contacted the editor-in-chief, Xudong Zhang, they were told that the removal of the essay 'should come as no surprise, since *FLSC* has its editorial office in Beijing and so must abide by normal Chinese censorship'.[133] Zhang rebuked the editors, telling them they should never have accepted the article in the first place. When the editors sought support from a member of the editorial board, a prominent professor at a prestigious US university, 'he merely shrugged: what did we expect?'[134] The editors went public about the incident and published the special issue elsewhere. Asking around, they uncovered similar instances of censorship of academic journals that had been kept private.[135]

The editors of the special issue wrote that they had trained themselves 'to read between the lines of work published on the Mainland, noting and compensating for the telling absences'.[136] However, they asked, 'What happens when it is no longer obvious where something was published and according to which rules?' For people who are not China-focused academics, the problem is compounded; they likely don't know they're expected to read between the lines.

China's unlawful territorial claims are another thing being subtly endorsed and reinforced by prestigious Western journals.[137] Articles have been published that incorporate maps of China showing the Nine-Dash Line. This line, first drawn in 1947, marks out China's claim to virtually all of the South China Sea and the islands and reefs within it. When the Philippines, whose fisherman had been bullied off their traditional fishing grounds, challenged China's jurisdiction within the line, a tribunal was convened in The Hague under the United Nations Convention on the Law of the Sea. In 2016 it ruled that there is 'no legal basis for China to claim'. The map appears in articles that have nothing to do with the South China Sea, such as on the distribution of butterflies or trees and grasses in China, and are purely political statements. When Western authors question the inclusion of the map in their articles, their Chinese co-authors say they can do nothing because the authorities require it, or they repeat the CCP line that the South China Sea is part of their homeland.[138]

13
Reshaping global governance

'Champion of multilateralism'

At the 2018 Central Foreign Affairs Conference, Xi Jinping called on China to 'lead the reform of the global governance system'.[1] This marked a shift from the careful terminology he had used at the same conference in 2014, where there was no talk of China 'leading'.[2] The more forthright language reflects Beijing's increasingly robust efforts to reshape international institutions and global regimes to suit the CCP's interests.

However, the CCP wants China to be seen as a *protector* of multilateral institutions, presenting itself as a much-needed counterweight to 'US unilateralism'. In 2018 at the United Nations General Assembly, foreign minister Wang Yi called China a 'champion of multilateralism'.[3] The following year, at the G20 Summit in Osaka, Xi Jinping 'led a chorus for safeguarding multilateralism',[4] while a joint EU–China statement in April stressed that both sides 'share common ground in upholding multilateralism'.[5]

The CCP's discontent with the present order should not come as a surprise; after all, it did not have much of a say in creating it, joining only in the 1970s. But when China's leaders speak of making the international order more inclusive, what they are calling for is acceptance of authoritarian systems, and for their values to be given the same status as democratic ones.[6] The CCP also wants to create new international organisations, with norms that stress national sovereignty and thereby impose minimal accountability on China.

The Party's *modus operandi* is to strengthen its position in large multilateral organisations, such as the United Nations, and chip away at those of its mechanisms it does not like, while simultaneously creating parallel institutions that China can dominate. Where it can, it will split nations off from multilateral groups and engage in bilateral relationships in which China will almost always be the stronger party. Pseudo-multilateral institutions (discussed below) follow the same approach. Beijing's position at the United Nations has been bolstered by its growing financial contribution, at a time when that of the US is declining, and by its large number of allies among developing countries and the non-Western world.

Through international bodies the CCP can set technical standards, gain support for policies like the BRI, insert 'Xi-speak' into discussions—phrases like 'community of shared future for mankind'—and spread its alternative definitions of 'human rights', 'terrorism' and 'internet governance'. This makes these bodies ideal platforms for increasing the Party's global 'discourse power' (*huayuquan*) and for spreading the 'China model'.

Sinicising the United Nations

China is a permanent member of the UN Security Council and under Xi Jinping has been actively expanding its influence there. It pursues the strategy of 'using the countryside to surround the city', challenging the established order by gradually building up bases on the periphery. The most prominent example is China's approach to the UN Human Rights Council, where it has been criticising 'Western' conceptions and promoting 'human rights with Chinese characteristics', persuading other countries to praise its human rights record. We look at this in detail later this chapter, but meanwhile there are many other signs of China's surging influence at the UN.

The Group of 77 (G77) was founded in 1964 to represent the interests of developing nations at the UN, and although China does not consider itself a member of the group it often works with it.

Membership of the G77 has grown substantially since its founding and today it numbers 134 countries, nearly 70 per cent of the UN's membership countries, giving China a substantial pool of allies with which to coordinate activity.[7] Though G77 countries do not always vote as a bloc, China can often mobilise enough of them to speak up on its behalf and to represent its interests in UN bodies.

Four of the UN's fifteen specialised agencies—the Food and Agriculture Organization, the International Telecommunications Organization, the International Civil Aviation Organization, and the UN Industrial Development Organization—are now run by Chinese nationals (by contrast, the US, the UK and France each head one).[8] Beijing has also gained effective control of large UN departments neglected by Western nations. One is the UN Department of Economic and Social Affairs, which is responsible for all kinds of activities, from the Sustainable Development Goals to following up on actions mandated by UN conferences and summits. It is headed by Liu Zhenmin, previously China's vice minister for foreign affairs, who also advises the UN secretary-general on internet governance.[9] A European diplomat has described the department as 'a Chinese enterprise ... Everybody knows it and everybody accepts it.'[10]

The Department of Economic and Social Affairs has worked closely with Chinese organisations to push the BRI onto the UN's agenda.[11] Its economic and policy division is implementing a major project linking the BRI to the UN's Sustainable Development Goals, part of its high-profile Agenda for Sustainable Development.[12] A Dutch think tank has written of China employing the UN to 'internationalise and legitimise its own domestic interests'.[13] A slew of UN agencies, including the World Meteorological Organization, the International Labour Organization, the International Civil Aviation Organization, and the International Telecommunication Union, have signed BRI agreements, all feeding into the CCP's narrative that the BRI is a global initiative rather than a Chinese one.[14]

The UN Development Program was the first at the UN to sign a BRI memorandum of understanding with China, in September 2016.[15] Helen Clark, former New Zealand prime minister and the administrator of the UNDP, lauded the BRI as 'a powerful platform for economic growth' and 'an important catalyst and accelerator for the sustainable development goals'.[16] The memorandum was followed in May 2017 by an action plan for cooperation between the UNDP and the Chinese government. The UNDP stressed that it 'commends the Government of China for enacting this initiative, and acknowledges the role of China in leading by example and reaffirms its desire to support China in its efforts'.[17]

Even UN Secretary General Antonio Guterres has praised the BRI, in opening remarks at the 2019 Belt and Road Forum for International Cooperation, held in Beijing. (He was accompanied on this trip by his under-secretary, Liu Zhenmin.[18]) Guterres commended China 'for its central role as a pillar of international cooperation and multilateralism'.[19]

China has also been wielding influence at the Economic and Social Council, one of the UN's six main bodies; it's been a member since 1971. Through its membership of the council's NGO accrediting committee, Beijing has blocked organisations it deems unfriendly. It prevented the Committee to Protect Journalists from being accredited as an NGO for four years. (The situation was only resolved when the United States called for a full vote.[20]) China also tried to have the consultative status of the Germany-based Society for Threatened Peoples withdrawn.[21] By contrast, CCP front groups like the China Foundation for Peace and Development were approved without delay.[22]

Beijing has also regularly used the accreditation process to demand that NGOs remove material it does not like from their websites, and to inform them that they must refer to Taiwan as 'Taiwan, Province of China'. Such orders are put even to NGOs that have nothing to do with China.[23] One NGO told Human Rights Watch that China complained about material concerning dissident Nobel Laureate Liu Xiaobo on its website. The NGO removed some of the 'offensive' material, but continued to see its application deferred by China when it did not comply with requests for information that would have put sources in China at risk.[24]

In 2015 UN headquarters in both New York and Geneva began to refuse entry to Taiwanese nationals, and even Taiwanese diplomats if they were carrying only their Taiwanese passports.[25] Whether this was done at Beijing's request or was a pre-emptive act, it indicates that China's efforts to erase Taiwan as a de facto independent nation are succeeding. The UN explained it only accepts documents issued by member states. (Taiwan hasn't been a member of the UN since it was replaced by the PRC in 1971. Its bids to join have been rejected several times.) Documents issued by Taiwan have often been accepted in practice, but refusal of Taiwan-issued identifications seems to be on the rise. In 2017 a group of Taiwanese students were denied entry to the Geneva headquarters to observe a session of the UN Human Rights Council. They were told that to be able to enter they needed to show 'Taiwan Compatriot Travel Documents', a type of permit issued by Chinese authorities to Taiwanese citizens wanting to travel to China.[26] And in 2018 a Taiwanese journalist was refused entry even after presenting this permit; she was told she needed a PRC passport to enter.[27]

Others have been ejected from UN premises under direct orders from Chinese members. Former UN Under-Secretary General Wu Hongbo admitted on Chinese national television that he had used his position to have the head of the World Uyghur Congress, Dolkun Isa, removed from UN premises during a forum on indigenous issues in April 2017, despite the fact that Dolkun was accredited as an NGO participant. Dolkun was given no reason for his expulsion and was not allowed to re-enter the premises.[28]

Pushing Taiwan off the international stage

Beijing has successfully pressured Western companies to treat Taiwan, a country of 23 million, as if it were a part of the PRC. Over the course of 2019 it aggressively courted those countries that still recognise Taiwan, leading some to switch recognition within a very short period.[29] For a long time, China has resisted the inclusion of Taiwan in the World Health Organization, thereby impeding the global fight against diseases. During the 2003 SARS epidemic, Taiwanese health organisations only received information about the dangerous disease through contacts at the US Centers for Disease Control and Prevention. After SARS broke out in a Taiwanese hospital, the WHO finally dispatched some experts to Taiwan, the first time in thirty-one years.[30] Following this debacle, Taiwan was occasionally allowed to participate in the WHO, with China's permission.[31] During the rapid spread of the novel coronavirus in early 2020, at Beijing's insistence WHO excluded Taiwan from meetings of countries affected by the outbreak.[32] China's foreign ministry claimed that China would tell Taiwan what it needed to know about the epidemic. Taiwan's foreign ministry said that China was not passing on all information, impeding its ability to protect its citizens.[33] At the same time, Nikkei Asian Review reported a diplomatic source in Beijing noting that 'China and the WHO have extremely close ties'.[34] China is the world's second-largest financial contributor to the U.N. Previously, *Nature* reported that the WHO's relationship with China grew especially close during the tenure of Margaret Chan, who led the organisation from 2006 to 2017. (Chan was rumoured to be in the running for the position of Hong Kong chief executive, but Beijing chose Carrie Lam instead.)[35] During the corona virus crisis, WHO's director-general Tedros Adhanom Ghebreyesus was criticised for backing Beijing's initial resistance to travel warnings and for giving high praise to President Xi's response. (Xi's wife, Peng Liyuan, is a longtime WHO goodwill ambassador.)

After Tsai Ing-wen was elected president of Taiwan in 2016, Beijing began blocking the country's participation in the World Health Assembly, presumably to punish it for electing a politician the CCP dislikes.[36] The WHA in Geneva has refused to accredit Taiwanese journalists trying to cover it for several years in a row.[37] Canadian journalist Yuli Hu was prevented from covering the assembly of the UN International Civil Aviation Organization in Montreal in 2016 because she was working for Taiwan's Central News Agency.[38]

Taiwan's Red Cross Society has not only been excluded from the WHO, it is not recognised by the International Committee of the Red Cross, which has been trying hard to ingratiate itself with Beijing. In March 2019 the committee signed an agreement with a Chinese Chamber of Commerce to 'pool and share their resources [to support] Chinese companies operating in complex environments abroad'.[39] The committee's special envoy to China, Jacques Pellet, praised China's contributions to humanitarian relief on China's international TV broadcaster CGTN.[40] In Xinjiang, where over a million ethnic minorities have disappeared into concentration camps, the International Committee has worked with China's Red Cross Society on a development project.[41] While the outcome may be beneficial to some, the presence of the international organisation lends legitimacy to policies that are, in effect, cultural genocide and crimes against humanity in the region.

Beijing's implacable campaign against Taiwan sends an unambiguous message to the world that Taiwan belongs to China. It is intended to intimidate Taiwan, showing the cost of refusing to follow the CCP's wishes. It is also meant to erode international resistance to Beijing's plan to incorporate Taiwan into the PRC, possibly by launching an armed attack, something that the hawks inside the CCP have long wanted to do.

Policing goes global

Around the world, the United Front Work Department has sponsored or encouraged the creation of Overseas Chinese Service Centers, known in some places as Chinese Community and Police Cooperation Centres.[42] Set up to protect overseas Chinese, whatever their citizenship, and to bring them together to 'share in the dream of national rejuvenation', they are also a means of keeping watch on the activities of dissidents and critics.[43] With the support of Chinese embassies, some sixty centres operate in forty countries, including the United States, Canada, France and Britain, and these have, according to a report from the official China News Agency, 'gradually penetrated into overseas Chinese communities'.[44] The centres work with local police, offering liaison and translation services, among other things, but they also spread the message that the CCP is everywhere. In Melbourne, for example, on the seventieth anniversary of the PRC, police in a district with a high ethnic Chinese population raised the Chinese flag over the station. The action was widely criticised, with one radio commentator saying, 'It's a police station honouring a police state.' Local Taiwanese, Uyghurs and Tibetans also objected.[45]

China has been expanding its cooperation with international organisations engaged in crime control. In April 2015 alone, Chinese authorities asked Interpol to post 500 red notices—requests for law enforcement agencies around the world to arrest those accused of crimes. This number was the same as the total for the prior thirty years combined.[46] Beijing is known to issue red notices for political dissidents. In 2016 Meng Hongwei became the first Chinese president of Interpol, and in April 2017 Europol, the EU's police cooperation agency, signed a strategic agreement with China's Ministry of Public Security, represented by Meng Hongwei, who was then still vice minister of public security.[47] Since then, Europol (which facilitates cross-border operations against criminals) has received Chinese representatives of the MPS to discuss closer cooperation.[48]

These developments have had noticeable effects. When in 2017 Italian police detained Dolkun Isa, president of the Munich-based World Uyghur Congress and a German citizen, they reportedly did so following a request from China, which had issued a red notice for Dolkun's arrest back in 2006. According to a Western diplomat, the Chinese government regularly requests European states to arrest Dolkun.[49] Interpol revoked his red notice in February 2018, and six weeks later the Party committee at China's Public Security Bureau expelled Meng Hongwei.[50] On a visit to Beijing a few months later, Meng simply disappeared, leaving Interpol mystified. It's unclear whether his disappearance was related to the red notice or some other infraction, but Bethany Allen-Ebrahimian wrote that CCP disciplinary authorities 'were treating Meng first and foremost as a party member who had strayed from the straight and narrow', rather than the leader of an international law enforcement agency.[51] In January 2020, after a one-day trial, he was convicted of bribery and sent to prison for thirteen and a half years.[52]

Extradition treaties are another way for the Chinese state to extend its long arm. The people of Hong Kong understand all too well what it means to be extradited to China, which is why they protested so vehemently in 2019 against a proposed extradition bill. The Beijing-friendly government was forced to abandon it. By contrast, seven EU countries have signed and ratified extradition treaties with China—France, Spain, Italy, Portugal, Romania, Bulgaria and Lithuania.[53]

Spain was the first Western country to sign such a treaty, which it ratified in 2007.[54] In December 2016 a joint Spanish–Chinese operation resulted in the arrest of 269 people accused of running a telecommunications fraud ring from Spain. Most of them were Taiwanese nationals, but because Spain does not formally recognise Taiwan, they were treated as 'Chinese nationals' by Spain's courts.[55] As of July 2019, Spain had extradited 218 of the arrested Taiwanese citizens to China, where they will not face a fair trial.[56] Kenya, Malaysia and Vietnam have also extradited Taiwanese citizens to China.

Italy ratified an extradition treaty with China in 2015. In addition, a 2016 police cooperation agreement sees Chinese police officers patrolling popular tourist spots in Rome, Venice and Prato.[57] Prato (near Florence) has a large ethnic Chinese population, many of whom work in textile and clothing factories. Although the ostensible purpose of the joint patrols is to protect Chinese tourists, the presence of Chinese police abroad is another means of sending the message to overseas Chinese that the state goes wherever they go. But for Beijing, the primary benefit of these police cooperation agreements is their role in helping tie foreign law enforcement into a network of obligations, information sharing, and possibly looking the other way when Beijing acts unlawfully.

France ratified an extradition treaty with China in 2015, and in September of the following year, Chinese national Chen Wenhua became the first person to be extradited under it.[58] Under the terms of the treaty, French nationals are protected from extradition to China, but citizens of other European nations have no such protection.[59] After France granted asylum to Grace Meng, the wife of Interpol president Meng Hongwei, China suspended all police cooperation with France.[60]

Despite the extradition treaty, Chinese authorities have kidnapped suspects in France. Unwilling to wait and go through the extradition process, Chinese authorities 'repatriated' Zheng Ning in February 2017 without informing French authorities.[61] A red notice had been issued for Zheng, who was accused of 'economic crimes', but undercover agents 'persuaded' him to return to China as part of Xi's notorious Operation Fox Hunt, the global extension of his anti-corruption campaign.[62] In fact, far more Chinese fugitives are 'persuaded' to return to China than are extradited or deported. This persuasion often involves threats to punish families in China, and to broadcast the photos and alleged crimes of the accused across the nation. Such was the case of 'Melbourne grandmother' Zhou Shiqin, accused of graft by the Party, who returned to China after her photo was plastered across state media and her sister's assets were frozen.[63]

This kind of extrajudicial intimidation is not uncommon and to date has been met with little resistance from Western countries when

Chinese officials harass and threaten dissidents and ethnic minorities. China's security services have tried to intimidate Uyghurs living in Belgium, France, Germany, Canada and many other countries.[64] In October 2017 the US State Department blocked the FBI from arresting four MSS officials who had entered the US on false pretenses and tried to 'persuade' wealthy dissident Guo Wengui (also known as Miles Kwok) to return to China.[65]

When Xi Jinping went to London in 2015, police arrested Chinese and Tibetan dissidents protesting his visit, and searched their homes.[66] A year earlier, when Xi visited Brussels, demonstrations were forbidden and pro-Tibet protesters were arrested.[67] The pattern was repeated in Switzerland in 2017.[68] Western governments are in this way allowing their police forces to assist the CCP in suppressing dissent. Tiananmen survivor Shao Jiang, whose London home was one of those searched, compared it to his experience in China: 'every time I was arrested the Chinese police would search my rooms and take things. It reminded me of that.'[69]

But a growing number of countries are declining to cooperate with Chinese authorities. In 2017 the Australian parliament stopped a move by the government to push through an extradition treaty with China, with members citing the corruption of China's judicial system, the fact that China's courts have a conviction rate of more than 99 per cent, and the widespread violation of human rights. In 2019 Chinese authorities celebrated Sweden's decision to extradite former Chinese official Qiao Jianjun. Sweden has no treaty with China, and the decision was based on the UN Convention against Corruption.[70] But a Swedish court blocked the extradition because of the 'real risk that the person will be subjected to persecution for political reasons in China', citing torture, degrading punishment and executions.[71] In recent times, Sweden has shown itself less easily cowed than others by Beijing's bullying. Perhaps it was this that led China's ambassador in Stockholm to comment, 'We treat our friends with good wine, but for our enemies we got shotguns.'[72]

Exporting Beijing's definition of 'terrorism'

Regional organisations in which China dominates provide an excellent opportunity to exert influence through cooperation agreements, bypassing larger international organisations where China does not yet call the shots. The Shanghai Cooperation Organization, and especially its Regional Anti-Terrorism Structure, is a prime example. The SCO is a China-dominated political, economic and security alliance with Russia, the Central Asian states and, since 2017, India and Pakistan. It was founded in Shanghai in 2001.

The organisation has adopted Beijing's Three Evils doctrine, which conflates terrorism with anything the CCP considers to be 'religious extremism' or 'separatism'.[73] Ethnic Uyghurs in Xinjiang have discovered that the CCP's current definition of 'religious extremism' includes growing a beard, refusing to eat pork, declining alcohol and praying, any of which can result in practitioners being sent to a concentration camp.[74]

The Regional Anti-Terrorism Structure has been stepping up cooperation with the UN Security Council's counterterrorism committee and has signed a memorandum of understanding to enhance the exchange of information.[75] The Structure has participated in Interpol activities, such as Project Kalkan, a working-group meeting used to exchange information on terrorist activities, where it reports on its work on countering the Three Evils.[76] In March 2019 the Structure signed a cooperation memorandum with the UN's Counter-Terrorism Committee.[77]

Memorandums like this are a way for the Party to legitimise its repressive interpretation of terrorism. Its efforts to brand dissidents as terrorists have already paid off. The Germany-based World Uyghur Congress has been listed as a terrorist organisation on World Check, a database used by governments and banks to screen for terrorists and people linked to financial crime.[78] As a result, Deutsche Bank and Western Union have blocked international money transfers of WUC president Dolkun Isa, without giving a reason. Dolkun was also prevented from exchanging money in Geneva while attending a meeting of the UN Human Rights Commission. Other members of the World Uyghur Congress have experienced similar obstacles.[79]

Creating parallel and pseudo-multilateral organisations

As we have seen, the Belt and Road Initiative is one example of how the CCP is trying to change the international order while simultaneously making use of existing organisations to promote it. Some have argued that the BRI is an ill-defined, disorganised 'package of everything and nothing', driven by vague and confused domestic policy.[80] Of course, the BRI serves domestic goals, such as generating growth in GDP at a time when China's infrastructure needs have been met, but it's also part of Beijing's strategy to create parallel global institutions that it dominates. The domestic and international aspects are united by the fact that the CCP, despite its claims to the contrary, is the architect and the primary beneficiary of both.

China expert Alice Ekman has argued, 'China is unhappy with the current security governance architecture and has the political determination ... to restructure it.'[81] Beijing invites everyone to join China's 'circle of friends', including security allies of the United States.[82] Ekman points out that China is the clear beneficiary of the ambiguity that results when old, formal alliances are supplemented with new, informal ones.[83]

Europe now plays a prominent role in the CCP's strategy of gradually chipping away at the existing international order. Long seen by the CCP as the United States' largely irrelevant junior partner, the continent is now a crucial player to be won over. Beijing wants to deepen the divide across the Atlantic, while at the same time use European support, or at least lack of public criticism, to give it legitimacy in the developing world. Parallel organisations help Beijing deal with EU countries one on one, and play them against one another.

Beijing is redrawing borders in Europe itself with the 17+1 summit, a pseudo-multilateral framework that could more accurately be described as seventeen bilateral relationships between European countries and their much bigger 'partner'.[84] Launched in Budapest in 2012 to deepen relations between China and Central and Eastern Europe and to promote the BRI, its secretariat is based in Beijing. Under the framework, the heads of government of the seventeen participating states meet annually with China's prime minister. The summit poses a challenge to the EU because it mixes EU member states and EU accession candidates with non-member states. Its parallel economic summits are attractive opportunities for countries that crave Chinese investment and are willing to 'stand up for China' in return.[85] However, the larger significance of 17+1 is the challenge it poses to the established order, the EU.

China has succeeded in derailing a number of EU initiatives by convincing individual member countries to boycott them. Due to the principle of unanimity, just one dissenting country is often sufficient to scotch a joint statement or policy. Under pressure from China, in July 2016 Hungary and Greece prevented the EU from speaking out on the South China Sea, and in March 2017 Hungary derailed the EU from signing a letter denouncing the torture of lawyers in China. In the same year, Greece blocked the EU from releasing a statement criticising the state of human rights in China.[86] In March 2018 the Hungarian ambassador to China was the only one of twenty-eight EU ambassadors not to sign a statement critical of the Belt and Road Initiative.[87]

Human rights with Chinese characteristics

In the early 1990s the CCP embarked on an aggressive mission to promote its own concept of human rights—namely, that the 'right to development' trumps all other rights. In 1991 the Party published its first white paper on human rights through the newly founded Office of External Propaganda, also known as the State Council Information Office.[88] The office has a Human Rights Bureau, currently headed by Li Xiaojun, dedicated to spreading the Party's notion of human rights. The basic idea is to downplay individual and political freedoms and focus instead on 'social and economic rights'.

The China Society for Human Rights Studies was founded in 1993 as one of the public faces of the Office of External Propaganda. It poses as an NGO and is a member of the United Nations Conference of Non-Governmental Organizations.[89] Its first director, Zhu Muzhi, also headed the Office of External Propaganda. The institutional link to the propaganda office is confirmed by the fact that Cui Yuying, former deputy director of the Propaganda Department and the Office of External Propaganda, served concurrently as deputy director of the China Society for Human Rights Studies.[90]

The strategic importance of the society became apparent in 1998 when it was among the first Chinese organisations to set up an English-language website.[91] The society publishes an annual report on human rights in China, and since 1998 has also published an annual report on human rights in the United States, a tit-for-tat response to the US annual report on human rights in China.[92] However, the main function of the China Society for Human Rights Studies is to spread a discourse that favours China.[93]

In 2006 the UN Human Rights Council replaced the UN Commission on Human Rights, which had been criticised for having members with poor records on human rights, and for its criticism of Israel. China was active in the setting up of rules for the new UNHRC, trying to ensure that country-specific resolutions would need to obtain a two-thirds majority, and arguing that country-specific reviews should be abolished, or at least radically limited.[94] While China failed to have the two-thirds rule made official, country-specific resolutions at the UNHRC are often voted down by the large number of Asian and African countries on the council.

Beijing has also been very adept at suppressing criticism of its human rights record at the UNHRC. Whenever its human rights record is reviewed at the UN, it works hard to fill speakers' spots with countries willing to praise that record. In 2019 the human rights 'recommendations' China received from these sympathetic countries included 'Continue to promote the Belt and Road Initiative to help other developing countries in their development endeavours, (Pakistan), 'Work on strengthening international cooperation in the field of human rights through [China's] National Human Rights Action Plan 2016–2020' (Turkmenistan), and 'Continue to fight against terrorism and extremism and separatist tendencies to safeguard its sovereignty and territorial integrity' (Syrian Arab Republic).[95] There were many similar points of praise for China disguised as recommendations. In July 2019 Hong Kong activist Denise Ho addressed the UNHRC. Overriding interruptions by China's delegates, she called for China's membership of the council to be suspended.[96] But China is too deeply embedded in the UN system for any such call to be heeded.

To spread its vision of human rights, the CCP has launched its own forums to normalise its repressive policies. For instance, Xinhua reported that at the sixth Beijing Forum on Human Rights, 'foreign experts' agreed with Chinese experts that regulating the internet is important for safeguarding human rights, thereby legitimising China's censorship policies.[97] The experts—Tom Zwart, director of the Netherlands School of Human Rights Research, and Kate Westgarth, former director of Chinese Affairs of the UK Foreign and Commonwealth Office—may not support the level of censorship the CCP promotes, but their participation in these dialogues and their apparent endorsement of China's policies through published statements like these lend the CCP legitimacy.

Human rights dialogues, like the annual EU-China Human Rights Dialogue and the Sino-German dialogue on human rights, also serve to legitimise the Party's position without improving human rights in China. In 2017 ten human rights organisations called on the EU to suspend its human rights dialogue with China until such time as the country undertakes meaningful reforms in the field.[98] Western governments have been reluctant to do so. However, in 2019 China cancelled its human rights dialogue with Germany, citing the 'lack of a constructive atmosphere' on the German side.[99]

When the CCP holds dialogues with Western partners on topics like human rights and the media, the West is not the only target audience. While Europe and North America have been weakening their pressure on China to respect human rights, the Party is well aware that it will not win over these countries for some time. And meanwhile the West can still undermine Beijing's claims in the eyes of countries in the global South.

In recent years, the CCP has been ramping up the promotion of its concept of human rights through Beijing-organised dialogues, UN resolutions and international meetings. In 2011 China published its first Human Rights Action Plan. In June 2017 it brought its first resolution to the UNHRC, called 'The contribution of development to the enjoyment of all human rights'.[100] In March 2018 it brought a second resolution, titled 'Promoting mutually beneficial cooperation in the field of human rights'.[101] Both resolutions were passed comfortably.

In December 2017 China hosted the 'South-South Human Rights Forum' in Beijing, resulting in the 'Beijing Declaration' that endorsed Xi's 'community of shared future for mankind' as central to human rights in the developing world.[102] The China Society for Human Rights Studies has been touring Europe to promote the CCP's version of human rights, and to defuse criticism of its system of concentration camps.[103] China argues that the camps holding a million-plus Uyghurs and other minorities, interned since 2017, are necessary in the fight against terrorism.[104] The society has also organised events at the UNHRC that praise the improvement in human rights in Xinjiang.[105] If the current state of Xinjiang is any indicator, China's 'community of shared future' is bad news for anyone who genuinely cares about human rights.

Exporting 'internet sovereignty' and standards for new technologies

The CCP's concept of 'internet sovereignty' replaces the idea of an open, borderless internet that promotes the free flow of information. Domestically it involves a censorship regime unparalleled in history—manipulation of search engines to block specific terms, an army of online censors, and tight regulation of internet companies. When Chinese government think tanks call for a 'democratic' global internet-governance system, this is simply another way of calling for 'internet sovereignty' by making the norms of autocratic countries equal in status to those of democratic countries, allowing each country to censor the internet within its borders as it pleases.[106]

Since 2014 China has organised the annual World Internet Conference in Wuzhen. Far from being a fringe event, the conference attracts high-profile participants, such as Apple's Tim Cook and Google CEO Sundar Pichai, both of whom have delivered public addresses.[107] Cook said he was proud to 'help build a community that will join a common future in cyberspace'.[108] The Chinese translation sounded very close to Xi's 'shared future for mankind'.

To spread 'internet sovereignty' globally, Beijing trains officials from other countries. In November 2017 China hosted a 'Seminar on Cyberspace Management for Officials of Countries along the Belt and Road Initiative', giving sessions on how to monitor negative public opinion and then spin it in a positive direction.[109]

While the Party is unlikely to win over the entire world to its ideas of internet governance, it has celebrated some successes. Vietnam's highly restrictive cyberspace law is modelled on China's.[110] Russia has backed the idea of 'internet sovereignty' with a 2019 law giving the government sweeping powers over what people can see on the internet inside Russia's borders.[111] Perhaps more importantly, China is exporting not just the concepts and expertise but the technology that enables the CCP's censorship and surveillance regime. The 'safe cities' that are being built around the world use the surveillance technology of companies like Huawei.[112] Huawei provided the 'safe city' infrastructure for Lusaka, where its employees have also reportedly helped the Zambian government track political opponents.[113]

Finally, China has paid close attention to the role of international standard-setting; that is, setting the requirements, norms and technical specifications for products or tasks. In 2015 it created a Leading Small Group for standardisation along the Belt and Road.[114] It has also secured leadership positions in the International Organization for Standardization, the International Electronic Commission, and the UN's International Telecommunication Union, among others.[115] Through the latter body, Chinese companies, including ZTE and the state-owned China Telecom, have proposed new facial-recognition standards, according to leaked documents first reported by the *Financial Times*.[116] Being able to set global standards based on their own proprietary technologies gives companies a distinct advantage in expanding their market share. In June 2019 ZTE and China Telecom proposed a standard to add video monitoring to smart street lights, precisely what protesters in Hong Kong have been concerned about. The standard was accepted.[117]

Afterword

How should the West respond to these threats to individual freedom and human rights? How are democracies to become more resilient? How can they better equip themselves to deal with interference by the CCP and other authoritarian regimes without coming to resemble them?

An active pushback strategy is required, not mere talk or wishful thinking. Democracies won't be able to change China, but they can defend their most important institutions. Effective responses will differ from country to country, but all must draw on the strengths of open societies while simultaneously addressing their weaknesses. Countries will be required to accept the short-term costs that will come with the end of unrestrained engagement with China. And better coordination among allies is vital.

The CCP prefers to operate in the shadows, and sunlight is often the best disinfectant. The responsibility for shedding light on the Party's activities lies with the news media, government agencies, scholars and political leaders. Of these, the media ought to be at the forefront. Free speech and a free media are the enemies of the Chinese Communist Party and must be protected at all costs. Tantrum diplomacy and fear of economic retribution must not be allowed to prevent governments and others from calling out Beijing for its interference activities.

Scholars, too, must step up, because the very idea of the university is under threat. Attacks on academic freedom, whether in the form of insidious self-censorship or institutions leaning on employees to temper their work, need to be called out vigorously. Remaining silent when acts of interference, censorship and harassment occur is the greatest danger. There ought to be zero tolerance from academics and students. If enough universities invited the Dalai Lama to speak, Beijing's threats would prove hollow.

Civil society also has a leading role to play in exposing the CCP. Political, business and university elites who acquiesce to or actively support Beijing deserve public scrutiny and robust criticism. Theatres, filmmakers, publishers—all cultural organisations in fact—should be exposed and condemned whenever they censor material under pressure from Beijing. Boycotts are often effective.

People of Chinese heritage have a vital role in the pushback against the CCP. It cannot be emphasised too strongly that the Chinese diaspora must be engaged, not least to neutralise the underhanded accusation that resistance to CCP influence is motivated by racism, or is somehow 'anti-China'. Chinese-heritage people in the West, and elsewhere, are the foremost targets of CCP intimidation. The threat to conform to Beijing's wishes or be punished is often severe. The rights of these people need protection; those among them willing to speak out must be supported, and those who threaten them should be prosecuted.

The language used in the pushback should never fall into the trap of conflating the CCP with the Chinese people. More people of Chinese heritage who are committed to democracy need to be involved in civic and political organisations, in order to counter the CCP's *huaren canzhang* program of promoting its own people. Political parties should be encouraging ethnic Chinese people with democratic values to run for office, and politicians must stop legitimising united front groups by associating with them.

The defence of democratic institutions rests with political parties, public service agencies, law enforcement, universities, cultural institutions, media organisations and businesses, all of which need to define and enforce clear rules for dealing with authoritarian regimes. In the political domain, much can be achieved by legislating for transparency in lobbying and by fixing loopholes in campaign-financing laws, thus preventing CCP proxies from buying political influence with donations, backing their favoured candidates, suppressing critical voices, and engaging in information campaigns to swing elections. Parliaments must also enact foreign interference laws where needed, to protect against new forms of political warfare and to defend against organisations and individuals that actively seek to subvert democratic institutions. Another weakness that urgently needs to be addressed is the underfunding of universities, many of which are now led by profit-oriented people who believe their success depends on good relations with Beijing. Academic freedom is more difficult to uphold when doing so risks financial punishment. Universities need more money to fund independent experts on China who will help the public understand the CCP's strategies.

Similarly, greater investment in public media will help counter those proprietors who have a financial interest in staying on Beijing's good side. Measures to expose and disable CCP control of Chinese-language media should include overcoming advertiser boycotts, which have driven many from the market. New companies may need public financial support.

The costs entailed in a nation reducing its vulnerability to CCP pressure will be worth it in the long run. Beijing wields its economic power like a great weapon. Its economic blackmail has proven highly effective, distorting decisions made by elected governments, frightening bureaucrats, silencing critics, and making countless companies beholden to it. That power is only amplified when Chinese companies answerable to Beijing own critical infrastructure in other countries. The West needs to inoculate itself against these pressures where it can, but where it can't it needs to make some hard choices and walk away.

All industries, including the education and tourism sectors, must understand the political risks of becoming heavily reliant on revenue flows from China. Short-term profit-making exposes them to long-term damage. When considering partnerships with Chinese organisations, much better due diligence is required, by people who are fluent in Chinese and have a strong understanding of how the CCP system works.

Governments need to make it clear that all companies that expose themselves to risk by becoming too dependent on China's market must bear the costs. Companies should not expect their governments to compromise human rights and civil freedoms to appease Beijing. As long as the current CCP regime rules China, prudent corporate management requires diversification of markets.

The United States cannot succeed in countering the CCP's spreading influence alone. By going it alone, it is playing into Beijing's hands. At the same time, other Western nations need to realise that a CCP-led China is not and never will be its friend. Other than those it controls, Beijing abhors alliances and does all it can to break them up. Democratic nations around the world must unite to protect universal human rights and democratic principles, and in this endeavour, alliances with developing nations will be as important as those among developed nations.

Despite the grim picture painted in this book, we remain hopeful that democracy and the will to freedom can prevail. In Hong Kong and Taiwan, people are fighting back against the CCP's attempts to control and intimidate them. It's true that many in the West are beset by cynicism and exhaustion when it comes to their own governance systems, yet more and more can see that the CCP represents a profound threat to the rights and freedoms that are frequently taken for granted. And it is reassuring to note that opposition to the CCP's influence, interference and intimidation crosses traditional political boundaries. People on the left and on the right who have opened their eyes to the threat posed by the CCP, including those who have left China to escape it, are banding together. The pushback is growing by the day and the Party bosses in Beijing are worried.

Acknowledgements

Dozens of people have helped improve this book with their generous contributions of time and knowledge.

We are especially grateful to those who read and commented on all or part of the manuscript—John Fitzgerald, Helena Legarda, Katja Drinhausen, Alex Joske and Matthew Turpin. Geoff Wade provided invaluable advice along the way. An academic colleague in Melbourne who wishes to remain anonymous made an enormous contribution to the research and carefully read each chapter.

Clive Hamilton would particularly like to express his thanks to the many people in Canada and the United States who met with him and volunteered their expertise: David Kilgour, Winnie Ng, Alex Bowe, Matt Southerland, Daniel Peck, Tom Mahnken, Toshi Yoshihara, Ely Ratner, Josh Rogin, Isaac Stone-Fish, Andrew Erikson, Joanna Chiu, Jeremy Nuttall, Ina Mitchell, Jonathan Manthorpe, Perrin Grauer, Calvin Chrustie, John Fraser, Reverend Dominic Tse, Joel Chipcar, Craig Offman, Dick Chan, Dimon Liu, Bob Suettinger, Vincent Chao, Russell Hsiao, Chris Walker, Jessica Ludwig, Orville Schell and Ian Easton.

He is especially grateful to Ivy Li, Fenella Sung and Natalie Hui for guiding him through the politics of CCP influence in Canada and for being a mine of information.

In Australia, in addition to those mentioned already, conversations with a number of colleagues added information and understanding to the subject: Charles Edel, Catherine Yeung, Nick McKenzie, Matthew Robertson and John Garnaut. In the UK, Keith Thomas, Martin Thorley and Charles Parton have been very helpful sources. In Europe, the contributions of Pradeep Taneja, Lucrezia Poggetti, Thorsten Benner, Roger Faligot and Jichang Lulu have all found their way into the book.

Mareike Ohlberg would like to thank her colleagues at MERICS who have provided invaluable feedback and support. The views expressed in this book do not necessarily reflect the views of any of her employers. She would also like to thank the participants of dozens of conferences, workshops and seminars on the topic across Europe. Many conversations on the side helped her draw new connections, gain new insights, and refine her understanding of CCP interference. Finally, she would like to thank her family and friends. Without their support, the completion of this book would not have been possible.

Our work has built upon the labours of a number of China scholars and analysts, and we hope that we have adequately reflected our debts to them in the text and the endnotes. We would particularly like to acknowledge the seminal work of Anne-Marie Brady, which has had a big influence on our understanding of the CCP's united front work.

Of course, all views expressed in this book are our own and should not be attributed to any of those named above. All remaining errors are also our own.

Glossary

Biaotai	表态	Short for *biaoshi taidu*, literally 'expressing one's attitude'. Can be used to refer to the politically significant act of expressing allegiance to the CCP by repeating and affirming its political phrases.
Big external propaganda	大外宣	Propaganda work targeted at foreigners that is done not just by propaganda departments but by all Party and government agencies, as well as society more broadly.
Borrowing boats	借舟出海	Literally 'borrowing boats to go out to sea': refers to using others (like foreign media) to spread the CCP's message.
China case	中国方案	Term used to describe the Chinese model of authoritarian government, which can be exported for other countries to learn from.
Document No. 9	9号文件	The colloquial term for an internal communique called Notice on the Current State of the Ideological Sphere, circulated by the Party Center in April 2013; it outlined seven 'false ideological trends'.
Enemy of the people	人民的敌人	A category of person that the CCP considers irrevocably hostile to its own goals. They are not part of 'the people'; i.e., the broad masses that the Party claims to speak for. A different set of rules applies to how the CCP treats anyone it considers an enemy.

Great Firewall	防火长城	Colloquial term for the regulations and technologies used to censor the internet in China.
Huaqiao	华侨	A person of Chinese ethnicity living outside China.
Huaren canzheng	华人参政	Literally 'ethnic Chinese participation in politics', a united front strategy to maximise political influence in democracies by promoting trusted people of Chinese heritage.
Huayuquan	话语权	Literally 'discourse power', a CCP term that refers to the ability to set the agenda and steer the direction of public discourse.
Kouhao	口号	A political slogan, very common in Chinese politics.
Lao pengyou	老朋友	'Old friend of China', an appellation used for foreigners of a certain standing who help the strategic interests of the CCP.
Leading Small Group	领导小组	A common coordinating and consulting mechanism used in the Chinese political system whereby leaders from different departments and ministries come together to coordinate their work in a specific area.
Liyong difang baowei zhongyang	利用地方包围中央	'Using the local to surround the centre'; one way of describing the tactic of using good relations with local actors to pressure national governments.
Nongcun baowei chengshi	农村包围城市	'Using the countryside to surround the city': using a place where the enemy is weak to surround the enemy's stronghold.
Peaceful evolution	和平演变	A CCP theory of the supposed attempt by Western governments to cause political change in China through peaceful means, most importantly the spreading of ideas that undermine the Chinese system from within (see Document No. 9).

Peaceful rise	和平崛起	A theory, coined by political adviser and former acting head of the Propaganda Department, Zheng Bijian, asserting that China's growing influence in the world would be peaceful; later changed to 'peaceful development'.
People-to-people diplomacy	民间外交	A form of international engagement used by the CCP since the 1950s. Originally used to bypass China's diplomatic isolation, it was maintained after China was fully recognised by other countries. Although ostensibly undertaken by ordinary people, it is carefully orchestrated by the Party through united front bodies. The Party considers itself to be the ultimate representative of 'the people'.
Positive energy	正能量	A term used by Xi Jinping and the Party to demand that media and others spread positive content rather than critical or 'negative' news.
Qiaowu	侨务	'Overseas Chinese affairs', a type of united front work targeted at overseas Chinese.
Thousand Talents Plan	千人计划	A program launched by the Chinese government in 2008 to recruit leading international researchers to come to China.
United front work	统战（统一战线）工作	The political work of building relationships with groups and individuals outside the Party. The goal is to build the broadest possible coalition against the principal enemy.
Wai yuan nei fang	外圆内方	'Round outside, square within', a united front principle that allows flexibility in strategy without compromising one's principles.

Xiao ma da bangmang	小骂大帮忙	'Big help with a little badmouth', a strategy of offering a little criticism on smaller issues in order to appear more credible when supporting the CCP (or another organisation) on larger issues.
Xinqiao	新桥	People of Chinese ethnicity who have recently settled outside China.
Yi shang bi zheng	以商逼政	Using business to pressure the government; i.e., getting foreign businesses to lobby their governments on China's/the CCP's behalf.
Youyi	友谊	'Friendship', a term associated with winning over foreigners to defend and advance the CCP's interests.

Acronyms

2PLA			The Second Department of the former General Staff Department of the PLA. Its successor is the Intelligence Bureau of the Joint Staff Department of the Central Military Commission.
3PLA			The Third Department of the former General Staff Department of the PLA; it was responsible for signals intelligence.
ABP	Advanced Business Park		A Beijing-based property development company which was granted a £1 billion deal to redevelop part of London's Royal Albert Dock by then mayor Boris Johnson.
ACPAI	America China Public Affairs Institute		A not-for-profit group that builds US–China relationships. Its president is Fred Teng, who is also the special US representative of CUSEF.
AfD	Alternative for Germany		A German far-right party.
AFROC	All-China Federation of Returned Overseas Chinese	中华全国归国华侨联合会	A united front body, established in 1956, whose target groups are foreign nationals of Chinese heritage who have moved to China and Chinese nationals who have returned after living overseas.

ANU	Australian National University		The national university of Australia, based in Canberra.
BC	British Columbia		The westernmost province of Canada.
BRI	Belt and Road Initiative	丝绸之路经济带和21世纪海上丝绸之路	A major Chinese government program that funds infrastructure projects worldwide. Also known as the Silk Road, and One Belt, One Road.
C100	Committee of 100	百人会	An organisation of prominent Chinese-Americans, founded in 1990, officially committed to advancing the full participation of Chinese-Americans in American society and promoting constructive relations between the US and Greater China.
CAFI	China Arts Foundation International	中国艺术基金会（纽约）	The New York branch of the China Art Foundation; it was established in 2014 to exert influence and gather intelligence through cultural activities. The China Art Foundation was set up in 2006 by Deng Xiaoping's daughter, Deng Rong, with the backing of the PLA-linked CAIFC.
CAIEP	China Association for International Exchange of Personnel	中国国际人才交流协会	A Chinese organisation officially dedicated to professional 'people-to-people' exchange, with offices in the US, Canada, Russia, Germany, the UK, Australia, Israel, Japan, Singapore and Hong Kong.

CAIFC	China Association for International Friendly Contact	中国国际友好联络会	A united front organisation under the Liaison Department of the Political Work Department of the Central Military Commission. It gathers intelligence and engages in propaganda campaigns.
CASS	Chinese Academy of Social Sciences	中国社会科学院	China's principal national-level organisation for research on the humanities and social sciences, founded in 1977. It has ministerial rank and is directly under the State Council.
CBBC	China-Britain Business Council	英中贸易协会	A British lobby group promoting trade and investment between the UK and China. It was founded as the China-Britain Trade Group in 1991 with the backing of the 48 Group Club.
CCG	Center for China and Globalization	中国与全球化智库	A Beijing-based think tank with strong united front ties, founded in 2008 and headed by Wang Huiyao.
CCIEE	China Center for International Economic Exchanges	中国国际经济交流中心	A Beijing-based, high-level think tank founded in 2009, supervised by the National Development and Reform Commission and headed by former vice premier Zeng Peiyan.
CCP	Chinese Communist Party	中国共产党	The sole governing party of the People's Republic of China.

CCPIT	China Council for the Promotion of International Trade	中国国际贸易促进委员会	A united front body founded in 1952 on the instructions of former Chinese premier Zhou Enlai. Its task at that time was to persuade foreign governments to trade with China, which was subject to a trade embargo after the 1949 communist takeover. Today it continues to promote trade between China and foreign countries and builds political networks.
CCPPNR	China Council for the Promotion of Peaceful National Reunification	中国和平统一促进会	A united front body dedicated to promoting the CCP's position on Taiwan and suppressing alternative voices, but also serving wider political goals of the Party.
CCTV	China Central Television	中央电视台	The principal national television broadcaster in China. In 2018 it merged with China National Radio and China Radio International to form the China Media Group, which is under the leadership of the CCP's Propaganda Department.
CEIBS	China Europe International Business School		A Shanghai-based business school established in 1994 under an agreement between the Chinese government and the European Commission.
CETC	China Electronics Technology Group Corporation	中国电子科技集团	A Chinese state-owned conglomerate specialising in communications equipment, computers, software and other electronic equipment, whose purpose is 'leveraging civilian electronics for the gain of the PLA'.

CGTN	China Global Television Network	中国环球电视网	The global arm of CCTV, with production centres in Washington D.C., Nairobi and London. Formerly known as CCTV International, it was rebranded in 2016.
CIC	China Investment Corporation	中国投资有限责任公司	Sovereign wealth fund managing part of the PRC's foreign exchange reserves.
CICIR	China Institutes of Contemporary International Relations	中国现代国际关系研究院	A Beijing-based think tank founded in 1965 and overseen by the Ministry of State Security.
CIPG	China International Publishing Group	中国国际出版集团	The external nameplate used by the CCP's Foreign Languages Bureau, an organisation under the Propaganda Department of the CCP Central Committee. It also goes by the name of China Foreign Languages Publishing Administration.
CITIC	China International Trust and Investment Corporation	中国中信集团有限公司	A state-owned investment corporation with links to the PLA.
CMC	Central Military Commission of the Communist Party of China	中央军事委员会	The CCP commission commanding the People's Liberation Army. It also goes by the name of Central Military Commission of the PRC.

CMG	China Media Group	中央广播电视总台	A media organisation formed in 2018 through the merger of China Central Television, China National Radio, and China Radio International. In China, it is usually referred to as the Central Broadcast and Television General Station. It takes orders from the CCP's Propaganda Department.
CNS	China News Service		China's second official news agency. It is part of the CCP's united front outfit and mainly targets overseas Chinese, as well as the people of Taiwan, Hong Kong and Macao.
CPAFFC	Chinese People's Association for Friendship with Foreign Countries	中国人民对外友好协会	A united front organisation founded in 1954 and now headed by Li Xiaolin, the daughter of former Chinese president Li Xiannian.
CPPCC	Chinese People's Political Consultative Conference	中国人民政治协商会议	The united front equivalent of the National People's Congress. Both the NPC and the CPPCC meet once every year in March in what is known as the Two Sessions.
CPSU	Communist Party of the Soviet Union		The ruling party of the former Soviet Union.
CRI	China Radio International	中国国际广播电台	China's official international radio broadcaster, since 2018 part of China Media Group.
CSSA	Chinese Students and Scholars Association	中国学生学者联合(谊)会	United front organisation for Chinese students and scholars studying abroad. CSSAs on campuses around the world are usually linked to the local Chinese embassy or consulate.

CUSEF	China-United States Exchange Foundation	中美交流基金会	A Hong Kong–based foundation founded in 2008. It is chaired by former Hong Kong chief executive Tung Chee-hwa, an important united front personage. It also has links to the PLA.
EDI Media		鹰龙传媒有限公司	A Los Angeles–based Chinese-American multimedia company with links to China Radio International. Its vice president James Su is also vice president of AFROC.
G77	Group of 77		A coalition of 135 developing nations at the United Nations, named after its 77 founding members. China, while not a formal member, regularly coordinates with it, so that joint statements are often issued under the name 'the Group of 77 and China'.
HNA Group	Hainan Airlines Group	海航集团有限公司	A Haikou-based Chinese conglomerate involved in various industries, including aviation, real estate and financial services, and believed to have links to top Party officials.
ICAS	Institute for China-America Studies	中美研究中心	A think tank based in Washington D.C. It was founded in 2015 as an outpost of the Chinese government's National Institute for South China Sea Studies and is funded by the Hainan Nanhai Research Foundation.
ICPT	International Committee for the Promotion of Trade		A Soviet front group created in 1952 to find ways around restrictions on trade with the Soviet Union.

ILD	International Liaison Department of the Communist Party of China (also known as the International Department)	中国共产党中央委员会对外联络部	A department of the CCP founded in 1951 and tasked with liaising with foreign political parties. Initially focused on communist parties, it broadened its mandate in the 1980s and started liaising with non-communist parties too.
MPS	Ministry of Public Security	中华人民共和国公安部	The principal police and domestic-security authority in China.
MSS	Ministry of State Security	中华人民共和国国家安全部	The principal government authority in China in charge of intelligence work and political security.
NAS	National Association of Scholars		A conservative advocacy group in the US with an interest in education.
NUDT	National University of Defense Technology	国防科技大学	One of China's key universities; it is under the leadership of the Central Military Commission and is based in Changsha, Hunan.
NYU	New York University		A private research university based in New York City and with degree-granting campuses in Shanghai and Abu Dhabi.
OBOR	One Belt, One Road	一带一路	Former English acronym for what is now called the Belt and Road Initiative (see BRI).
OCAO	Overseas Chinese Affairs Office	国务院侨务办公室	A former Chinese government agency in charge of managing relations with overseas Chinese. It was merged into the United Front Work Department in 2018, although the name is still used in public.

PLA	People's Liberation Army	中国人民解放军	The armed wing of the Communist Party of China.
PLAIEU	People's Liberation Army Strategic Support Force Information Engineering University	中国人民解放军战略支援部队信息工程大学	A military academy based in Zhengzhou, Henan.
PRC	People's Republic of China	中华人民共和国	The official name of China, not to be confused with the Republic of China (ROC), which is the formal name of Taiwan.
RMB	Renminbi	人民币	The currency of the People's Republic of China, also known as the Chinese yuan.
SAFEA	State Administration of Foreign Experts Affairs	国家外国专家局	An agency, under the State Council, responsible for certifying foreign experts working in the PRC. It is in charge of granting the Friendship Award.
SAIS	School of Advanced International Studies		A top US graduate school of international relations at Johns Hopkins University.
SARS	Severe acute respiratory syndrome	严重急性呼吸系统综合症	A viral respiratory disease.
SASTIND	State Administration for Science, Technology and Industry for National Defense	国家国防科技工业局	A Chinese government agency subordinate to the Ministry of Industry and Information Technology. It superseded the Commission for Science, Technology and Industry for National Defense (COSTIND).

SCO	Shanghai Cooperation Organization	上海合作组织	A Eurasian security organisation dominated by China. Founded in Shanghai in 2001, its members also include Russia, Kazakhstan, Kyrgyzstan, Tajikistan, Uzbekistan, India and Pakistan.
SCOBA	Silicon Valley Chinese Overseas Business Association	硅谷留美博士企业家协会	An association of businesspeople and technical experts, including both mainland Chinese and Chinese-Americans. Some members serve as advisers to Chinese national and provincial government agencies.
SOE	State-owned enterprise	国有企业	An enterprise with majority government ownership.
SPD	Social Democratic Party of Germany		A centre-left German party.
UFWD	United Front Work Department	中共中央统一战线工作部	An agency of the CCP that manages relations with organisations and individuals outside the Party, both domestically and internationally. Target groups include religious organisations, industry federations, minorities, overseas Chinese, and people in Hong Kong, Macau and Taiwan. Its mandate has been expanded in the Xi era, and in 2018 it absorbed a number of government agencies.
UNDP	United Nations Development Program	联合国开发计划署	The UN's global-development network.

UNHRC	United Nations Human Rights Council	联合国人权理事会	A UN body tasked with promoting and protecting human rights. It was founded in 2006 and replaced the UN Commission on Human Rights.
USCPFA	U.S.-China Peoples Friendship Association	美中人民友好协会	US-based 'friendship' organisation founded in 1974.
USSR	Union of Soviet Socialist Republics		The official name of the former Soviet Union.
WHA	World Health Assembly	世界卫生大会	The forum through which the World Health Organization is governed; it is composed of health ministers from member states.
WHO	World Health Organization	世界卫生组织	An agency of the United Nations concerned with international public health.
ZJUKA	Zhejiang UK Association	英国浙江联谊会	A hometown association (united front body) for people from the province of Zhejiang now living in the UK.

Notes

Chapter 1 An overview of the CCP's ambitions

1 Shaun Rein, China Market Research Group, Shanghai, quoted by Anon., 'Beijing's new weapon in economic war: Chinese tourists', *Inquirer.net*, 26 June 2017.

2 Clive Hamilton, *Silent Invasion: China's influence in Australia*, Melbourne: Hardie Grant Books, 2018, p. 145.

3 Norman Lebrecht, 'Eastman dean explains why he dropped Korean students from China tour', *Slipped Disk*, 26 October 2019.

4 Javier Hernández, 'Caught in U.S.-China crossfire, Eastman Orchestra cancels tour', *The New York Times*, 30 October 2019.

5 James Palmer, 'The NBA is China's willing tool', *Foreign Policy*, 7 October 2019.

6 Ben Cohen, Georgia Wells and Tom McGinty, 'How one tweet turned pro-China trolls against the NBA', *The Wall Street Journal*, 16 October 2019.

7 Sopan Deb, 'N.B.A. commissioner defends Daryl Morey as Chinese companies cut ties', *The New York Times*, 8 October 2019.

8 Ben Mathis-Lilley, 'The NBA forgot that it has American fans too', *Slate*, 7 October 2019.

9 Perry Link, 'China: the anaconda in the chandelier', *Chinafile*, 11 April 2002.

10 Jason Thomas, 'China's BRI negatively impacting the environment', *Asean Post*, 19 February 2019.

11 Devin Thorne and Ben Spevack, 'Harbored ambitions: how China's port investments are strategically reshaping the Indo-Pacific', C4ADS, 2017, p. 19.

12 Nadège Rolland, 'Beijing's vision for a reshaped international order', *China Brief* (*Jamestown Foundation*), 26 February 2018.

13 The leading intellectual Zheng Wang observes, 'the Chinese feel a strong sense of chosenness and are extremely proud of their ancient and modern achievements'. Zheng Wang, *Never Forget National Humiliation: Historical memory in Chinese politics and foreign relations*, New York: Columbia University Press, 2012, p. 17.

14 Martin Hála and Jichang Lulu, 'Lost in Translation: "economic diplomacy" with Chinese characteristics', *Sinopsis*, 10 March 2019, p. 7.

15 Qiao Liang, 'One belt, one road', *Limes* (Revista Italiana di Geopolitica), 17 July 2015.
16 Tom Wright and Bradley Hope, 'China offered to bail out troubled Malaysian fund in return for deals', *The Wall Street Journal*, 7 January 2019. The projects turned into a major graft scandal.
17 Ben Blanchard and Robin Emmott, 'China struggles to ease concerns over "Belt and Road" initiative as summit looms', *Japan Times*, 11 April 2019.
18 Nayan Chanda, 'The Silk Road – Old and New', *YaleGlobal Online*, 26 October 2015.
19 Ariana King, 'China is "champion of multilateralism," foreign minister says', *Nikkei Asian Review*, 29 September 2018.
20 Zhonggong zhongyang xuanchuanbu ganbuju 中共中央宣传部干部局 [Cadre Bureau of the Central Propaganda Department of the CPC Central Committee], ed., *Xin shiqi xuanchuan sixiang gongzuo* 新时期宣传思想工作 [Propaganda and thought work in the new period], Beijing: Xuexi chubanshe, 2006, p. 2.
21 Melanie Hart and Blaine Johnson, 'Mapping China's global governance ambitions', Center for American Progress, 28 February 2019. The CCP's switch to attack as the best form of defence is discussed in chapter two.
22 Anon., 'Why does the Western media hate the GFW so much?', *Global Times*, 11 April 2016. Like many other *Global Times* editorials that are dismissed as radical or only representing a fringe opinion inside the Chinese government, we'll see that it actually represents mainstream thinking inside the CCP leadership.
23 Party theorists have studied Michel Foucault. See 'Guoji huayuquan jianshe zhong ji da jichuxing lilunxing wenti' 国际话语权建设中几大基础性理论问题 [Some big basic theoretical questions in building international discourse power], State Council Information Office, 27 February 2017, <http://archive.is/jIjRm>.

Chapter 2 A Leninist party goes out to the world

1 'China urges US to abandon zero-sum Cold War mindset', CGTN YouTube channel, 19 December 2017, <https://www.youtube.com/watch?v=zZ-yPDLJmZE>; 'China calls on US to "cast away Cold War mentality"', AP Archive YouTube channel, 6 February 2018, <https://www.youtube.com/watch?v=ZYdaY8Ptp78>. For official news agency Xinhua, the US Department of Defense's 2018 National Defense Strategy was also a sign of America's 'Cold War mentality'. Anon., '"Cold War" mentality for U.S. to play up "Chinese military threat": spokesperson', *Xinhua*, 1 January 2018.
2 Anon., 'Huawei victim of high-tech McCarthyism', *Global Times*, 1 July 2019.
3 Liu Xiaoming, '"Gunboat diplomacy" does not promote peace', *The Telegraph*, 20 March 2019. It is not just the United States that suffers from a 'Cold War' mindset. Germany has the same problem, if the *Global Times* is to be believed,

and Australia. Li Chao, 'Germany's skepticism of China unfounded', *Global Times*, 14 March 2018. When Lithuania included China in its 2019 National Threat Assessment, the Chinese ambassador 'reminded' Lithuania 'not to look at Chinese investment through the lens of "cold war"'. Joel Gehrke, 'China lashes Lithuania for sounding alarm on espionage', *Washington Examiner*, 8 February 2019.

4 Anon., 'China rejects U.S. accusations on human rights', *People's Daily Online*, 15 March 2019.

5 Laurie Chen, 'Overreaction to China threat could turn into McCarthyite Red Scare, says former US official', *South China Morning Post*, 31 March 2019.

6 Chen, 'Overreaction to China threat could turn into McCarthyite Red Scare'.

7 John Kennedy, 'Xi Jinping's opposition to political reforms laid out in leaked internal speech', *South China Morning Post*, 28 January 2013; Gao You 高瑜, 'Nan'er Xi Jinping' 男儿习近平 [Real man Xi Jinping], *Deutsche Welle*, 25 January 2013.

8 E.g., Angus Grigg, 'How did we get Chinese leader Xi Jinping so wrong', *Financial Review*, 18 January 2019.

9 Xi Jinping 习近平, 'Guanyu jianchi he fazhan Zhongguo tese shehui zhuyi ji ge wenti' 关于坚持和发展中国特色社会主义的几个问题 [A few issues regarding upholding and developing socialism with Chinese characteristics], *Qiushi*, no. 7, 31 March 2019, <http://www.qstheory.cn/dukan/qs/2019-03/31/c_1124302776.htm>.

10 For a translation, see Anon., 'Document 9: a *ChinaFile* translation', *ChinaFile*, 8 November 2013, <http://www.chinafile.com/document-9-chinafile-translation>.

11 Carry Huang, 'Paranoia from Soviet Union collapse haunts China's Communist Party, 22 years on', *South China Morning Post*, 8 November 2013. In the same year, cadres were asked to watch a documentary, jointly produced by the CCP's Central Disciplinary Inspection Commission and the Chinese Academy of the Social Sciences, called *In Memory of the Collapse of the Communist Party of the Soviet Union*. Just like Xi Jinping's speeches, it blamed the fall of the Soviet Union on the loosening of Party control in the ideological sphere.

12 Also see Jeremy Goldkorn, 'Silent Contest', *The China Story*, 2014.

13 Huang Jingjing, '"Silent Contest" silenced', *Global Times*, 17 November 2013.

14 For campaigns at universities, see Tom Phillips, '"It's getting worse": China's liberal academics fear growing censorship', *The Guardian*, 6 August 2015; Tom Phillips, 'China universities must become Communist party "strongholds", says Xi Jinping', *The Guardian*, 9 December 2016; Steven Jiang, 'Communist Party cracks down on China's famous Peking University', *CNN*, 15 November 2018. For tightened controls over media, see David Bandurski, 'The spirit of control', *Medium*, 24 February 2016.

15 John Garnaut, 'Engineers of the soul: ideology in Xi Jinping's China by John Garnaut', republished in *Sinocism Newsletter*, 17 January 2019, <https://nb.sinocism.com/p/engineers-of-the-soul-ideology-in>.

16 Garnaut, 'Engineers of the soul'.

17 Anne-Marie Brady, *Marketing Dictatorship: Propaganda and thought work in contemporary China*, Lanham, MD: Rowman & Littlefield, 2008, pp. 51ff.

18 Joseph Nye, *Bound to Lead: The changing nature of American power*, New York: Basic Books, 1990.

19 *Meiguo dingneng lingdao shijie ma?* 美国定能领导世界吗? [Is It Certain that America Can Lead the World?], trans. He Xiaodong 何小东 and Gao Yuyun 盖玉云, Beijing: Junshi yiwen chubanshe, 1992, p. 4.

20 *Meiguo dingneng lingdao shijie ma?*, pp. 2–3.

21 Sha Qiguang 沙奇光, 'Dui shiji chu guoji yulun xingshi ji yingdui cuoshi de ji dian sikao' 对 世纪初国际舆论形式及应对措施的几点思考 [Reflections on form of international public opinion and response measures in the beginning of the century], *Duiwai xuanchuan cankao*, no. 12, 2000, p. 9.

22 Zhang Guofan 张国祚, 'Zenme kandai yishi xingtai wenti' 怎样看待意识形态问题 [How to view the question of ideology], *Qiushi*, 23 April 2015, originally published in *Hongqi wengao*, no. 8, 2015, <https://web.archive.org/web/20191205120449/http://www.qstheory.cn/dukan/hqwg/2015-04/23/c_1115069696.htm>.

23 See for example chapter 4, 'The Chinese discourse on Communist party-states', in David Shambaugh, *China's Communist Party: Atrophy and adaptation*, Berkeley: University of California Press; Washington, D.C.: Woodrow Wilson Center Press, 2008.

24 Bruce Gilley and Heike Holbig, 'In search of legitimacy in post-revolutionary China: bringing ideology and governance back', *GIGA Working Paper* no. 127, 8 March 2010, available at SSRN: <https://ssrn.com/abstract=1586310 or http://dx.doi.org/10.2139/ssrn.1586310>.

25 'The west is strong and China is weak' is an assessment of the state on the 'public opinion front' (舆论战线) that both top party leaders and others have made repeatedly. See for example Zhang Zhizhou 张志洲, 'Qieshi gaibian guoji huayuquan "Xi qiang wo ruo" geju' 切实改变国际话语权'西强我弱'格局 [Thoroughly change the pattern of 'the West is strong and China is weak' in international discursive power], *People's Daily Online*, 20 September 2016, <http://theory.people.com.cn/n1/2016/0920/c40531-28725837.html>.

26 Yang Jinzhou 杨金洲 and Yang Guoren 杨国仁, 'Xingshi, renwu, tiaozhan, jiyu – xie zai xin shiji kaiyuan zhi ji' 形势·任务·挑战·机遇—写在新世纪开元之际 [The situation, responsibilities, challenges, opportunities—Written on the occasion of the new century], *Duiwai xuanchuan cankao*, no. 1, 2001, p. 4.

27 Wang Huning 王沪宁, 'Zuowei guojia shili de wenhua: ruanquanli' 作为国家实力的文化：软权力 [Culture as a part of a country's power: soft power], *Fudan xuebai (shehui kexueban)*, no. 3, 1993, p. 91.

28 See Banyan, 'The meaning of the man behind China's ideology', *The Economist*, 2 November 2017.

29 In the early 2000s, the CCP still pushed the idea of 'China's peaceful rise', an idea proposed by former deputy director of the Central Propaganda Department Zheng Bijian, and not to be confused with 'peaceful evolution'. The slogan was later turned into 'China's peaceful development'—to avoid the threatening connotations of the word 'rise'—and then dropped entirely. See for example R.L. Suettinger, 'The Rise and descent of "peaceful rise"', *China Leadership Monitor*, no. 12, 2004.

30 Zhonggong zhongyang xuanchuanbu ganbuju 中共中央宣传部干部局 [Cadre Bureau of the Central Propaganda Department of the Central Committee of the Communist Party of China], ed., *Xin shiqi xuanchuan sixiang gongzuo* 新时期宣传思想工作 [Propaganda and thought work in the new period], Beijing: Xuexi, 2006, p. 188. A few months later, in April 2004, China upgraded the External Propaganda Work Small Group to the status of Leading Small Group in order to better coordinate policy-making and implementation. Zhu Muzhi 朱穆之, *Fengyun jidang qishi nian* 风云激荡七十年 [Seven turbulent decades], vol. 2, Beijing: Wuzhou chuanbo chubanshe, 2007, p. 248. The group may have been merged with the Leading Small Group for Propaganda and Thought Work under Xi, but since neither is officially publicly acknowledged, that's unclear.

31 'Quansheng duiwai xuanchuan gongzuo huiyi tichu: jianli da waixuan geju kaichuang waixuan gongzuo xin jumian' 全省对外宣传工作会议提出:建立大外宣格局开创外宣工作新局面 [The province's foreign propaganda work meeting suggests: establish a big external propaganda pattern to create a new situation of external propaganda work], Jinri Hainan, no. 7, 2004, p. 7.

32 Anne-Marie Brady, *Magic Weapons: China's political influence activities under Xi Jinping*, Washington D.C.: Wilson Center, 2017, p. 9.

33 Wu Nong 吴农, 'Lun duiwai xuanchuan yu jiaqiang dang de zhizheng nengli jianshe' 论对外 宣传与加强党的执政能力建设 [On external propaganda and building the ability of the Party to rule], *Duiwai xuanchuan cankao*, no. 4, 2005, p. 17.

34 Joseph Fewsmith, 'Debating "the China Model"', *China Leadership Monitor*, no. 35, summer 2011.

35 Chen Fengying 陈凤英, 'Shijiu da baogao quanshi quanqiu zhili zhi Zhongguo fang'an: Zhongguo dui quanqiu zhili de gongxian yu zuoyong' 十九大报告诠释全球治理之中国方案—中国对全球治理的贡献与作用 [The 19th Party Congress Report explains the China Case for global governance: China's contribution and function for global governance], *People's Daily Online*, 14 December 2017, <https://web.archive.org/web/20191205121135/http://theory.people.com.cn/n1/2017/1214/c40531-29706473.html>; 'Tegao: Zhongguo fang'an de shijie huixiang—xie zai renlei mingyun gongtongti linian shouci zairu Anlihui jueyi zhi ji' 特稿：中国方案的世界回响—写

在人类命运共同体理念首次载入安理会决议之际 [Special report: the world's echo of the China Case—Written on the occasion of the first inclusion of the idea of the concept of the community of shared destiny for mankind in the Security Council], *Xinhua*, 23 March 2017, <https://web.archive.org/web/20180725121415/http://www.xinhuanet.com/2017-03/23/c_129516885.htm>.

36 'Chinese democracy in the eyes of an American', New China TV YouTube channel, 2 March 2019, <https://www.youtube.com/watch?v=AUxbZ07q7j0>.

37 'Pojie quanqiu zhili 4 da chizi, Xi Jinping zai Bali jichu "Zhongguo fang'an"' 破解全球治理4大赤字，习近平在巴黎给出'中国方案' [To break through the four major deficits of global governance, Xi Jinping offers the 'China case' in Paris], *China Peace Net*, 27 March 2019, <https://web.archive.org/web/20190404193447/http://www.chinapeace.gov.cn/2019-03/27/content_11513080.htm>.

38 Juan Pablo Cardenal, Jacek Kucharczyk, Grigorij Mesežnikov and Gabriela Pleschová, *Sharp Power: Rising authoritarian influence*, Washington D.C.: International Forum for Democratic Studies, 2017.

39 Jasmin Gong, Bertram Lang and Kristin Shi-Kupfer, 'European crises through the lens of Chinese media', *MERICS China Monitor*, 12 July 2016.

40 Peter Mattis, 'China's "three warfares" in perspective', *War on the Rocks*, 30 January 2018.

41 'Zhonggong zhongyang yin "Shenhua dang he guojia jigou gaige fang'an"' 中共中央印发《深化党和国家机构改革方案》[The Central Committee of the Communist Party of China issues the 'Plan to deepen the reform of party and state organisations'], *Xinhua*, 21 March 2018, <https://web.archive.org/web/20191130114748/http://www.xinhuanet.com/politics/2018-03/21/c_1122570517.htm>.

42 Tasking a party member with keeping an eye on Chinese delegations going abroad is not an entirely new phenomenon, but it appears to be more strictly enforced under Xi Jinping.

43 David Shambaugh, 'China's "quiet diplomacy": the International Department of the Chinese Communist Party', *China: An International Journal*, vol. 5, no. 1, March 2002, pp. 26–54.

44 Larry Diamond and Orville Schell, eds, *China's Influence & American Interest: Promoting constructive vigilance*, Stanford: Hoover Institution Press, 2018, pp. 160–1. As part of a large-scale restructuring in 2017 and 2018, the ILD was merged with the Office of the Central Leading Group on Foreign Affairs. Anne-Marie Brady, 'Exploit every rift: United Front Work goes global', *Party Watch Annual Report 2018*, p. 35.

45 Julia G. Bowie, 'International liaison work for the new era: generating global consensus?', *Party Watch Annual Report 2018*, p. 42, cited from 'Xi Jinping: nuli kaichuang Zhongguo tase dagga waijiao xin jumian' 习近平：努力开

创中国特色大国外交新局面 [Xi Jinping: work hard to start a new phase of great power relations with Chinese characteristics], *Xinhua*, 23 June 2018, <https://web.archive.org/web/20191130115541/http://www.xinhuanet.com/2018-06/23/c_1123025806.htm>.

46 Brady, 'Exploit every rift', pp. 35–6.

47 See Michael Martina, 'Exclusive: In China, the Party's push for influence inside foreign firms stirs fears', *Reuters*, 24 August 2017.

48 Alex Joske, 'The Party speaks for you', Canberra, Australian Strategic Policy Institute, 2020.

49 Brady, 'Exploit every rift', p. 34. Also see Charlotte Gao, 'The 19th Party Congress: a rare glimpse of the United Front Work Department', *The Diplomat*, 24 October 2017.

50 Gerry Groot, 'The expansion of the United Front under Xi Jinping', in *The China Story*, Australian Centre on China in the World, ANU, 2015, p. 168. See also Gerry Groot, 'The long reach of China's United Front Work', *Lowy Interpreter*, 6 November 2017, and Gerry Groot, 'United Front Work after the 19th Party Congress', *China Brief* (*Jamestown Foundatio*n), 22 December 2017.

51 Anon., 'Tongyi zhanxian shi yi men kexue de youlai' 统一战线是一门科学的由来 [The origin of united front as a science], *United Front News Net*, 8 May 2014, <https://tinyurl.com/uvz6jwe>.

52 Anon., 'Woguo shou jie tongzhanxue shuoshi biye—lai kan yixia' 我国首届统战学硕士毕业—来看一下 [China's first batch of United Front master students graduated—take a look], *Sohu*, 4 July 2018, <https://web.archive.org/web/20191130134628/http://m.*sohu*.com/a/239312861_358054.>

53 Anne-Marie Brady, 'Chinese interference: Anne-Marie Brady's full submission', *Newsroom*, 8 May 2019.

54 Groot, 'The expansion of the United Front under Xi Jinping', p. 168.

55 Gerry Groot, 'The United Front in an age of shared destiny', in *Shared Destiny: The China Story yearbook*, ed. Geremie Barmé et al., Canberra: ANU Press, 2015, p. 130.

56 Brady, *Magic Weapons*, p. 8.

57 Zheng Bijian, 'China's "peaceful rise" to great-power status', *Foreign Affairs*, September/October 2005.

58 'Zheng Bijian: jiefang "san ge li" zhiguan quanju' 郑必坚：解放"三个力"事关全局 [Zheng Bijian: liberating the 'three forces' matters to the big picture], originally published in *Tong zhou gong jin*, no. 12, 2008, <https://tinyurl.com/srcgwy2>; Zheng Bijian, Bo'ao Forum for Asia, 17 December 2013, <https://tinyurl.com/wwt5bmj>. A 2015 article outlined the varying roles of six former senior advisers to Chinese leaders, including Zheng Bijian, <https://tinyurl.com/qoc5uwl>.

59 Lü Jianzhong 吕建中, <https://tinyurl.com/u3zzbpd>. Baidu Baike is China's equivalent of Wikipedia. See also 'Xi'an Datang Xishi wenhua chanye touzi youxian gongsi' 西安大唐西市文化产业投资有限公司董事长吕

建中 [Lü Jianzhong, Chairman of Xi'an Datang West Cultural Industry Investment Co., Ltd.], *ifeng.com*, 20 March 2013, <https://tinyurl.com/qne7n6j> and 'Lü Jianzhong shou yao danren Zhonguo guoji wenti yanjiu jijinhui teyao fu lishizhang' 吕建中受邀担任中国国际问题研究基金会特邀副理事长 [Lü Jianzhong invited to be Vice Chairman of the China Foundation for International Studies], Jin Merchants Club, 12 August 2016, <https://tinyurl.com/surttjk>.

60 See Russell L.C. Hsiao, 'Chinese political warfare in the 21st century', *Asia Dialogue*, 21 October 2013. The PLA's General Political Department was disbanded as part of the military reform of 2015–16 and superseded by the Political Work Department of the Central Military Commission.

61 Previously, the State Council Information Office and the Office of External Propaganda were referred to as 'one organisation with two nameplates under the Central Committee'. See 'Guowuyuan guanyu jigou shezhi de tongzhi' 国务院关于机构设置的通知 [Notice by the State Council on organisational set up], *People's Daily Online*, 24 April 2008, <https://tinyurl.com/w23mode>. According to the official website of the Chinese government, the State Council Information Office now has a nameplate under the Central Propaganda Department. See 'Zhonghua renmin gongheguo guowuyuan' 中华人民共和国国务院 [State Council of the People's Republic of China], website of the Chinese government, <http://www.gov.cn/guowuyuan/zuzhi.htm>. According to David Shambaugh, 'As a result of the sweeping reorganisation of the State Council at the 13th National People's Congress (NPC) in March 2018, it appears that the EPLG [External Propaganda Leading Group] has been reabsorbed back within the Central Propaganda Department—thus no longer enjoying its semi-autonomous status—but this is not entirely clear.' David Shambaugh, 'China's external propaganda work: missions, messengers, mediums', *Party Watch Annual Report*, October 2018, p. 29.

62 'Xueyuan jieshao' 学院简介 [Introduction to the institute], website of the Central Institute of Socialism, 25 June 2018, <https://tinyurl.com/vm5v3h9>; Website of the Academy of Chinese Culture, <https://tinyurl.com/utzlpha>.

63 Quote: '特别是与外国合作以商业面貌出现'. Benkan teyue jizhe 本刊特约记者, 'Tixian shidaixing, bawo guilüxing, fuyu chuangzaoxing: ji 2003 nian quanguo waixuan gongzuo huiyi' 体现时代性 把握规律性 富于创造性—记 2003 年全国外宣工作会议 [Embody the characteristics of the times, grasp the rules, be rich in innovation—Notes from the nationwide work meeting for external propaganda in 2003], *Duiwai xuanchuan cankao*, no. 2, 2003, p. 3.

64 Peter Mattis, 'Everything we know about China's secretive State Security Bureau', *The National Interest*, 9 July 2017.

65 Anon., 'Guo Yezhou: quan fangwei, kuan lingyu, duo cengci de zhengdang waijiao xin geju yijing xingcheng' 郭业洲：全方位、宽领域、多层次

的政党外交新格局已经形成 [Guo Yezhou: a new pattern of all-round, wide-ranging and multi-level government–party diplomacy has already taken shape], *Xinhua*, 21 October 2017, <https://tinyurl.com/sownfcg>.

66 Anne-Marie Brady, *Making the Foreign Serve China: Managing foreigners in the People's Republic*, Lanham MD: Rowman & Littlefield, 2003.

67 Brady, *Making the Foreign Serve China*, p. 8.

68 See Nick Knight, *Marxist Philosophy in China: From Qu Qiubai to Mao Zedong, 1923–1945*, Springer, 2005 p. 149. It wasn't published until 1952, and some scholars have argued it wasn't written in 1937 but was used retroactively to justify the alliance with the KMT with the benefit of hindsight.

69 'Xinhuawang: dangqian yishi xingtai lingyu hongse heise huise san ge didai jiaoshi' 新华网：当前意识形态领域红色黑色灰色三个地带交织 [Xinhuanet: in the ideological field, the red, black and grey zones are intertwined], CCTV, 7 September 2013, <https://web.archive.org/web/20191130145054/http://news.cntv.cn/2013/09/07/ARTI1378549535599959.shtml.>. Also see Binchun Meng, *The Politics of Chinese Media: Consensus and contestation*, New York: Palgrave Macmillan, 2018, p. 131.

70 The latter instruction is from a speech from late 2015. See 'Xi Jinping: zai quanguo dangxiao gongzuo huiyi shang de jianghua' 习近平：在全国党校工作会议上的讲话 [Xi Jinping: speech at the national party school work conference], *Qiushi*, republished on *CPC News*, 1 May 2016, <https://tinyurl.com/rd5fckq>.

71 See 'Zhonggong zhongyang guanyu jiaqiang he gaijin duiwai xuanchuan gongzuo de tongzhi' 中共中央关于加强和改进对外宣传工作的通知 [Note by the Central Committee of the Communist Party of China on reinforcing and improving external propaganda work], Central Circular No. 21 (1990) in *Dang de xuanchuan gongzuo wenjian xuanbian (1988–1992)*, 1922; and 'Zeng Jianhui tongzhi tan waixuan gongzuo de ji ge wenti' 曾建徽同志 谈外宣工作的几个问题 [Comrade Zeng Jianhui talks about a number of problems in external propaganda work], *Duiwai baodao cankao*, no. 7, 1990, p. 3.

72 Although in recent years, Party theorists have argued again that some arguments that are presented as academic issues are in fact political issues 'dressed up' as academic issues. This is part of the politicisation of an increasing number of issues under Xi, which means there is an ever smaller number of topics on which academics can dissent from the Party line. See Zhou Liangshu 周良书, 'Ruhe qufen zhengzhi yuanze, sixiang renshi he xueshu guandian wenti' 如何区分政治原则、思想认识和学术观点问题? [How to distinguish between issues of political principles, ideological grasp and academic views], *Banyuetan*, 12 December 2017, <https://tinyurl.com/qmfrswx>. *Banyuetan* ('Bimonthly commentary') is a journal run by Xinhua News Agency on behalf of the Central Propaganda Department.

45 Anon., 'White House hawks ratchet up trade hostilities with China', *Financial Times*, 18 September 2018.

46 Edward Helmore, 'Jared Kushner's company under renewed scrutiny over Chinese and Israeli deals', *The Guardian*, 8 January 2018.

47 Matthew Carney, 'Donald Trump heaps praise on Xi Jinping, makes no breakthrough on North Korea or trade', *ABC News* online, 10 November 2017.

48 Mo Yu, 'Chinese-American businesswoman accused of selling access to Trump', *Voice of America* online, 30 March 2019.

49 Lee Fang and Jon Schwarz, 'A "desperate" seller: Gary Locke, while Obama's ambassador to China, got a Chinese tycoon to buy his house', *The Intercept*, 4 August 2016. Locke had been described as 'the most successful American politician of Chinese descent in history', and had been providing services to the couple's company for some years.

50 Jon Schwarz and Lee Fang, 'Citizens united playbook', *The Intercept*, 4 August 2016.

51 Fang and Schwarz, 'A "desperate" seller'.

52 Lee Fang, Jon Schwarz and Elaine Yu, 'Power couple', *The Intercept*, 4 August 2016.

53 Dominic Faulder, 'George H.W. Bush's China connection', *Nikkei Asian Review*, 1 December 2018.

54 Maureen Dowd, '2 US officials went to Beijing secretly in July', *The New York Times*, 19 December 1989.

55 <https://www.aspph.org/texas-am-dean-named-senior-academic-advisor-for-the-bush-china-u-s-relations-foundation/>.

56 <https://www.aspph.org/texas-am-dean-named-senior-academic-advisor-for-the-bush-china-u-s-relations-foundation/>.

57 Anne-Marie Brady, *Making the Foreign Serve China: Managing foreigners in the People's Republic*, Lanham: Rowman & Littlefield, 2003, p. 7.

58 Zhang Qi, 'Ireland willing to help China reach out to EU—deputy PM', *Xinhua*, 25 May 2019.

59 Zhang Mengxu, 'China, US have more in common than what divides them', *People's Daily*, 24 June 2019.

60 CGTN, 'Exclusive interview with Neil Bush', CGTN channel on YouTube, 27 August 2019, <https://www.youtube.com/watch?v=DNT7Hth6XzA>.

61 Lee Jeong-ho, 'US must stop treating China as an enemy, says son of former president George HW Bush', *South China Morning Post*, 10 July 2019.

62 CGTN, 'Exclusive interview with Neil Bush', CGTN channel on YouTube, 27 August 2019, <https://www.youtube.com/watch?v=DNT7Hth6XzA>.

63 It was previously under the General Political Department of the PLA. With the restructuring of the PLA in 2016, it seems likely that the functions of the General Political Department were assumed by the new Political Work Department of the Central Military Commission. Alexander Bowe, 'China's overseas United Front Work: background and implications for the

United States', U.S.-China Economic and Security Review Commission, Washington, 24 August 2018, p. 9 note.

64 Geoff Wade, 'Spying beyond the façade', *The Strategist*, Canberra: Australian Strategic Policy Institute, 13 November 2013.

65 Mark Stokes and Russell Hsiao, 'The People's Liberation Army General Political Department: political warfare with Chinese characteristics', Project 2049 Institute, 14 October 2013, p. 15. See also Zheping Huang, 'An intricate web ties the woman who paid $16 million for Trump's condo to China's power elite', *Quartz*, 17 March 2017.

66 Stokes and Hsiao, 'The People's Liberation Army General Political Department'.

67 Angela Chen's Chinese name is Chen Xiaoyan (陈晓燕) but she also goes by Chen Yu.

68 Andy Kroll and Russ Choma, 'Businesswoman who bought Trump penthouse is connected to Chinese intelligence front group', *Mother Jones*, 15 March 2017.

69 Wade, 'Spying beyond the façade'. See also Roger Faligot, *Chinese Spies: From Chairman Mao to Xi Jinping*, London: Hurst & Company, 2019 (updated from the 2015 second French edition), pp. 247–8. He writes that China's military intelligence 'employs tens of thousands of agents—scientists, students, tourists, shopkeepers and businessmen' overseas. For links between CAFI and CAIFC, see the detailed discussion in chapter ten.

70 Stokes and Hsiao, 'The People's Liberation Army General Political Department', p. 24. In 2015 the usually well-informed *South China Morning Post* referred to CAIFC as 'a Chinese military intelligence agency'. (Minnie Chan, 'Chinese military intelligence chief Xing Yunming held in graft inquiry', *South China Morning Post*, 4 March 2015.)

71 John Garnaut, 'Chinese military woos big business', *The Sydney Morning Herald*, 25 May 2013; Bowe, 'China's overseas United Front work'.

72 John Garnaut, 'China gets into the business of making friends', *The Sydney Morning Herald*, 25 May 2013.

73 Chan, 'Chinese military intelligence chief Xing Yunming held in graft inquiry'.

74 Wade, 'Spying beyond the façade'.

75 Stokes and Hsiao, 'The People's Liberation Army General Political Department', p. 24.

76 Garnaut, 'China gets into the business of making friends'. For Owens's bio, see <https://www.eastwest.ngo/node/2032>.

77 Garnaut, 'China gets into the business of making friends'.

78 Garnaut, 'China gets into the business of making friends'.

79 Bill Gertz, 'Chinese communists influence US policy through ex-military officials', *Washington Free Beacon*, 6 February 2012; Shirley A. Kan, 'US-China military contacts: issues for Congress', report of the US Congressional

Research Service, 25 October 2012; Bill Owens, 'America must start treating China as a friend', *Financial Times*, 17 November 2009.

80 Gertz, 'Chinese communists influence US policy through ex-military officials'.

81 Kan, 'US-China military contacts'.

82 <https://web.archive.org/web/20180508000126/https://red-bison.com/about-us/>.

83 Kan, 'US-China military contacts: issues for Congress'.

84 Gertz, 'Chinese communists influence US policy through ex-military officials'.

85 Ralph Hallow, 'Republicans fear exchange program put national security at risk', *The Washington Times*, 19 April 2012.

86 Jace White, 'U.S.-China Sanya Initiative Dialogue: report from the 10th anniversary meeting', EastWest.ngo, 17 January 2019, <https://web.archive.org/web/20191208182022/https://www.eastwest.ngo/idea/us-china-sanya-initiative-dialogue-report-10th-anniversary-meeting>.

87 Michael Kranish, 'Trump's China whisperer: how billionaire Stephen Schwarzman has sought to keep the president close to Beijing', *The Washington Post*, 12 March 2018.

88 Kranish, 'Trump's China whisperer'.

89 Dasha Afanasieva, 'Blackstone sells Logicor to China Investment Corporation for $14 billion', *Reuters*, 3 June 2017.

90 Quoted by Kranish, 'Trump's China whisperer'.

91 Anon., 'Stephen Schwarzman's remarks from the Schwarzman Scholars inaugural convocation', website of the Schwarzman Scholars, 10 September 2016, <https://web.archive.org/web/20191208182433/https://www.schwarzmanscholars.org/news-article/stephen-schwarzmans-remarks-at-the-schwarzman-scholars-inaugural-convocation/>.

92 Kranish, 'Trump's China whisperer'.

93 'Schwarzman College', website of Schwarzman Scholars, not dated, <https://www.schwarzmanscholars.org/about/schwarzman-college/>; <https://en.wikipedia.org/wiki/Tsinghua_clique>.

94 Sam Dangremond, 'Steve Schwarzman hosted an epic 70th birthday party in Palm Beach', *Town & Country*, 13 February 2017.

95 Tony Munroe, 'Refinitiv blocks Reuters stories on Tiananmen from its Eikon platform', *Reuters*, 4 June 2019.

96 Matthew Belvedere, 'Blackstone's Schwarzman: China's economic "miracle" came at the expense of the US and the West', *CNBC*, 17 September 2019.

97 Jonathan Manthorpe, *Claws of the Panda: Beijing's campaign of influence and intimidation in Canada*, Toronto: Cormorant Books, 2019, pp. 157–67.

98 Nicholas Kristof, 'Chinese bank is an anomaly', *The New York Times*, 4 May 1987.

99 Faligot, *Chinese Spies*, pp. 203–4.

100 Faligot, *Chinese Spies*, p. 204, quoting from Agnès Andrésy, *Princes Rouge, les nouveaux puissants de Chine*, Paris: L'Harmattan, 2003. Cain Nunns, 'China's Poly Group: the most important company you've never heard of', *GlobalPost*, 25 February 2013.

101 Mark Mackinnon and Nathan Vanderklippe, 'The inglorious exit of Bo Xilai, Canada's closest ally in China's power structure', *The Globe and Mail*, 25 October 2013.

102 Sandra Martin, 'Behind the scenes, Paul Desmarais was a force in Canadian politics', *The Globe and Mail*, 9 October 2013. For the paper mill, see Yongjin Zhang, *China's Emerging Global Businesses: Political economy and institutional investigations*, Basingstoke: Palgrave Macmillan, 2003, p. 137.

103 Li Hede 李禾德, 'Bo Guagua zai Jianada dagong qian chu yu Suoluosi de guanxi' 薄瓜瓜在加拿大打工 牵出与索罗斯关系 [Bo Guagua works in Canada, pulls relationship with Soros], *Next Magazine*, 4 December 2018, <https://web.archive.org/web/20191208194657/https://hk.nextmgz.com/article/2_641390_0>.

104 Anne Kingston, 'Brian Mulroney: from scandal-adjacent elitist to magnanimous statesman', *Macleans*, 19 February 2019.

105 Martin, 'Behind the scenes, Paul Desmarais was a force in Canadian politics'.

106 Jason Kirby, 'Chretien's sell-out plan to keep China happy', *Macleans*, 14 June 2019.

107 Manthorpe, *Claws of the Panda*, p. 127.

108 Geoffrey York, 'Chrétien builds links with Chinese conglomerate', *The Globe and Mail*, 6 February 2004.

109 Manthorpe, *Claws of the Panda*, p. 127.

110 Andrew Mitrovica and Jeff Sallot, 'China set up crime web in Canada, report says', *The Globe and Mail*, 29 April 2000.

111 Manthorpe, *Claws of the Panda*, pp. 157–67.

112 <https://www.primetimecrime.com/Articles/RobertRead/Sidewinder%20page%201.htm>. Although the CCP's use of triads in Taiwan and Hong Kong is well known, the links between organised crime and Beijing's political influence operations in the West is little studied or understood.

113 Manthorpe, *Claws of the Panda*, pp. 157–9.

114 Robert Fife and Steven Chase, 'Influential Chinese-Canadians paying to attend private fundraisers with Trudeau', *The Globe and Mail*, 2 December 2016.

115 Fife and Chase, 'Influential Chinese-Canadians paying to attend private fundraisers with Trudeau'.

116 Jen Gerson, 'At Toronto fundraiser, Justin Trudeau seemingly admires China's "basic dictatorship"', *National Post*, 8 November 2013.

117 See the account in Manthorpe, *Claws of the Panda*, pp. 179–81.

118 Craig Offman, 'CSIS warned this cabinet minister could be a threat. Ontario disagreed', *The Globe and Mail*, 16 June 2015 (updated 15 May 2018).

119 At the time of writing the case had not been concluded.

120 Craig Offman, 'Ontario minister Michael Chan defends China's human-rights record', *The Globe and Mail*, 8 June 2016.

121 Tom Blackwell, 'Former Ontario Liberal cabinet minister headlines pro-Beijing rally near Toronto', *National Post*, 20 August 2019; Xiao Xu, 'Former Ontario minister sides with Beijing, pins Hong Kong protests on "outside" forces', *The Globe and Mail*, 15 September 2019. Interviewed by China News in September 2019, Chan said the Hong Kong police's behaviour is 'the most non-violent violence' (最不暴力的暴力) <https://tinyurl.com/uot4t9p>.

122 Walt Bogdanich and Michael Forsythe, 'How McKinsey has helped raise the stature of authoritarian governments', *The New York Times*, 15 December 2018.

123 Bogdanich and Forsythe, 'How McKinsey has helped raise the stature of authoritarian governments'.

124 Geoff Zochodne and Naomi Powell, 'Will Dominic Barton's experience in China help or hurt him as Canada's new man in Beijing?', *Leader Post*, 6 September 2019.

125 Jeremy Nuttall, 'Chinese politician's role on Teck board worries watchdog', *The Tyee*, 7 July 2016; <https://tinyurl.com/wdqtk7n>; for Quan's bio see <https://tinyurl.com/yx6cdjfk>.

126 Matthew Fisher, 'Canada's new foreign minister must figure out how to deal with China', *Global News*, 24 November 2019.

127 Steve Chase, 'François-Philippe Champagne takes helm at Department of Global Affairs during critical period in Canada-China relations', *The Globe and Mail*, 20 November 2019.

128 Michelle Carbert, 'Trudeau no-show leads to cancellation of Munk debate on foreign policy', *The Globe and Mail*, 24 September 2019.

Chapter 4 Political elites at the centre: Europe

1 For a good overview of the ILD, see David Shambaugh, 'China's "Quiet Diplomacy": the International Department of the Chinese Communist Party', *China: An International Journal*, vol. 5, no. 1, March 2007, pp. 26–54. In English, the ILD is referred to as the International Department.

2 '习近平总书记说，"党的对外交往工作是党的一条重要战线，是国家总体外交的一个重要组成部分"', See Anon., 'Guo Yezhou: hanwei guojia liyi shi suoyou duiwai jiaowang gongzuo de yingyou zhi yi' 郭业洲：捍卫国家利益是所有对外交往工作的应有之义, *Xinhua*, 21 October 2017, <http://www.xinhuanet.com/politics/19cpcnc/2017-10/21/c_129724190.htm>. According to an editor of *Party Watch Initiative*, Julia Bowie, the ILD operates by 'encouraging foreign political parties, politicians, and political organizations to understand and respect China's values and interests'. Julia Bowie, 'International liaison work for the new era: generating global consensus?', in Julia Bowie and David Gitter, eds, *Party Watch Annual Report*

2018, Washington D.C.: Center for Advanced China Research, 19 October 2018, p. 43.

3 Bowie, 'International liaison work for the new era', p. 43. At the 19th Party Congress in 2017, the deputy head of the ILD, Guo Yezhou, said the CCP maintains regular contact with over 400 political parties in over 160 countries, <http://www.xinhuanet.com/politics/19cpcnc/zb/zb7/index.htm>.

4 Bowie, 'International liaison work for the new era', p. 44.

5 Bowie, 'International liaison work for the new era', p. 44.

6 Hu Ping, 'Do "we", the world's political parties, know that "we" have issued an initiative extolling the CCP's global leadership for a better world?', *China Change*, 5 December 2017.

7 <http://language.chinadaily.com.cn/2017-12/04/content_35199254.htm>.

8 Bowie, 'International liaison work for the new era', p. 48.

9 See the banner at the top of their website, <http://www.idcpc.org.cn/english/>.

10 Meetings are recorded in English at <http://www.idcpc.org.cn/english/news/>.

11 <http://www.idcpc.org.cn/english/news/201905/t20190523_100451.html>.

12 Email to authors, 6 May 2019.

13 <http://www.idcpc.org.cn/english/news/201812/t20181211_99054.html>.

14 <http://www.idcpc.org.cn/english/news/201905/t20190505_100353.html>.

15 Examples include Hans-Peter Friedrich, vice president of the German Bundestag and former minister of the interior, whom we will meet again, <http://www.idcpc.org.cn/english/news/201904/t20190420_100067.html>; Lars Klingbeil, general secretary of the Social Democratic Party of Germany, <http://www.idcpc.org.cn/english/news/201812/t20181221_99149.html>; and Morten Wold, vice president of the Norwegian Parliament, <http://www.idcpc.org.cn/english/news/201812/t20181211_99051.html>.

16 Bowie, 'International liaison work for the new era', p. 47.

17 <http://www.gbcc.org.uk/about-us/our-board>.

18 <http://www.idcpc.org.cn/english/news/201905/t20190515_100405.html>. These words are the ILD's, presumably paraphrased from Mandelson's comments.

19 Peter Mandelson, 'Trump is wrong on China, and we must tell him', *The Sunday Times*, 16 June 2019.

20 Peter Mandelson is chairman and co-founder of Global Counsel, a consulting firm, <https://tinyurl.com/qvhl94a>. On 7 May 2019 he went to Beijing and met with senior members of the China Council for International Investment Promotion (under the Ministry of Commerce). Jin Ligang, a principal of Albright Stonebridge Group (chaired by Madeleine Albright) joined them, as did the chairman of ASG China.

21 Angela Gui, 'Damned if you do, damned if you don't? I won't', *Medium*, 13 February 2019.

22 Gui, 'Damned if you do, damned if you don't?'
23 Gui, 'Damned if you do, damned if you don't?'
24 Kris Cheng, '"Threats, verbal abuse, bribes, flattery" won't silence me: Sweden probes unauthorised meeting with daughter of bookseller detained in China', *Hong Kong Free Press*, 14 February 2019.
25 Anon., 'Ex-Swedish envoy to China Anna Lindstedt suspected of crime after setting up "unofficial" meetings over detained bookseller', *Hong Kong Free Press*, 10 May 2019; Iliana Magra and Chris Buckley, 'Sweden charges ex-ambassador to China over secret meetings', *The New York Times*, 9 December 2019.
26 Anon., 'Ola Wong: "Sverige har varit som en sömngångare om Kina"', *Expressen*, 23 February 2019; Anon., 'Tung diplomat byter sida—hjälper Ericssons ärkerival', *Dagens SP*, 7 November 2012.
27 'Serge Abou', *Corporate Europe Observatory*, <https://corporateeurope.org/revolvingdoorwatch/cases/serge-abou>.
28 'Serge Abou', *Corporate Europe Observatory*.
29 Ren Ke, 'Interview: BRI to become model for culture exchanges: former German ambassador to China', *Xinhua*, 22 March 2019.
30 'Advisory Board', *Deutsch-Chinesische Wirtschaftsvereinigung e.V.*, <https://www.dcw-ev.de/en/about-dcw/advisory-board.html>.
31 'Dr. Michael Schaefer', MERICS, <https://www.merics.org/de/team/dr-michael-schaefer>.
32 Michael Schaefer, 'Co-driving the new silk road', *Berlin Policy Journal*, 12 January 2016.
33 Philip Bilsky, 'Schaefer: "Man tut sich sehr schwer"', *Deutsche Welle*, 17 February 2015.
34 Bilsky, 'Schaefer'.
35 David Bandurski, 'China's new science of sycophantology', *China Media Project*, 21 June 2018.
36 Peter Martin and Alan Crawford, 'China's influence digs deep into Europe's political landscape', *Bloomberg*, 4 April 2019.
37 Martin and Crawford, 'China's influence digs deep into Europe's political landscape'.
38 Martin and Crawford, 'China's influence digs deep into Europe's political landscape'.
39 Martin and Crawford, 'China's influence digs deep into Europe's political landscape'.
40 See for example, 'International Conference: "EU-China 2020 Strategic Agenda for Cooperation"', <https://www.coleurope.eu/events/international-conference-eu-china-2020-strategic-agenda-cooperation>.
41 <https://www.vsse.be/nl/wat-we-doen/dreigingen/spionage>.
42 Christoph B. Schiltz, 'Hunderte Spione in Brüssel—Vor dem Betreten einiger Lokale wird gewarnt', *Die Welt*, 9 February 2019.

43 <http://www.chinamission.be/eng/fyrjh/t1636626.htm>.

44 Jörg Diehl and Fidelius Schmid, 'Ex-Diplomat soll für China spioniert haben', *Der Spiegel*, 15 January 2020. Matthew Karnitschnig, 'The man at the center of Brussels spy probe', *Politico*, 22 January 2020.

45 Alan Crawford and Peter Martin, 'How Belgium became Europe's den of spies and a gateway for China', *Bloomberg*, 29 November 2019.

46 'Ouzhou Huiyi Ou Zhong youhao xiaozu' 欧洲议会欧中友好小组 [EU-China Friendship Group of the European Parliament], website of the EU-China Friendship Association, not dated, <https://web.archive.org/web/20190616092022/http://www.eu-cfa.com/lists/OZYHOZYHXH.html>; Zhang Jie 张杰, 'Ouzhou yihui yiyuan zhuli Gai Lin jiangshu ta de gongzuo gushi' 欧洲议会议员助理盖琳讲述他的工作故事, *People's Daily Online*, 27 March 2014, <https://web.archive.org/web/20191208211535/http://world.people.com.cn/n/2014/0327/c1002-24756505.html>.

47 Jichang Lulu, 'Repurposing democracy: the European Parliament China friendship group', *Sinopsis*, 26 November 2019.

48 'Ouzhou Huiyi Ou Zhong youhao xiaozu zhuxi: ceng dangmian bochi Rebiya' 欧洲议会欧中友好小组主席：曾当面驳斥热比娅 [Chairman of the EU-China Friendship Group of the European Parliament: I once refuted Rebiya in person], website of the EU-China Friendship Association, 17 October 2016, <https://web.archive.org/web/20191020051201/http://www.eu-cfa.com/detail/218.html>; Darren Ennis, 'EU assembly to consider Beijing Olympics boycott', *Reuters*, 21 March 2008.

49 'EU-China Friendship Groups visits Tibet', *China.org.cn*, 27 August 2016, <https://web.archive.org/web/20191208211327/http://www.china.org.cn/china/2016-08/27/content_39179710.htm>.

50 Daqiong and Palden Nyima, 'Friendship group praises Tibet after 3-day field trip', *China Daily*, 27 August 2016.

51 The term used was 著名的对华友好人士. Zhang Xiaofang 张晓芳, 'Ouzhou Huiyi Ou Zhong youhao xiaozu zhuxi: ceng dangmian bochi Rebiya' 欧洲议会欧中友好小组主席：曾当面驳斥热比娅 [Chairman of the EU-China Friendship Group of the European Parliament: I once refuted Rebiya in person], *Huanqiuwang*, 17 March 2014, <http://world.huanqiu.com/exclusive/2014-03/4909357.html?agt=622>.

52 Anon., 'Český europoslanec na Hedvábné stezce', *Sinopsis*, 17 May 2019.

53 Gai Lin (盖琳), in Li Xia, 'Spotlight: two-year mark of global community towards a shared future', *Xinhua*, 20 January 2019; <http://www.europarl.europa.eu/meps/en/4556/NIRJ_DEVA/assistants#mep-card-content>. For the claim that he became the first EU public servant of Chinese nationality, see 'Ouzhou yihui Ou Zhong youhao xiaozu zhuxi: ceng dangmian bochi Rebiya' 欧洲议会欧中友好小组主席：曾当面驳斥热比娅, Huanqiuwang, 17 March 2014, <http://world.huanqiu.com/exclusive/2014-03/4909357.html?agt=622>; <https://tinyurl.com/selw4g3>.

54 'Ouzhou huiyi li de Zhongguo miankong' 欧洲议会里的中国面孔 [The Chinese face in the European Parliament], *CRI Online*, 19 October 2014, <https://web.archive.org/web/20191208205839/http://news.cri.cn/gb/42071/2014/10/19/6891s4732552.htm>. '最后，盖琳被聘为"议员顾问"，开始了他在欧洲议会的职业生涯。'

55 Zhang Jie, 'Ouzhou yihui yiyuan zhuli Gai Lin jiangshu ta de gongzuo gushi'.

56 Zhang Jie, 'Ouzhou yihui yiyuan zhuli Gai Lin jiangshu ta de gongzuo gushi'.

57 The ILD and the UFWD are listed on the Friendship Association's Chinese website as its 'partners', although this is not mentioned on its English site. The Friendship Association is officially separate from the less transparent Friendship Group but it is run by some of the same people, including Gai Lin, <https://web.archive.org/web/20180824075929/http://eu-cfa.com/lists/HZZZ-01.html>.

58 On Huawei, see Martin and Crawford, 'China's influence digs deep into Europe's political landscape'. On Xinjiang, see <https://www.youtube.com/watch?v=AdWGS-_UHM8>; Zhang Xiaofang, 'Ouzhou Huiyi Ou Zhong youhao xiaozu zhuxi'.

59 Zhang Xiaofang, 'Ouzhou Huiyi Ou Zhong youhao xiaozu'.

60 Yang Yi, 'Chinese NPC Tibetan delegation visits European Parliament', *Xinhua*, 12 December 2018.

61 Martin and Crawford, 'China's influence digs deep into Europe's political landscape'.

62 EU–China relations: <https://www.youtube.com/watch?v=IhLXWznZts4>; Trade with China: <https://www.youtube.com/watch?v=rTwvtA3ym_o>. In March 2019 Nirj Deva's organisation launched the Policy Coordination Committee of the Belt and Road Initiative in Europe, <https://tinyurl.com/yx4tgt25>.

63 New China TV (TV channel run by Xinhua News Agency), <https://www.youtube.com/watch?v=aaAW1RVE9mM>.

64 Martin and Crawford, 'China's influence digs deep into Europe's political landscape'.

65 'About', blog of EU-China Friendship Association, not dated, <https://web.archive.org/web/20191208215049/https://euchinafa.wordpress.com/about/>; Zhang Xiaofang, 'Ouzhou Huiyi Ou Zhong youhao xiaozu'.

66 Zhang Xiaofang, 'Ouzhou Huiyi Ou Zhong youhao xiaozu zhuxi'.

67 Derek Vaughan has had a number of roles in pro-Beijing groups, such as honorary president of the EU-China Joint Innovation Centre. 'Derek Vaughan zhuxi daibiao Oumeng Zhongguo lianhe chuangxin zhongxin wei 2019 Zhong Ou chengshi Keyan chuangxin chanye fazhan luntan kaimu zhici', Derek Vaughan主席代表欧盟中国联合创新中心为2019中欧城市科研创新产业发展论坛开幕致辞[Chairman Derek Vaughan gives opening speech on behalf of the EU-China Joint Innovation Center at the opening of the 2019 China-EU Urban Scientific Innovation Industry

Development Forum], website of EU-China Joint Innovation Center, 18 May 2019, <https://web.archive.org/web/20190827184202/http://cn.eucjic.org/index.php?id=81>.

68 Anon., 'Český europoslanec na Hedvábné stezce'. The Chinese report cited by *Sinopsis* can be found at <https://web.archive.org/web/20200104212113/http://www.zgqt.zj.cn/5337641.html>.

69 Lulu, 'Repurposing democracy'.

70 Lulu, 'Repurposing democracy', p. 13.

71 Screenshot of an email sent by Deva to prospective participants at the European Parliament. The committee is also referenced on the website of the Chinese Mission to the EU, <https://tinyurl.com/rsj6fd2>.

72 European Commission, 'Member States publish a report on EU coordinated risk assessment of 5G networks security', European Commission, 9 October 2019.

73 'A public debate: sustaining an open global digital ecosystem with Huawei: a European perspective', Huawei, 15 Otober 2019, <https://web.archive.org/web/20191016153007/https://huawei.eu/events/public-debate-huawei>.

74 In Belgium, the parliamentary group has facilitated trips to China for parliamentarians. 'Qian Hongshan meets with Belgian multi-party parliamentarian delegation', website of the ILD, 18 March 2019, <https://web.archive.org/web/20191208220359/http://www.idcpc.org.cn/english/news/201903/t20190322_99883.html>.

75 Alexei Chikhachev, 'From apprehensions to ambitions: the French approach to China', Russian International Affairs Council, 11 April 2019.

76 'About us', website of the All Party Parliamentary China Group, not dated, <https://web.archive.org/web/20191208220625/https://appcg.org.uk/about-us/>.

77 For members, see <https://www.the48groupclub.com/about-the-club/whos-who/>; for history, see <https://tinyurl.com/uu3wu4d>.

78 Ji Chaozhu 冀朝铸 was an interpreter for Mao Zedong, Zhou Enlai and Deng Xiaoping. He is the younger brother of Ji Chaoding, mentioned later. On Ji Chaozhu see: David Barboza, 'The Man on Mao's right, at the center of history', *The New York Times*, 17 February 2012; <http://www.chinese-embassy.org.uk/eng/ambassador/lrds/trans1/t229791.htm>; Geoffrey Fowler, 'Reunion in Beijing', *Harvard Magazine*, undated, <https://harvardmagazine.com/2000/01/reunion-in-beijing-html>.

79 <https://www.the48groupclub.com/about-the-club/>; Lord Davidson is represented on the board of CBBC by Katie Lee of Ensis Strategic.

80 Anon., 'Lord Mayor of London leads fintech delegation to China to promote trade and investment', press release, City of London Corporation, 18 March 2019.

81 'Belt and Road report: a guide to UK services (April 2019)', website of the China-Britain Business Council, <http://www.cbbc.org/

belt-and-road-publications-2019/>; <https://appcg.org.uk/about-us/>; CBBC still hosting meetings with the CCPIT: see 'Roundtable meeting with CCPIT Xiamen (London)', <http://www.cbbc.org/events/2019/july/roundtable-meeting-with-ccpit-xiamen-(london)/>.

82 'Xi reiterates China's commitment to free trade, globalization', *Xinhua*, 16 October 2018, <https://web.archive.org/save/http://www.xinhuanet.com/english/2018-10/16/c_137537109.htm>. See also An Baijie and Cao Desheng, '10 foreigners given medals for roles in reform, opening-up', *China Daily*, 19 December 2018.

83 Stephen Perry, 'China and the world', website of China Global Impact, 11 June 2019, <https://web.archive.org/web/20191208221526/https://chinaglobalimpact.com/2019/06/11/china-and-the-world-2/>; Stephen Perry, 'New China', website of China Global Impact, 30 May 2019, <https://web.archive.org/web/20191208221648/https://chinaglobalimpact.com/2019/05/30/new-china/>.

84 Stephen Perry, 'Stephen Perry, Chairman of the 48 Group Club, honoured as one of ten foreigners who have supported and helped China's reform and opening up over the past 40 years', website of China Global Impact, 24 December 2018, <https://tinyurl.com/tac8to6>.

85 <http://www.chinagoabroad.com/en/expert/dr-robert-lawrence-kuhn>; <https://en.wikipedia.org/wiki/Robert_Lawrence_Kuhn>. When in August 2019 Xinhua reported Robert Kuhn calling for the Hong Kong protests to be shut down, the Party newspaper described him as 'an American investment banker and author of a propaganda book eulogizing former Chinese Communist Party chair Jiang Zemin', <http://www.xinhuanet.com/world/2019-08/14/c_1124876756.htm>.

86 <https://chinaglobalimpact.com/>.

87 <https://chinaglobalimpact.com/>.

88 <https://www.youtube.com/watch?v=PJl507uI1Qw>.

89 The clues are all to be found in Tom Buchanan, *East Wind: China and the British left, 1925–1976*, Oxford: Oxford University Press, 2012, pp. 156–8. See also Wen-guang Shao, *China, Britain and Businessmen: Political and commercial relations, 1949–57*, Basingstoke: Macmillan, 1991, pp. 148–9.

90 From a detailed account, published by the *People's Daily*, of the establishment and early years of the CCPIT. 'Maoyi xian xing yi min cu guan—Zhou Enlai zhidao Maocuhui duiwai gongzuo de sixiang yu shijian' 贸易先行　以民促官—周恩来指导贸促会对外工作的思想和实践 [Trade advances first, using the people to push the officials—thought and practise of how Zhou Enlai guided the external work of CCPIT], *People's Daily Online*, not dated, <https://web.archive.org/web/20191208222236/http://www.people.com.cn/GB/shizheng/8198/9405/34150/2543935.html>.

91 <https://www.cia.gov/library/readingroom/docs/CIA-RDP78-00915R000600210003-9.pdf>, p. 63.

92 <https://www.cia.gov/library/readingroom/docs/CIA-RDP78-00915R000600210003-9.pdf> p. 63; 'Chi Cha'o-ting' and 'Nan Hanch'en' are listed as committee members. Ji Chaoding is the pinyin translation of Chi Cha'o-ting 冀朝鼎.

93 Nan Hanchen 南汉宸 (1895-1967). This account is drawn in part from Jiang Mengying 蒋梦莹, 'Huode guojia lingdaoren huijian, Yingguo 48 Jia jituan julebu you he lai tou' 获得国家领导人会见，英国48家集团俱乐部有何来头？ [What is the origin of the 48 Group Club that received a meeting with national leaders?], *The Paper*, 17 October 2018, <https://tinyurl.com/s4keutp>.

94 'Nan Hanchen', in Wolfgang Bartke, *Who Was Who in the People's Republic of China*, München: Saur, 1997, p. 347.

95 Joseph Needham quoted by Buchanan, *East Wind*, p. 96. See also this obituary in *The New York Times* on 10 August 1963: <https://tinyurl.com/yxwsky35>, p. 17.

96 Ch'en Li-fu, *The Storm Clouds Clear over China: The memoir of Ch'en Li-fu, 1900–1993*, Sidney Chang and Ramon Myers, eds, Stanford: Hoover Institution Press, 1994, pp. 181–2.

97 Peter Mattis and Matthew Brazil, *Chinese Communist Espionage: An intelligence primer*, Annapolis: Naval Institute Press, 2019.

98 Buchanan, *East Wind*, p. 155–7; <https://www.cia.gov/library/readingroom/docs/CIA-RDP78-00915R000600210003-9.pdf>, p. 63. In a now-declassified telegram of May 1952 to the British embassy in Paris concerning the Moscow conference, the Foreign Office wrote: 'We must be careful not to let Communist propaganda persuade people to think of economics apart from politics and so obscure the real reasons for the limitations upon East-West trade', telegram from UK Foreign Office Northern Department to Commercial Department, British embassy, Paris, 14 May 1952.

99 Buchanan, *East Wind*, pp. 156–7.

100 On Roland Berger, see <https://discovery.nationalarchives.gov.uk/details/r/C16282412>. On Bernard Buckman, see Alan Campbell and John Mcilroy, '"The Trojan Horse": Communist entrism in the British Labour Party, 1933–43', *Labor History*, March 2018. Berger's work for the BCPIT was 'deemed so sensitive by the [British] Communist Party that the career of his wife Nancy … was deliberately held back for fear of jeopardizing it'. Buchanan, *East Wind*, p. 156.

101 Ming Liu, 'Buckman collection in spotlight at London auction', *China Daily*, 14 November 2016. SOAS offers a Bernard Buckman Fellowship, <https://www.soas.ac.uk/registry/scholarships/bernard-buckman-scholarship.html>.

102 <https://hansard.parliament.uk/commons/1953-02-05/debates/c06a6587-b990-4157-a4ef-69ee2efbc909/CouncilForPromotionOfInternational Trade>.

103 Buchanan, *East Wind*, p. 157.

104 Dave Renton, *Fascism, Anti-Fascism and Britain in the 1940s*, Basingstoke: Macmillan, 2000, p. 96. Jack Perry, who was Jewish, had battled Mosley's Blackshirts in the East End in the 1930s and he remained an antifascist activist. When Perry died he was eulogised in the *China Daily*: Zhang Haizhou, 'Father-and-son team bridged Chinese business with West', *China Daily*, 3 December 2010.

105 See Anon., 'The rise & fall of Maoism: the English experience', p. 35, <https://www.marxists.org/history/erol/uk.firstwave/uk-maoism.pdf>; Buchanan, *East Wind*, p. 202.

106 <https://www.the48groupclub.com/about-the-club/>.

107 Jin Jing and Gu Zhenqiu, 'The "icebreaker" who helps bond China with West', *Xinhua*, 23 October 2018.

108 <http://en.ccpit.org/info/info_4028811760d8d5d401668610b98301d2.html>.

109 Stephen Perry, 'President Xi and Stephen Perry Meeting—Xi reiterates China's commitment to free trade, globalization', 22 October 2018, on Perry's blog <https://chinaglobalimpact.com/2018/10/22/president-xi-and-stephen-perry-meeting-xi-reiterates-chinas-commitment-to-free-trade-globalization/>.

110 Anon., 'Three generations of British family play important role in warming China-UK trade relations', *Global Times*, 20 October 2015.

111 <https://web.archive.org/web/20191020112028/http://europe.chinadaily.com.cn/epaper/2010-12/03/content_11993942.htm>.

112 <http://www.chinese-embassy.org.uk/eng/EmbassyNews/t1655714.htm>.

113 <https://web.archive.org/web/20191020113023/http://www.chinese-embassy.org.uk/eng/EmbassyNews/t1652772.htm>.

114 See, for example, Cecily Liu, 'New book explains role China is playing in global development', *China Daily*, 11 April 2018.

115 <https://www.amazon.com/Chinas-Role-Shared-Human-Future/dp/1910334340>.

116 Anon., '*China Daily* Global Edition wins admiration from across the world', *China Daily*, 11 January 2019.

117 <http://www.martinjacques.com/articles/no-time-for-wishful-thinking/>.

118 Interview with Martin Jacques, 'How to make sense of the Hong Kong protests?', *CGTN* online, 5 July 2019.

119 Ian McGregor organises visits by Chinese diplomats to The Telegraph Media Group's offices so that they may put their point of view: see for example <https://www.fmprc.gov.cn/ce/ceuk/eng/EmbassyNews/t1677779.htm>. At a meeting in January 2019 Ambassador Liu praised the *The Daily Telegraph* and *The Sunday Telegraph* for 'playing a positive role in enhancing the mutual understanding between China and western countries', and *The Sunday Telegraph*'s editor Allister Heath is reported to have replied that the two newspapers 'attach great importance to China-related reports and stay

committed to covering China's development comprehensively to contribute to the understanding and cooperation between China and the UK', <http://www.chinese-embassy.org.uk/eng/ambassador/dshd/t1633606.htm>. The Telegraph Group has struck a deal with Beijing according to which it receives £750,000 each year to publish in *The Daily Telegraph* paid propaganda inserts supplied by CCP news outlet *China Daily*. (Louisa Lim and Julia Bergin, 'Inside China's audacious global propaganda campaign', *The Guardian*, 7 December 2018.)

120 With thanks to Lucrezia Poggetti for helpful comments on this section.

121 Andre Tartar, Mira Rojanasakul and Jeremy Scott Diamond, 'How China is buying its way into Europe', *Bloomberg*, 23 April 2018.

122 Anon., 'China, Italy sign BRI MoU to advance connectivity', *China Daily*, 23 March 2019.

123 John Follain and Rosalind Mathieson, 'Italy pivots to China in blow to EU efforts to keep its distance', *Bloomberg*, 5 October 2018.

124 Follain and Mathieson, 'Italy pivots to China in blow to EU efforts to keep its distance'. Geraci's boss, minister of economic development and second deputy prime minister Luigi Di Maio, leads the Five Star Movement. He has been a firm supporter of closer ties with China. The BRI was opposed by the foreign minister, Enzo Moavero Milanesi, and his officials.

125 Stuart Lau, 'Italian PM Giuseppe Conte ignores US warnings and pushes for closer cooperation with China's belt and road plan', *South China Morning Post*, 12 March 2019.

126 Lau, 'Italian PM Giuseppe Conte ignores US warnings'.

127 Lucrezia Poggetti, 'Italy's BRI Blunder', *Project Syndicate*, 21 March 2019.

128 Philippe Le Corre wrote: 'There is a strong possibility that Southern Europe might become a zone of strong Chinese influence in the future. In an economically weakened region with rising anti-European sentiment, citizens might be looking at alternative options', <https://carnegieendowment.org/2018/10/30/this-is-china-s-plan-to-dominate-southern-europe-pub-77621>.

129 François Godement and Abigaël Vasselier, *China at the Gates: A new power audit of EU-China relations*, London: European Council on Foreign Relations, 2017, p. 112.

130 François Godement, 'Hand-outs and bail-outs: China's lobbyists in Italy', blog post, European Council on Foreign Relations, 12 October 2018.

131 Lucrezia Poggetti, 'Italy charts risky course with China-friendly policy', blog post, Mercator Institute of China Studies, 11 October 2018.

132 <https://data.consilium.europa.eu/doc/document/ST-6551-2019-ADD-2/en/pdf>.

133 Godement, 'Hand-outs and bail-outs'; Crispian Balmer, 'Italy's drive to join China's Belt and Road hits potholes', *Reuters*, 15 March 2019.

134 Giulia Pompili, 'Chi Mise la Cina al governo', *Il Foglio*, 7 March 2019.

135 Stuart Lau, 'The Sinophile driving Italy's hopes of a New Silk Road deal with China', *South China Morning Post*, 16 March 2019.

136 John Follain, 'Trump's Huawei threats dismissed in Italian pivot toward China', *Bloomberg*, 19 February 2109.

137 Pompili, 'Chi Mise la Cina al governo'.

138 <http://www.beppegrillo.it/la-cina-e-il-governo-del-cambiamento/>.

139 Editors, 'The Chinese panacea?', *Made in China*, 19 March 2019.

140 Not all China experts at the University of Nottingham are CCP sympathisers. Rian Thum, a senior research fellow, wrote in respect of the persecution of Uyghurs, 'Xi's Communist Party is an organization that's willing to go to greater extremes of repression than I think any outside observer expected', Peter Martin, 'Inside Xinjiang: a 10-day tour of China's most repressed state', *Bloomberg*, 25 January 2019.

141 <https://web.archive.org/web/20190620130525/http://www.globalthinktank.org.cn/Director/View.aspx?Id=4964>. See also Jonas Parello-Plesner, 'The Curious case of Mr. Wang and the United Front', blog post, Hoover Institute, 11 May 2018.

142 Lau, 'The Sinophile driving Italy's hopes of a New Silk Road deal with China'.

143 <https://tinyurl.com/rulzryq>; <https://www.linkedin.com/pulse/italy-china-link-ecco-come-porteremo-investimenti-cinesi-maria-moreni>.

144 Anon., 'Italy aims to develop closer trade ties with China through Belt and Road', *China Daily*, 16 May 2019.

145 <https://web.archive.org/web/20180819042607/http://agcci.com/trend/info/772?cid=19>; https://web.archive.org/web/20190406012753/http:/agcci.com/style/info/742>.

146 <https://web.archive.org/web/20170829042923/http://www.chinaqw.com/sqjg/2017/08-29/159363.shtml>.

147 Many overseas Chinese are concentrated in the industrial city of Prato, with a population of some 50,000 migrants from China, and many working in fast fashion factories. A delegation of senior united front officials visited in July 2019 to 'promote the unity of overseas Chinese', <http://italiapratohuashanghui.com/a/info/2019/0718/424.html>.

148 <https://tinyurl.com/tzxe4wl>.

149 <https://tinyurl.com/tzxe4wl>.

150 <https://web.archive.org/web/20180903040709/http://oborit.org/about-us.html>.

151 European Commission, *EU-China—A strategic outlook*, report, 12 March 2019, p. 1.

152 They can be found at <https://tinyurl.com/w22oe57> and <https://tinyurl.com/ur7bnkx>.

153 Stuart Lau, 'Italy may be ready to open up four ports to Chinese investment under "Belt and Road Initiative"', *South China Morning Post*, 19 March 2019.

154 <https://tinyurl.com/w22oe57>. Note also collaboration agreement between private media conglomerate Class Editori and China Media Group. Class Editori will jointly organise events with CMG and broadcast programs produced by it, <https://tinyurl.com/u4m6lde>.

155 The League is part of Bannon's coalition of European right-wing parties. Earlier in March 2019 Bannon met with leaders of the League party and warned against China's 'predatory capitalism', including the BRI. Jason Horowitz, 'Defying allies, Italy signs on to New Silk Road with China', *The New York Times*, 23 March 2019.

156 Elvira Pollina, 'Huawei to invest $3.1 billion in Italy but calls for fair policy on 5G: country CEO', *Reuters*, 15 July 2019.

157 Juan Pedro Tomás, 'Italy will not push emergency legislation on 5G "golden power": Report', *RCRWireless News*, 19 July 2019. However, PM Conte was reported to be cooling on the China relationship and making reassuring comments to Europe. Stuart Lau, 'Is Italy experiencing buyer's remorse after signing up to China's belt and road scheme?', *South China Morning Post*, 30 July 2019.

158 Anon., 'Cai Mingpo: the financier helping to build bridges between France and China', *Intelligence Online*, 20 May 2019.

159 Bezard's appointment to Cathay Capital attracted controversy because he had been a member of the supervisory committee of a state-owned financial institution involved in making a loan to the company. Laurent Mauduit, 'Direction du Trésor: le sulfureux pantouflage de Bruno Bézard', *Mediapart*, 25 May 2016.

160 Anon., 'Cai Mingpo'.

161 Anon., 'Cai Mingpo'.

162 Anon., 'Cai Mingpo'.

163 On united front ties, see 'Hubei Shengwei tongzhan fubuzhang Chen Changhong dao Changjiang Guoji Shanghui diaoyan' 湖北省委统战部副部长陈昌宏到长江国际商会调研 [Chen Changhong, vice head of the United Front Work Department of Hubei Provincial Committee, inspects the Yangtze River International Chamber of Commerce], *Sina*, 1 November 2019, <https://tinyurl.com/uqkjct6>. Also see their website <https://tinyurl.com/uortmoz>. Cai Mingpo is a friend of the renowned New York–based artist Cai Guo-Qiang, and bankrolled the French publication of the artist's book. Cai Guo-Qiang is close to Rupert Murdoch's former wife Wendi Deng, who is suspected by US intelligence—and by her former husband—of being a spy for the MSS. Graham Ruddick and Nicola Slawson, 'US officials "briefed Jared Kushner on concerns about Wendi Deng Murdoch"', *The Guardian*, 17 January 2018.

164 Anon., 'Cai Mingpo'.

165 Clive Hamilton, *Silent Invasion: China's influence in Australia*, Melbourne: Hardie Grant Books, 2018, p. 201.

166 <http://www.ceibs.edu/media/news/events-visits/14535>.

167 The Russian political scientist Alexei Chikhachev has written: 'Several former politicians of different affiliations, including former ministers, are now employed by Chinese companies, including Jean-Louis Borloo, who is with Huawei, and Bruno Le Roux, who is with CRRC. Both houses of the French parliament have France–China friendship groups ... However, the key vigilantes when it comes to China are not individual politicians, but some very reputable international experts. President of the French Institute of International Relations (IFRI) Thierry de Montbrial says that China is "playing the intra-European controversies," using a "quasi-imperial" strategy in its efforts to implement the Belt and Road Initiative and striving to become the leading world power in the next few decades ... France is extremely wary of potential Chinese espionage (including, but not limited to, industrial espionage).' Alexei Chikhachev, 'From apprehensions to ambitions: the French approach to China', Russian International Affairs Council, 11 April 2019. For CEIBS, see their website, where all three are listed as distinguished professors.

168 Steven Chase, 'New Chinese ambassador praises Canadian communist supporter Isabel Crook, jailed during Cultural Revolution', *The Globe and Mail*, 24 October 2019.

169 Anon., 'Xi confers highest state honors on individuals ahead of National Day', *Xinhua*, 29 September 2019.

170 Anon., 'France backs China on Taiwan', *Deutsche Welle*, 21 April 2005.

171 Pierre Tiessen and Régis Soubrouillard, *La France Made in China: la France peut-elle résister à la puissance chinoise?*, Paris: Michel Lafon, 2019; Philippe Grangereau, 'Le petit livre rouge de Raffarin', *Libération*, 27 October 2011.

172 Andrew Moody, 'Raffarin supports ideas of president', *China Daily*, 30 July 2018.

173 Philippe Branche, 'Comprendre La Chine: questions/réponses à Jean-Pierre Raffarin', *Forbes*, 19 June 2018.

174 'France's former prime minister Jean-Pierre Raffarin joins CEIBS', website of CEIBS, 23 February 2018, <https://tinyurl.com/uxot3vy>.

175 Anon., 'Cai Mingpo'.

176 Anon., 'Patrice Cristofini, fondateur du club Paris Shanghai: "rapprocher la France et la Chine va permettre d'apaiser les tentations protectionnistes"', *Opinion Internationale*, 13 June 2018.

177 On Raffarin's role in the France China Foundation, see Anon., 'China-France meeting of minds calls for continued globalization', *Chinawatch*, 19 October 2018; Bruna Bisini, 'Qui sont les relais de l'influence chinoise en France?', *Le Journal du Dimanche*, 30 October 2017. For the foundation's partnership with the CPIFA, see <https://tinyurl.com/s4rlf4b>. Raffarin is also the chairman of Fondation Prospective et Innovation, responsible for a stream of pro-Beijing books and commentary, along with various seminars

and workshops promoting the BRI. A *China Daily* report on a 2018 'Young Leaders Program' tour organised by the France China Foundation and CPIFA, although painful to read, shows how easy it is for the CCP's united front operations to draw 'young leaders' into the Party's worldview, with French young leaders gushing about 'people-to-people exchanges' and a 'community of shared values'.

178 Diamond and Schell, eds, *China's Influence & American Interests*, p. 12. See also Robert Fife, Steven Chase and Xiao Xu, 'Beijing foots bill for Canadian senators, MPs to visit China', *The Globe and Mail*, 1 December 2017; Andrew Tillett, 'The new diplomatic dance with Beijing', *Australian Financial Review*, 4 November 2018. The twitter hashtag #cpifa provides a useful insight into the CPIFA's global influence operations: see <https://twitter.com/hashtag/CPIFA?src=hashtag_click>.

179 See 'Partners', website of the France China Foundation, capture from 26 January 2018, <https://tinyurl.com/wseqw28>.

180 'Strategic Committee', website of the France China Foundation, undated, <https://tinyurl.com/up8xvwo>.

181 Anon., 'In wolves' clothing', *The Economist*, 12 February 2015.

182 On CITIC's PLA links, see elsewhere in this book via the index. On Everbright's PLA link, see U.S-China Security Review Commission, documentary annex to 'Report to Congress of the U.S.-China Security Review', Washington D.C., July 2002, p. 26.

183 Véroniques Groussa, 'Emmanuel Macron, membre du club des Young Leaders China', *Le Nouvel Observateur*, 4 August 2018.

184 CPIFA also sponsors a Young Leaders Program in Australia, <https://twitter.com/EichtingerM/status/983464348671758336>.

185 <https://tinyurl.com/wa8by6z>. Financial supporters include retail giant Carrefour, high-end jeweller Chaumet, and restauranteur Alain Ducasse Group.

186 Diamond and Schell, eds, *China's Influence & American Interests*, p. 14.

187 The founder of the organisation is said to be Chinese-French businessman Hua Bin (华宾, French name Gérard Houa), <https://tinyurl.com/wa8by6z>. Hua is a business partner of HNA Group. Anon., 'Aigle Azur: l'actionnaire à l'origine du coup de force se dit soutenu par les deux autres', *Le Figaro*, 1 September 2019.

188 One of the five honorary members is France's former ambassador to China, distinguished diplomat Jean-Pierre Lafon, <http://fondation-france-chine.com/?page_id=112>. (Directeur du Centre de R&D du Conseil des Affaires d'Etat.)

189 <https://tinyurl.com/wa8by6z>. To further complicate matters, in 2011 Cathay Capital founded a third foundation with a very similar name, the France Chine Entreprendre Fondation. It is chaired by Sciences Po journalism professor, and brother of Cathay Capital's co-founder Edouard

Moinet, Paul-Henri Moinet. Paul-Henri Moinet is also the editor of a French website named *Sinocle* that promotes closer Sino-French connectivity and aims to 'remove the ignorance, prejudice and ideology that distort Europe's view of China'. *Sinocle* publishes endless puff pieces about the wonders of the BRI, often quoting experts from the Peterson Institute for International Economics. Its principal purpose seems to be to promote the New Silk Road, <http://*sinocle*.info/en/2019/01/23/>.

190 Johnny Ehrling, 'China trauert um den "alten Freund" Helmut Schmidt', *Die Welt*, 11 November 2015.

191 Anon., 'Helmut Schmidt: "Wir sehen China ganz falsch"', *Westdeutsche Zeitung*, 13 April 2008.

192 Helmut Schmidt, *Nachbar China: Helmut Schmidt im Gespräch mit Frank Sieren*, Berlin: Ullstein, 2006.

193 Anon., 'Altkanzler Schmidt verteidigt Tian'anmen-Massaker', *Welt*, 13 September 2012.

194 Helmut Schmidt, 'Xi Jinping: the governance of China book review', State Council Information Office, 25 April 2017.

195 Anon., 'Fuß gefaßt', *Der Spiegel*, 11 June 1984.

196 Sabine Pamperrien, 'Die China-Versteher und ihre demokratischen Freunde', *Deutschlandfunk*, 3 October 2013.

197 David Charter, 'Angela Merkel benefits as Gerhard Schröder joins Rosneft board', *The Times*, 17 August 2017.

198 Andreas Lorenz, 'Hugging the panda: Gerhard Schröder opens doors for German companies in China', *Der Spiegel*, 6 November 2009.

199 Nina Trentmann, 'Ex-Politiker als gut bezahlte Türöffner nach China', *Die Welt*, 12 April 2012.

200 Lorenz, 'Hugging the panda'.

201 Anon., 'Keine bohrenden Nachfragen', *Deutsche Welle*, 8 April 2002.

202 Anon., 'Schröder calls for end to arms embargo against China', *Deutsche Welle*, 2 December 2003.

203 Lorenz, 'Hugging the panda'.

204 Trentmann, 'Ex-Politiker als gut bezahlte Türöffner nach China'; Lorenz, 'Hugging the panda'.

205 Matthias Kamp, 'Altkanzler Schröder verteidigt Seidenstraßen-Initiative', *Wiwo*, 26 November 2018.

206 Anon., 'Hamburger China-Konferenz mit Steinmeier und Ex-Kanzler Schröder', *Business Insider*, 20 November 2016.

207 'Die Laudatio der Verleihung des "China-Europe Friendship Awards" 2016 an Gerhard Schröder', Gesellschaft für Deutsch-Chinesische Verständigung e.V., 30 March 2017.

208 Kamp, 'Altkanzler Schröder verteidigt Seidenstraßen-Initiative'.

209 Anon., 'Scharping: Sachsen müssen in China ihre Nischen suchen', *RND*, 27 November 2017.

210 Trentmann, 'Ex-Politiker als gut bezahlte Türöffner'.

211 Anon., 'Ludaofu Shaerping—Deguo zhengzhijia, Zhong De hezuo jiaolicu tuidongzhe' 鲁道夫·沙尔平—德国政治家、中德合作交流推动者 [Rudolf Scharping—German politician and promoter of Sino-German cooperation and exchange], *Sohu*, 27 January 2018, <https://www.*sohu*.com/a/219447838_99901145>; Zhu Dianyong 朱殿勇: 'Wang Guosheng huijian Ludaofu Shaerping' 王国生会见鲁道夫·沙尔平 [Wang Guosheng meets Rudolf Scharping], *Henan ribao*, 29 September 2018, <https://baijiahao.baidu.com/s?id=1612940937639689321&wfr=spider&for=pc>.

212 For example, 'One Belt, One Road: die Neue Seidenstrasse', <https://www.bhv-bremen.de/tiding/one-belt-one-road-die-neue-seidenstrasse/>.

213 'Chinas neue Rolle in der *Welt*—die "Road and Belt" Initiative', 11 July 2018, <https://www.spdhessensued.de/2018/07/11/chinas-neue-rolle-in-der-welt-die-road-and-belt-initiative/>.

214 'Introduction to China Economic Cooperation Center', CECC, 6 June 2014, <http://en.cecc.net.cn/Detail.aspx?newsId=1026&TId=44>.

215 See the programs at <https://bri-rsbk.de/de/>.

216 Cathrin Shaer, 'Huawei can work on German 5G networks: here's why critics say that's a very bad idea', ZDNet, 16 October 2019.

217 Matthew Miller, 'China's HNA charity turns to former German official for leadership', *Reuters*, 14 December 2017; Anon., 'Who owns HNA, China's most aggressive dealmaker?', *Financial Times*, 2 June 2017. 'Hainan Cihang said it planned to contribute up to $200 million toward charitable undertakings over the next five years, including $30 million in pledges to Harvard University, the Massachusetts Institute of Technology and Calvary Hospital in New York.'

218 Anon., 'Zeichen gegen US-Eskalation setzen—Rüstungsexporte für Taiwan stoppen', *Die Linke*, 21 August 2019.

219 Anon., 'Trumps Treibjagd nicht unterstützen', *Die Linke*, 11 December 2018.

220 Anon., 'Was ist für Dich links, Norbert?', *Die Linke*, 9 July 2019.

221 'Besorgt über die Lage religiöser Minderheiten in China', *Bundestag*, 8 May 2019, <https://www.bundestag.de/dokumente/textarchiv/2019/kw19-pa-menschenrechte-634964>.

222 Andreas Rinke, 'Annäherung statt Abgrenzung—Neues Netzwerk China-Brücke', *Reuters*, 15 January 2020. See also Torsten Rieke, 'CSU-Politiker Hans-Peter Friedrich schlägt Brücke zu China', *Handelsblatt*, 15 January 2020.

223 Lyndon LaRouche is said to be the author of 'the most baroque conspiracy theories ever put into circulation'. Scott McLemee, 'The LaRouche Youth Movement', *Inside Higher Ed*, 1 July 2007.

224 Anon., 'Foreign experts applaud China's development concepts', CCTV Plus, 16 March 2019; Chen Weihua, 'Identifying with China', *China Daily*, 18 August 2017.

225 Bethany Allen-Ebrahimina, 'Lyndon LaRouche is running a pro-China party in Germany', *Foreign Policy*, 18 September 2017.

226 'Movisol conference on BRI in Milan', <https://tinyurl.com/uo8xxvp>; Anon., 'Michele Geraci, from professor to Belt and Road player', *Belt & Road News*, 18 April 2019; Stuart Lau, 'The Sinophile driving Italy's hopes of a New Silk Road deal with China', *South China Morning Post*, 16 March 2019.

227 'Ambassador Gui Congyou meets with head of the Schiller Institute in Sweden', Chinese embassy in Sweden, 26 July 2018, <http://www.chinaembassy.se/eng/sgxw/t1580316.htm>.

228 'About us', <http://brixsweden.com/what-is-the-brix/?lang=en>.

Chapter 5 Political elites on the periphery

1 Jichang Lulu, 'Confined discourse management and localised interactions in the Nordics', *Sinopsis*, 22 October 2018. See also Jichang Lulu's revealing Twitter thread, <https://twitter.com/jichanglulu/status/1059542849291726850>.

2 Anon., 'Prime Minister Scott Morrison, Victorian Premier Daniel Andrews clash over China deal', *ABC News* online, 7 November 2018.

3 Gay Alcorn, 'Victorian opposition will make Belt and Road deal with China public if elected', *The Guardian*, 7 November 2018.

4 Nanette Asimov and Rachel Swan, 'Amid protests, SF board names Chinatown subway station after Rose Pak', *San Francisco Chronicle*, 21 August 2019; Mark Eades, 'Beijing-by-the-Bay: China's hidden influence in San Francisco', Foreign Policy Association, 9 June 2016.

5 Asimov and Swan, 'Amid protests, SF board names Chinatown subway station after Rose Pak'.

6 Asimov and Swan, 'Amid protests, SF board names Chinatown subway station after Rose Pak'.

7 Lulu, 'Confined discourse management'.

8 <https://twitter.com/XHNews/status/1163352605420130310>. See also the follow-up Xinhua story: Anon., 'U.S. state, local officials still eye China opportunities despite trade tensions', *Xinhua*, 17 August 2019.

9 <https://twitter.com/XHNews/status/1163352605420130310>.

10 Phila Siu, 'US-China trade war may cut Los Angeles' economic growth to zero, mayor Eric Garcetti warns during Hong Kong trip', *South China Morning Post*, 1 August 2018.

11 <https://twitter.com/XHNews/status/1163352605420130310>.

12 May Zhou, 'Ex-Missouri governor: American heartland seeks China relations', *China Daily*, 15 February 2019. Holden endorsed the efficacy of the CCP's tactic of 'use the countryside to surround the city' when he told *China Daily*: 'We are working with cities and states to have them actively involved in this. I believe that the real changes come from the bottom up, not top down. After

all, all politics are local.' Kong Wenzheng, 'Ex-governor is working to connect US heartland, China', *China Daily*, 7 August 2019.

13 Zhou, 'Ex-Missouri governor'.

14 <https://usheartlandchina.org/about>.

15 Tung is vice-chairman of the CPPCC. Jeffie Lam and Peace Chiu, 'Former Hong Kong leader Tung Chee-hwa blames liberal studies at secondary schools for encouraging violent protests among young people', *South China Morning Post*, 3 July 2019.

16 <https://drive.google.com/file/d/1vwkDkznV3dInH8ULSOdGBickOMpWW3xF/view>.

17 <https://efile.fara.gov/ords/f?p=181:130:6416909505612::NO::P130_CNTRY:CH>; Elizabeth Redden, 'Thanks, but no, thanks: UT Austin says it will not accept funding from a foundation', *Inside Higher Ed*, 16 January 2018. CUSEF's 'special representative is Fred Teng, also the president of the America China Public Affairs Institute (ACPAI), whose explicit aim is to establish good relations with individual governors of states so as to encourage all 50 of them to promote good bilateral trade ties with China. 'America China Public Affairs Institute', Chinese language self-introduction, <https://tinyurl.com/rybn978>. This statement is only on the Chinese-language version of the website. Teng is also a council member of the United Front–linked think tank the Centre for China and Globalization, <https://tinyurl.com/sbg84zy>, and was honoured to be one of only 35 overseas members to attend the CPPCC meeting in 2018, <https://tinyurl.com/vvwnqy6>.

18 Anne-Marie Brady, '*Magic weapons: China's political influence activities under Xi Jinping*', Wilson Center, September 2017.

19 Jichang Lulu, 'Repurposing democracy: the European Parliament China friendship cluster', *Sinopsis*, 29 November 2019.

20 Anne-Marie Brady describes how various mayors in New Zealand were co-opted by the CPAFFC. See her *Magic Weapons*, pp. 33–4.

21 Brady, *Magic Weapons*, p. 34.

22 See <https://tinyurl.com/um34hkm> where it says it organises educational tours of China in conjunction with the CPAFFC. See also May Zhou, 'Bilateral relationship's benefits celebrated in Houston', *China Daily*, 29 October 2018.

23 <http://mnchinagarden.org/board-members/>. In 2018 the Houston chapter of the USCPFA hosted a gala event at which Ed Gonzales, the sheriff of Harris County, which takes in Houston, was made a Friendship Ambassador by the CPAFFC. Gonzales heads the third-largest police force in the United States and was a prominent member of the Houston City Council.

24 <https://www.cgccusa.org/en/us-china-governors-collab-summit/>.

25 John Dotson, 'China explores economic outreach to U.S. states via united front entities', blog post, *Jamestown Foundation*, 26 June 2019.

26 Quoted in Dotson, 'China explores economic outreach to U.S. states via united front entities'.

27 Owen Churchill and John Power, 'For US and Chinese regional officials, economic summit was a chance to heal frayed ties. For the White House, it rang alarm bells', *South China Morning Post*, 9 August 2019.
28 Anon., 'U.S. state, local officials still eye China opportunities despite trade tensions', *Xinhua*, 17 August 2019.
29 Anon., 'U.S. state, local officials still eye China opportunities despite trade tensions'.
30 Dotson, 'China explores economic outreach to U.S. states via united front entities'.
31 Churchill and Power, 'For US and Chinese regional officials, economic summit was a chance to heal frayed ties'.
32 Quoted by Bill Bishop, *Sinocism Newsletter*, 30 July 2019. Original article: Huang Renwei 黄仁伟, 'Zhong Mei jinru zhanlüe xiangchi jieduan, jiang chong su daguo pingheng'中美进入战略相持阶段，将重塑大国平衡 [China and the United States enter a strategic stalemate phase which will reshape the balance of powers], *Guancha*, 1 March 2019.
33 Kong Wenzheng and May Zhou, 'China, US city leaders gather', *China Daily*, 18 July 2019.
34 Wenzheng and Zhou, 'China, US city leaders gather'.
35 Kyle Munson, 'Glad in Muscatine: what one Chinese businessman and his millions mean to this Iowa river town', *Des Moines Register*, 1 March 2018.
36 Kyle Munson, 'The rise of the "Iowa mafia" in China, from a governor to Xi's "old friends"', *Des Moines Register*, 9 November 2017.
37 Munson, 'The rise of the "Iowa mafia" in China, from a governor to Xi's "old friends"'.
38 The CPAFFC sponsored the China International Friendship Cities Association in 1992, a national civil organisation of the People's Republic of China with the status of a legal person, <https://tinyurl.com/wx2w33e>. See the section headed 'sister cities seeking', <https://tinyurl.com/yx5zwtej>.
39 Mike Ferguson, 'Muscatine woman a friend of China', *Globe Gazette*, 21 October 2013. Gary Dvorchak, who as a teenager in 1985 gave up his bedroom for the visiting Xi to sleep in, was one of only twelve foreigners invited to the grand military parade in Beijing to celebrate the seventieth anniversary of the founding of the PRC. Cate Cadell, 'A dozen hand-picked foreigners join China's parade of soldiers and tanks', *Reuters*, 1 October 2019.
40 Rusty Schrader, 'Lande resigns as director of Iowa Department of Natural Resources', *Muscatine Gazette*, 25 May 2012.
41 Cynthia Beaudette, 'Water under the bridge: Chinese students visit Muscatine and put their finger on the pulse of one of America's main arteries', *Muscatine Gazette*, 23 July 2012.
42 Beimeng Fu, 'A Chinese businessman wants to turn a small Iowa town into the Midwest's China hub', *Buzzfeed News*, 3 January 2017.
43 Brady, *Magic Weapons*, p. 34.

44 Melissa Nightingale, '$100k banquet in Wellington for Chinese Mayoral Form', *New Zealand Herald*, 5 April 2018.
45 Jeremy Nuttall, 'Chinese government woos local politicians with UBCM event', *The Tyee*, 13 September 2017.
46 Observation to author.
47 Renee Bernard, 'Delta mayor to boycott reception hosted by Chinese government', *Citynews*, 28 June 2019.
48 Anon., 'Carried away by communism', *The Globe and Mail*, 14 September 2010.
49 <https://tinyurl.com/uvxxkpc>.
50 <https://www.youtube.com/watch?v=xR9287AdGV4>.
51 Anon., 'Nanjing Massacre Victims Monument launched in Canada', *Xinhua*, 10 December 2018.
52 <https://tinyurl.com/rwxzymz>.
53 Paul Robinson and Emilia Terzon, 'Taiwan flag design painted over by council ahead of beef industry event', *ABC News* online, 9 May 2018.
54 Didi Kirsten Tatlow, 'Mapping China-in-Germany', *Sinopsis*, 2 October 2019.
55 Tatlow, 'Mapping China-in-Germany'.
56 <https://www.dcw-ev.de/de/partner/ccpit.html>. The United Front links of the CCPIT are especially conspicuous in New Zealand, <https://tinyurl.com/qlpffrl>.
57 Tatlow, 'Mapping China-in-Germany'.
58 Tatlow, 'Mapping China-in-Germany'.
59 Tatlow, 'Mapping China-in-Germany'. The agreement is available at <https://tinyurl.com/ro84czp>.
60 'One Belt One Road Forum 14.5.2017', <https://tinyurl.com/rugjfwb>.
61 According to this 2019 post on the Chinese embassy website, <https://tinyurl.com/we39krd>, Pflug was also a former chair of the German-Chinese Parliamentary Group of the Bundestag. On China Bridge, see Andreas Rinke, 'Annäherung statt Abgrenzung—Neues Netzwerk China-Brücke', *Reuters*, 15 January 2020.
62 'Johannes Pflug wird China-Beauftragter der Stadt', 22 April 2016, <https://tinyurl.com/uf8zev2>.
63 'One Belt One Road—Die neue Seidenstraße', Rheinmaintv, 29 March 2018, <https://www.youtube.com/watch?v=z6Cg_LMrlas>; Jeffrey Möller, 'Johannes Pflug: China hat mich frühzeitig eingenommen', Renminwang, 28 June 2018, <https://tinyurl.com/u58owqp>.
64 'CBND-China Business Network Duisburg', <http://www.cbnd.de/de/ueber-uns>.
65 'Chinesische Unternehmen setzen weiter auf Nordrhein-Westfalen und Düsseldorf', Chinese General Consulate in Düsseldorf, 18 January 2019, <http://dusseldorf.china-consulate.org/det/xwdt_6/t1630608.htm>.
66 Annika Schulz, 'Huawei soll Duisburg digitalisieren', *Tagesspiegl*, 6 December 2018.

67 'Huawei vertieft Kooperation mit Duisburg, um den deutschen Industriestandort in eine neue Smart City zu verwandeln', *Presseportal*, 3 September 2018, <https://www.presseportal.de/pm/100745/4051263>. Both Link and Pflug were interviewed in the March 2019 edition of the journal of the Chinese Industry and Trade Association in Germany. See <https://www.cihd.de/de/leistungen/download/Magazin39-D.PDF>.

68 Anon., 'Was vom Tage übrig blieb: Huawei mauschelt mit Duisburg und Cambridge Analytica rettet sich in die Pleite', *Netzpolitik*, 18 April 2019.

69 Anon., 'Chinese Chamber of Commerce opens office in Hamburg', *Hamburg News*, 20 March 2017.

70 '40 Jahre Öffnungspolitik in China: Präsidentin Veit lobt Beziehungen zur Volksrepublik', website of the Chinese consulate in Hamburg, 29 January 2019, <https://tinyurl.com/v2ovou8>.

71 'Chinesischer Vize-Ministerpräsident Liu He im Rathaus—Chancen für Hamburg durch "Neue Seidenstraße" von Asien nach Europa', website of the Chinese consulate in Hamburg, 27 November 2018, <http://hamburg.china-consulate.org/det/lgxwldhd/t1632457.htm>.

72 At least this is what the report written by the Chinese consulate that stands online, unchallenged, claims, <https://tinyurl.com/yxy5z2o3>.

73 Lulu, 'Repurposing democracy', p. 21–2. See also Olga Lomová, Jichang Lulu and Martin Hala, 'Bilateral dialogue with the PRC at both ends: Czech-Chinese "friendship" extends to social credit', *Sinopsis*, 28 July 2019.

74 In Prague, for example. See Manuel Eckert and Richard Turcsányi, 'Prague vs. Beijing: estranged sister cities', *The Diplomat*, 8 October 2019.

75 Brady, *Magic Weapons*.

76 Diamond and Schell, eds, *China's Influence & American Interests*, pp. 20–1.

77 <https://en.wikipedia.org/wiki/List_of_federal_installations_in_Maryland>.

78 In 1999, after complaints from Chinese diplomats, the governor of Maryland rescinded a proclamation honouring Li Hongzhi, exiled leader of Falun Gong. See Steven Mufson, 'Falun Gong honors rescinded', *The Washington Post*, 11 December 1999. The mayors of Seattle, Baltimore and San Francisco followed suit. For USA-China Sister School Association, see <https://montgomerycountymd.galaxydigital.com/agency/detail/?agency_id=76841#toggle-sidebar>. Rockville, Maryland has a sister-city relationship with Yilan city in Taiwan, <http://www.rockvillesistercities.org/wp/>.

79 Len Lazarick, 'Chinese sister state promoting more trade with Maryland', *Maryland Reporter*, undated.

80 Lazarick, 'Chinese sister state promoting more trade with Maryland'.

81 <https://globalmaryland.umd.edu/offices/confucius-institute-maryland/frequently-asked-questions>. For competing views on UM's Confucius Institute, see Don Lee, 'Confucius Institutes: do they improve U.S.-China ties or harbor spies?', *Los Angeles Times*, 23 January 2019.

82 Bethany Allen-Ebrahimian, 'China's long arm reaches into American campuses', *Foreign Policy*, 7 March 2018.
83 Simon Denyer and Congcong Zhang, 'A Chinese student praises the fresh air of free speech at a U.S. college, then came the backlash', *The Washington Post*, 23 May 2017.
84 <https://www.umdrightnow.umd.edu/news/university-statement-regarding-2017-student-commencement-speaker>.
85 Elizabeth Redden, '"A flood to a trickle"? Pence on Maryland's China Programs', *Inside Higher Ed*, 8 October 2018. Student enrolments from China have grown rapidly in recent years, reaching 2511 in 2017, making up 48 per cent of all international students and 6.2 per cent of the total student body, <https://tinyurl.com/ro5n4le>.
86 Although not named, the case of Columbia is discussed in Section 2 of Diamond and Schell, eds, *China's Influence & American Interests*.
87 <https://tinyurl.com/r3eb7ow>.
88 <https://www.sohu.com/a/212396602_246081>; <https://tinyurl.com/vqfmo5r>.
89 <https://tinyurl.com/sw7qe29>.
90 <https://tinyurl.com/r3eb7ow>.
91 Janene Holzberg, 'Columbia poised to add China's Liyang as sister city', *Baltimore Sun*, 15 June 2018.
92 <https://tinyurl.com/vqfmo5r>. Ms Han (韩军) has a number of united front links. She is vice chair of the Chinese Alumni Associations of Greater Washington (2018 to 2020), <https://web.archive.org/web/20180902104155/http://caagw.org/node/227>, which is active in talent transfer, <https://tinyurl.com/ufgobj3>. She is also deputy secretary general of the Coordination Council of Chinese America Associations, <http://archive.today/2019.10.23-094929/http://www.chinaqw.com/hqhr/hd2011/2016/11-09/1132.shtml>, which is active in *huaren canzheng* events. (<https://tinyurl.com/t8l4vru>; <https://tinyurl.com/v7yo9lp>)
93 <http://archive.today/upzHG>. In January 2018 Sun Diantao, ACM's editor-in-chief, was elected deputy secretary general of the National Association for China's Peaceful Unification in Washington D.C., a leading United Front group, <http://archive.today/CauBc>; <http://archive.today/YQP6H>. Sun was president of the Hebei Association of Greater Washington. ACM's president, Wei Dahang, used to work for CCTV as editor/producer: see <http://archive.today/EwV9k>.
94 <https://tinyurl.com/rejmmex>.
95 <https://web.archive.org/web/20190311223717/https://chaowu.org/meet-chao-wu/>.
96 Information provided by Chinese-American residents of Maryland.

97 He Xiaohui 何晓慧, <https://tinyurl.com/so8sppc>. See also Bethany Allen-Ebrahimian, 'China built an army of influence agents in the U.S.', *Daily Beast*, 18 July 2018.

98 <https://tinyurl.com/y5yhs9ky>.

99 Allen-Ebrahimian writes: 'Lily Qi, a current Democratic nominee for Maryland state delegate, described He as "one of those great connectors to pay attention to local level"'. (Allen-Ebrahimian, 'China built an army of influence agents in the U.S.')

100 See this article on the CCPPNR website: <https://tinyurl.com/so8sppc>.

101 Manuel Eckert and Richard Turcsanyi, 'Prague vs. Beijing: estranged sister cities', *The Diplomat*, 8 October 2019; Stuart Lau, 'Prague cuts sister-city ties with Beijing amid "tangible anger" over pro-China policies', *South China Morning Post*, 8 October 2019; Lenka Ponikelska, 'Beijing takes aim at Prague after "One-China" dispute deepens', *Bloomberg*, 9 October 2019.

102 Holmes Chan, 'Prague ditches Beijing for Taipei in new sister city deal', *Hong Kong Free Press*, 5 December 2019.

Chapter 6 The Party-corporate conglomerate

1 Bonnie Girard, 'The real danger of China's national intelligence law', *The Diplomat*, 23 Febraury 2019.

2 George C. Chen, 'Le droit, c'est moi: Xi Jinping's new rule-by-law approach', Oxford Human Rights Hub, 26 July 2017.

3 Jennifer Duggan, 'China targets lawyers in new human rights crackdown', *The Guardian*, 13 July 2015.

4 Anon., 'Xi stresses CPC leadership of state-owned enterprises', *China Daily*, 12 October 2016.

5 Zhang Lin, 'Chinese Communist Party needs to curtail its presence in private businesses', *South China Morning Post*, 26 November 2018; 'China says foreign firms welcome benefits from internal Communist Party cells', *Reuters*, 19 October 2017. Technically, Party cells have long been mandated in private enterprises under Chinese law, but this has been enforced much more tightly since ca. 2017.

6 In 2016 the respected Caixin finance news group reported on the 'growing number of Chinese state-owned enterprises that are merging the two roles' of chairman and Party secretary. Lu Bingyang and Teng Jing Xuan, 'Train manufacturer merges jobs of chairman, party secretary', *Caixin*, 28 November 2016.

7 Wang Jiamei and Huang Ge, 'SOEs to unify Party, board chairman posts', *Global Times*, 18 December 2016. See also Bingyang and Jing Xuan, 'Train manufacturer merges jobs of chairman, party secretary'.

8 Patricia Adversario, 'China's Communist party writes itself into company law', *Financial Times*, 14 August 2017.

9 Alexandra Stevenson, 'China's Communists rewrite the rules for foreign businesses', *The New York Times*, 13 April 2018.

10 Yi-Zheng Lian, 'China, the party-corporate complex', *The New York Times*, 12 February 2017.

11 John Garnaut, 'Chinese leader's family worth a billion', *The Sydney Morning Herald*, 30 June 2012; Anon., 'Panama Papers: family of China's President Xi implicated', *Straits Times*, 4 April 2016.

12 David Barboza and Michael Forsythe, 'Behind the rise of China's HNA: the chairman's brother', *The New York Times*, 27 March 2018.

13 Ting Chen and James Kai-sing Kung, 'Busting the "Princelings": the campaign against corruption in China's primary land market', *The Quarterly Journal of Economics*, vol. 134, no. 1, February 2019, pp. 185–226.

14 Minxin Pei, *China's Crony Capitalism: The dynamics of regime decay*, Cambridge, Mass.: Harvard University Press, 2016.

15 Chua Kong Ho, 'Huawei founder Ren Zhengfei on why he joined China's Communist Party and the People's Liberation Army', *South China Morning Post*, 16 January 2016.

16 While this claim has been challenged by Huawei in a legal deposition, Samantha Hoffmann and Elsa Kania have pointed out that the requirement to assist in intelligence work is consistent across several laws. See Samantha Hoffmann and Elsa Kania, 'Huawei and the ambiguity of China's intelligence and counter-espionage laws', *ASPI Strategist*, 12 September 2018.

17 Lin, 'Chinese Communist Party needs to curtail its presence in private businesses'.

18 Lin, 'Chinese Communist Party needs to curtail its presence in private businesses'.

19 Gwynne Guilford, 'Jack Ma: mowing down demonstrators in Tiananmen Square was the "correct decision"', *Quartz*, 17 July 2013. On Jack Ma's wealth, see <https://www.*forbes*.com/profile/jack-ma/#58d5da4f1ee4>.

20 Josh Horwitz, 'China's annual Communist Party shindig is welcoming a handful of new tech tycoons', *Quartz*, 5 March 2018.

21 Arjun Kharpal, 'Alibaba's Jack Ma has been a Communist Party member since the 1980s', *CNBC* online, 27 November 2018.

22 Horwitz, 'China's annual Communist Party shindig is welcoming a handful of new tech tycoons'.

23 Quoted by Elsa Kania, 'Much ado about Huawei (part 2)', *ASPI Strategist*, 28 Mar 2018.

24 Greg Levesque, 'China's evolving economic statecraft', *The Diplomat*, 12 April 2017.

25 Anon., 'Civil-military fusion: the missing link between China's technological and military rise', Council on Foreign Relations, blog post, 29 January 2018.

26 Doug Palmer, 'Navarro tells Wall Street "globalist billionaires" to end "shuttle diplomacy" in U.S.-China trade war', *Politico*, 9 November 2018. See also <https://www.youtube.com/watch?v=PROpS3U_FIY>.

27 Alexandra Stevenson, Kate Kelly and Keith Bradsher, 'As Trump's trade war mounts, China's Wall St allies lose clout', *The New York Times*, 16 September 2018.

28 Joseph Kahn, 'China leader concentrates on capitalism in New York', *The New York Times*, 14 April 1999.

29 Stevenson, Kelly and Bradsher, 'As Trump's trade war mounts, China's Wall St allies lose clout'.

30 Kahn, 'China leader concentrates on capitalism in New York'.

31 Stevenson, Kelly and Bradsher, 'As trade war rages, China's sway over the U.S. fades'.

32 Josh Rogin, 'China's infiltration of U.S. capital markets is a national security concern', *The Washington Post*, 13 June 2019.

33 On the influence of Goldman Sachs in the Obama White House, see Michael Sainato, 'Trump continues White House's Goldman Sachs revolving door tradition', *The Hill*, 12 December 2016.

34 Stevenson, Kelly and Bradsher, 'As Trump's trade war mounts, China's Wall St allies lose clout'.

35 Personal communication, April 2019.

36 William Stanton, 'Another PRC sharp power: foreign "friends"', *Global Taiwan Brief*, vol. 3, no. 24, 12 December 2018.

37 Paul Blustein, 'The untold story of how George W. Bush lost China', *Foreign Policy*, 2 October 2019.

38 Blustein, 'The untold story of how George W. Bush lost China'.

39 'Professor John L. Thornton honored with Friendship Award', Tsinghua SEM, 13 October 2008, <https://web.archive.org/web/20190824184433/http://cms.sem.tsinghua.edu.cn/semcms/News1/36101.htm?tempContent=full>.

40 Yun Li, 'Larry Fink just revealed how BlackRock is going to keep growing at its torrid pace: China', *CNBC*, 8 April 2019; James Hatton, 'Canadian ambassador's marriage to BlackRock APAC boss raises conflict of interest concerns', *Mingtiandi*, 25 September 2019.

41 Tony Tang Xiaodong, LinkedIn; Anon., 'Larry Fink says BlackRock focused on onshore presence in China', *Reuters*, 8 April 2019.

42 <https://citywireasia.com/manager/helen-zhu/d26476>.

43 Barbara Demick, 'In China, "red nobility" trumps egalitarian ideals', *Los Angeles Times*, 4 March 2013.

44 David Lynch, Jennifer Hughes and Martin Arnold, 'JPMorgan to pay $264m in penalty for hiring "princelings"', *Financial Times*, 18 November 2016.

45 Jessica Silver-Greenberg and Ben Protess, 'Chinese official made job plea to JPMorgan Chase chief', *The New York Times*, 9 February 2014.

46 Anon., 'JP Morgan under scrutiny over hiring of Chinese minister's son: WSJ', *Reuters*, 6 February 2015.

47 Gwynn Guilford, 'JP Morgan isn't the only big financial firm to have hired Chinese Communist Party scions', *Quartz*, 20 August 2013.

48 Kris Cheng, '"Little darlings summer camp": CY Leung faces fresh questions over his daughter's JP Morgan internship', *Hong Kong Free Press*, 24 November 2016.

49 Neil Gough, 'Former top China JPMorgan banker said to be arrested in Hong Kong', *The New York Times*, 22 May 2014; Wang Duan, 'Former JPMorgan executive arrested by HK's graft fighter', *Caixin*, 24 May 2014; Cendrowski, 'J.P. Morgan's dealmaker in China steps down', <https://huecri.wordpress.com/tag/fang-fang/>.

50 As a postscript, in 2014 Fang Fang was arrested by Hong Kong's anti-graft agency. Although some said he had agreed to become a 'tainted witness', spilling the beans on J.P. Morgan's practice of hiring princelings, a more plausible explanation may be that he was caught up in a CCP factional struggle. (Some say he is aligned with former CCP boss Zeng Qinghong, once aligned with Jiang Zemin and then a backer of Xi Jinping.) Whatever the reason, it does not seem to have done him much harm. After leaving J.P. Morgan he set up an investment group. He retains his prestigious role on the CPPCC and remains a vice chairman of the advisory council of the Center for China and Globalization.

51 Neil Gough, 'Top China banker for JPMorgan to retire amid hiring inquiry', *The New York Times*, 25 March 2014.

52 Scott Cendrowski, 'J.P. Morgan's dealmaker in China steps down. Who's next?', *Fortune*, 25 March 2014.

53 Cheng, '"Little darlings summer camp"'. For Hua Jing Society, see <http://www.hua-jing.org/default.php>.

54 For example, <https://www.ntdtv.com/gb/2014/05/26/a1111869.html>.

55 Cendrowski, 'J.P. Morgan's dealmaker in China steps down'.

56 <https://archive.fo/2019.05.01-014840/http:/english.ccg.org.cn/Director/Member.aspx?Id=1806>. The president of the Centre for China and Globalization is Wang Huiyao, a senior fellow at Harvard Kennedy School, and a CCP operative (see also Diamond and Schell, eds, *China's Influence & American Interests*, p. 64). CCG is funded by Ronnie Chan, also a big Harvard donor. For the CCG's tight Party links, see Tony Cheung, 'New mainland think tank hopes to take "objective" view on Hong Kong issues', *South China Morning Post*, 12 November 2017.

57 Matt Levine, 'JP Morgan's mistake was not hiring princelings fast enough', *Bloomberg*, 30 December 2013.

58 Gwynn Guilford, 'JP Morgan isn't the only big financial firm to have hired Chinese Communist Party scions', *Quartz*, 20 August 2013.

59 It's perhaps worth noting that Australia's former finance minister and prime minister Paul Keating was appointed to the CDB's international advisory board (whose membership included Kissinger and Dominic Barton). He became so enamoured of Chen Yuan that he wrote the foreword to Chen's book.

60 In 2011, Chen Xiaodan was courting Li Wangzhi, the son of Bo Xilai, a potential 'royal marriage' (Peter Foster, 'Photos leaked online fuel rumours of romance between China's red royals', *The Telegraph*, 21 February 2011). Both studied at Harvard. Bo Guagua went from Harrow to Oxford to Harvard and drove a red Ferrari.

61 James Follows, 'Internship at a Chinese bank? Only if you go to Harvard or MIT', *The Atlantic*, 20 February 2011.

62 Anon., 'Heirs of Mao's comrades rise as new capitalist nobility', *Bloomberg*, 27 December 2012.

63 Edward Wong and Amy Qin, 'Son of fallen Chinese official enrolls at Columbia Law School', *The New York Times*, 29 July 2013.

64 'Headhunter Tan says market knowledge and communication skills now trump family connections when young mainland graduates apply to global banks', <https://news.efinancialcareers.com/au-en/318785/finance-job-princeling-asia>.

65 Michael Forsythe, David Enrich and Alexandra Stevenson, 'Inside a brazen scheme to woo China: gifts, golf and a $4,254 wine', *The New York Times*, 14 October 2019.

66 Levine, 'JP Morgan's mistake was not hiring princelings fast enough'.

67 Forsythe, Enrich and Stevenson, 'Inside a brazen scheme to woo China'.

68 Forsythe, Enrich and Stevenson, 'Inside a brazen scheme to woo China'; Anon., 'Wang Xisha, daughter of Chinese vice premier Wang Yang; the couple's extravagant lifestyle has frequently caught the attention of Hong Kong's paparazzi and tabloids', *Bamboo Innovator*, 23 June 2014.

69 Matt Robinson and Patricia Hurtado, 'Credit Suisse to pay $77 million to settle princeling probes', *Bloomberg*, 6 July 2018.

70 Robinson and Hurtado, 'Credit Suisse to pay $77 million to settle princeling probes'.

71 Alexandra Rogers, 'City Corporation slammed for decision to ban Taiwan float from Lord Mayor's show', *City A.M.*, 14 May 2019.

72 Wieland Wagner, 'Exchange rates and reserve currencies: China plans path to economic hegemony', *Der Spiegel*, 26 January 2011.

73 Martin Thorley, 'Shadow play: elite Chinese state influence strategies and the case of Renminbi internationalisation', Parts 1 and 2, *Asia Dialogue*, 19 July 2018.

74 'Gaining currency: the rise of the Renminbi', Brookings website, event held on 3 November 2016, <https://www.brookings.edu/events/gaining-currency-the-rise-of-the-renminbi-2/>.

75 Anon., eds., *Currency Internationalization and Macro Financial Risk Control*, International Monetary Institute, London: Palgrave, 2018.
76 See <https://tinyurl.com/u4e2be3 and https://tinyurl.com/vn4wqn3>.
77 <https://twitter.com/OMFIF/status/1012246109413134336>.
78 <https://hansard.parliament.uk/Lords/2014-05-07/debates/14050796000304/ChinaInvestmentIntoTheUnitedKingdom>.
79 Quoted by Thorley, 'Shadow play'.
80 Nikou Asgari, 'City of London cements dominance of renminbi trading', *Financial Times*, 17 April 2019.
81 Anne Peters, 'Human rights à la Chinoise: impressions from the 6th Human Rights Forum in Beijing on the eve of the second UPR of China, Part II', blog of the *European Journal of International Law*, 24 September 2013, <https://tinyurl.com/w49glem>.
82 Anon., 'British Labour MP criticized for role in China's Tibet propaganda', *Tibetan Review*, 16 August 2014.
83 <https://www.theyworkforyou.com/lords/?id=2018-11-01b.1428.2>.
84 Lord Woolf of Barnes, former Lord Chief Justice and chairman of the Bank of England Financial Markets Law Committee, is also a fellow of the 48 Group Club.
85 <https://www.parliament.uk/biographies/lords/lord-davidson-of-glen-clova/3781/register-of-interests>.
86 <https://www.berggruen.org/work/berggruen-china-center/>.
87 Anon., 'Lord Mayor of London leads fintech delegation to China to promote trade and investment', press release, City of London Corporation, 18 March 2019.
88 <https://www.youtube.com/watch?v=IrAz-lQDrAo>, minute 2.00 and 19.30.
89 Anon., 'Lord Mayor of London leads fintech delegation to China to promote trade and investment'.
90 Anon., '*China Daily* Global Edition wins admiration from across the world', *China Daily*, 11 January 2019.
91 <https://sgc.frankfurt-school.de/>; Zhou Wa, 'Giving currency to yuan's spread', *China Daily*, 2 October 2015.
92 Mark Sobel has written for the journal Shenglin edits, the *International Monetary Review* (see the January 2019 issue).
93 Ben Moshinsky, 'Terrifying highlights from Ray Dalio's note on the China bubble', *Business Insider*, 24 July 2015.
94 Alicia Gonzales, '"China is dealing with a heart transplant," says Bridgewater head', *El Pais*, 26 August 2015.
95 Alan Cheng, 'How Ray Dalio broke into China', *Institutional Investor*, 18 December 2017.
96 Amanda Cantrell, 'Ray Dalio is worried about markets—but bullish on China', *Institutional Investor*, 15 November 2018.

97 Linette Lopez, 'It's time to stop listening to Ray Dalio on China', *Institutional Investor*, 4 January 2019.
98 Cheng, 'How Ray Dalio broke into China'.
99 Samuel Wade, 'Minitrue: rules on stock-market reporting', *China Digital Times*, 9 July 2015.
100 Amie Tsang, 'Caijing journalist's shaming signals China's growing control over news media', *The New York Times*, 6 September 2015.
101 PEN America, 'Darkened screen: constraints on foreign journalists in China', PEN America, 22 September 2016.
102 Based on discussions with financial market experts.
103 Anon., 'UBS is curbing some China travel after banker detained', *Bloomberg*, 20 October 2018.
104 Anon., 'UBS is curbing some China travel after banker detained'.
105 Anon., 'Lone analyst who cut Cathay to sell says he faces huge pressure', *Straits Times*, 23 August 2019.
106 Anon., 'Lone analyst who cut Cathay to sell says he faces huge pressure'.
107 John Pomfret, 'What America didn't anticipate about China', *The Atlantic*, 16 October 2019.
108 Brian Stelter, 'ESPN faces criticism over its coverage of Hong Kong tweet and the NBA', *CNN Business*, 9 October 2019; Alex Lindner, 'ESPN uses map of China complete with nine-dash line, Taiwan, and Arunachal Pradesh', *Shanghaiist*, 10 October 2019.
109 Anon., 'China takes a bite out of Apple privacy claims', *Deutsche Welle*, 28 February 2018.
110 Frank Tang, 'Apple CEO Tim Cook joins influential Beijing university board as company's China woes continue', *South China Morning Post*, 21 October 2019.
111 Martin Hala and Jichang Lulu, 'The CCP's model of social control goes global', *Sinopsis*, 20 December 2018.
112 <https://tariffshurt.com/>.
113 Scott Reeves, 'Tariffs hurt "heartland" companies, letter says', *China Daily*, 15 June 2019.
114 <https://tinyurl.com/w7hjs87>; Bethany Allen-Ebrahimian, 'Meet the U.S. officials now in China's sphere of influence', *Daily Beast*, 23 July 2018.
115 Moritz Koch, Dietmar Neuerer and Stephan Scheuer, 'Merkel öffnet 5G-Netz für Huawei' [Merkel opens 5G network for Huawei], *Handelsblatt*, 14 October 2019.
116 'The People's Republic of China is again Germany's main trading partner', German Federal Office of Statistics, <https://tinyurl.com/rco2uvo>; Mu Xueqian, 'China remains Germany's most important trading partner', *Xinhua*, 18 February 2019.
117 Elisa Simantke, Harald Schuhmann and Nico Schmidt, 'Wie gefährlich China für Europa wirklich ist', *Tagesspiegel*, 15 September 2019. See also

<https://www.euronews.com/2019/04/09/bei-ching-the-figures-behind-the-eu-s-trade-with-china>.

118 See for example Matthias Breitinger and Zacharias Zacharakis, 'Auto Macht Deutschland', *Die Zeit*, 24 July 2017; Martin Seiwert and Stefan Reccius, 'So abhängig ist Deutschland von der Autoindustrie', *Wirtschaftswoche*, 27 July 2017.

119 Anon., 'VW, BMW und Daimler wachsen in China gegen den Trend', *Manager Magazin*, 10 February 2019.

120 'Weekly brief: BMW's latest kowtow chasing Chinese driverless cash', *TU-Automotive*, 22 July 2019, <https://www.tu-auto.com/weekly-brief-bmws-latest-kowtow-chasing-chinese-driverless-cash/>.

121 Tim Bartz et al., 'China pressures foreign companies to fall in line on protests', *Der Speigel* online, 28 August 2019.

122 Interview with Robin Brant, 'VW boss "not aware" of China's detention camps', *BBC News* online (video), 16 April 2019.

123 Joe McDonald, 'Mercedes-Benz apologises to China for quoting Dalai Lama on Instagram', *The Independent*, 6 February 2018.

124 Anon., 'Audi apologizes for inaccurate China map', *Global Times*, 16 March 2017.

125 Gerhard Hegmann, 'Siemens-Chef warnt davor, Chinas Führung zu kritisieren', *Welt*, 8 September 2019.

126 'Siemens embraces Belt and Road Initiative', Siemens website, 6 June 2018, <https://tinyurl.com/tfsw8ff>.

127 Anon., 'Merkel will friedliche Lösung für Hongkong', *Frankfurter Rundschau*, 8 September 2019.

128 'About APA', <https://www.asien-pazifik-ausschuss.de/en/about-apa>.

129 Julian Röpcke, 'China-Lobbyisten fordern Ende deutscher Werte-Politik', *Bild*, 19 March 2019.

130 Author's personal experience.

131 Andrew Chatzky and James McBride, 'China's Massive Belt and Road Initiative', Backgrounder, Council on Foreign Relations, 21 May 2019; see also <https://tinyurl.com/r9ygvx2>.

132 Chatzky and McBride, 'China's Massive Belt and Road Initiative'.

133 Raissa Robles, 'China can turn off the Philippine national power grid, officials say', *South China Morning Post*, 20 November 2019.

134 Hamilton, *Silent Invasion*, pp. 121, 159.

135 Anon., 'As Trump bashed China, he sought deals with its government-owned energy firm State Grid', *South China Morning Post*, 18 October 2016.

136 Andre Tartar, Mira Rojanasakul and Jeremy Scott Diamond, 'How China is buying its way into Europe', *Bloomberg*, 23 April 2018.

137 Ronald Linden, 'The new sea people: China in the Mediterranean', IAI Papers 18, Istuto Affari Internazionali, July 2018.

138 Tartar, Rojanasakul and Scott Diamond, 'How China is buying its way into Europe'.

139 Devin Thorne and Ben Spevack, 'Harbored ambitions: how China's port investments are strategically reshaping the Indo-Pacific', C4ADS, 2017, p. 4.

140 Quoted by Thorne and Spevack, 'Harbored ambitions', p. 19.

141 <https://iias.asia/the-newsletter/article/one-belt-one-road-chinas-reconstruction-global-communication-international> (Xiang Debao 相德宝)

142 See Nadège Rolland, 'Beijing's vision for a reshaped international order', *China Brief*, vol. 18, no. 3 (*Jamestown Foundatio*n), 26 February 2018.

143 Jing Xin and Donald Matheson, 'One Belt, competing metaphors: the struggle over strategic narrative in English-language news media', *International Journal of Communication*, no. 12, 2018, pp. 4248–68. The CCP's 'Culture Going Global' strategy is also tied into the BRI. As Party theorists put it in 2015, 'the consensus on culture [that is, global acceptance of CCP values] is the foundation for the BRI'. Anon., 'Direction and aspects of the culture industry's development in BRI', *China Economy*, 28 March 2015.

144 Haoguang Liang and Yaojun Zhang, 'International discourse power: Belt and Road is not starting from "scratch"', in Anon., eds, *The Theoretical System of Belt and Road Initiative*, Singapore: Springer, 2019, p. 52.

145 In a study of foreign media reporting of the BRI, Jing Xin and Donald Matheson found that it often relies on metaphors of 'vision' and 'dream' to describe the larger meaning of BRI in the world. While Pakistani media tend to use phrases like 'game changer', 'economic catalyst' and 'a new wave of globalization', India's media are more likely to deploy the negative imagery of 'colonialism' and 'Trojan horse'. So, world media both reproduce Party discourse and undermine it. Chinese-language media abroad mostly follow three scripts: China as a historical victim committed to peaceful development, the 'China Dream' of returning to strength and self-confidence, and 'a new, more collaborative style of great-power relations, in contrast to cold war thinking'. Xin and Matheson, 'One Belt, competing metaphors'.

146 And to developing the sister-city networks and 'people-to-people exchanges'. ('Belt and Road, here is the Italy and China memorandum of understanding', *Affaritaliani.it*, 12 March 2019, <https://tinyurl.com/qm8yeno>. Italy's accession to the BRI was welcomed enthusiastically by the Schiller Institute. 'In an interview with Chinese journalists, Italian President Mattarella spoke at length about the ancient bonds between Italy and China and the future perspective for cooperation', <https://tinyurl.com/s3zh398>.

147 Dan Harrison, 'Victorian government releases agreement with China on Belt and Road Initiative', *ABC News* online, 12 November 2018.

148 'Joint communique of the leaders' roundtable of the 2nd Belt and Road Forum for International Cooperation', 27 April 2019, <https://tinyurl.com/qmn2fm8>.

Chapter 7 Mobilising the Chinese diaspora

1 James Jiann Hua To, *Qiaowu: Extra-territorial policies for the overseas Chinese*, Leiden: Koninklijke Brill, 2014, pp. 115, 184. There have been some important changes to united front structures and operations since James To wrote his book.

2 Marcel Angliviel de la Beaumelle, 'The United Front Work Department: "magic weapon" at home and abroad', *China Brief (Jamestown Foundation)*, 16 July 2017.

3 To, *Qiaowu*.

4 James Kynge, Lucy Hornby and Jamil Anderlini, 'Inside China's secret "magic weapon" for worldwide influence', *Financial Times*, 26 October 2017.

5 To, *Qiaowu*, p. 188.

6 James To, 'Beijing's policies for managing Han and ethnic-minority Chinese communities abroad', *Journal of Current Chinese Affairs*, no. 4, 2012, pp. 186–87.

7 Groot, 'The expansion of the United Front under Xi Jinping', p. 169.

8 For example, companies are threatened with loss of business in China and official displeasure unless they withdraw advertising from Chinese-language media that do not bend to Beijing's will.

9 To, *Qiaowu*, p. 189.

10 <https://tinyurl.com/u24p6ud>.

11 <http://www.upholdjustice.org/node/181#report181_24>; 'Quan guo Qiaoban zhuren huiyi jingshen chuanda tigang' 全国侨办主任会议精神传达提纲 [Main message from the directors' meeting of China's Overseas Office], Chongqing Overseas Chinese Affairs website, 5 April 2007, <https://tinyurl.com/tfz5zfa>.

12 'Quan guo Qiaoban zhuren huiyi jingshen chuanda tigang' (paragraph 7).

13 With thanks to Alex Joske for advice on the chart.

14 Joske, 'The Party speaks for you'.

15 <https://web.archive.org/web/20110801030857/http://www.gdsy.com.cn/new7.htm>.

16 Quoted in <http://www.upholdjustice.org/sites/default/files/201709/record/2008/181-report_a4_report.pdf>. See also Anne-Marie Brady, 'On the correct use of terms', *China Brief*, vol. 19, no. 9, 9 May 2019.

17 Jichang Lulu, 'Repurposing democracy: the European Parliament China friendship cluster', *Sinopsis*, 26 November 2019, p. 21, n105.

18 'The children of two other CCP grandees, Chen Yi and Chen Yun, have also held CPAFFC posts.' Lulu, 'Repurposing democracy', n104.

19 To, *Qiaowu*, p. 76. *Qiaowu* work is a subset of UFWD work because it is limited to influencing ethnic Chinese, while united front work has a much broader audience. Officially, *qiaowu* policies and directives come from the OCAO.

20 Alex Joske, 'Reorganizing the United Front Work Department: new structures for a new era of diaspora and religious affairs work', *China Brief*, vol. 19,

no. 9 (*Jamestown Foundation*), 9 May 2019. Joske notes that some OCAO staff were redeployed to AFROC or CPPCC positions.

21 For Australia, they are detailed in Clive Hamilton and Alex Joske, 'Submission to the Parliamentary Joint Committee on Intelligence and Security', 22 January 2018, Submission No. 20 at <https://tinyurl.com/yd922bwz>.

22 'Wei qiao fuwu xingdong nian quanmian luoshi ba xiang huiqiao jihua' 为侨服务行动年 全面落实八项惠侨计划 [Action year for serving overseas Chinese: fully implement the eight plans for benefiting overseas Chinese], website of the Chinese government, 2 March 2015, <https://tinyurl.com/yx554pfv>.

23 Joske, 'Reorganizing the United Front Work Department'.

24 <https://twitter.com/geoff_p_wade/status/1116480563613851648>.

25 <https://tinyurl.com/s2ccyp6>.

26 <http://www.ejinsight.com/20140805-chinese-french-citizenship/>. Some 500 people from China have obtained French citizenship this way. It's especially popular for young people from the city of Wenzhou. The first to take this route was a student from Wenzhou on the advice of his professor at the University of Paris 3 in 1979.

27 <https://www.youtube.com/watch?v=NoWc3tEGuu4>.

28 <http://news.66wz.com/system/2015/04/02/104404281.shtml>.

29 'Yingguo huaren laobing lianyihui Lundun "ba yi" da juhui' 英国华人老兵联谊会伦敦"八一"大聚会, Huashangbao, 1 August 2016, <http://archive.today/BK0uo>. See also <https://tinyurl.com/racdqwu>.

30 Tom Blackwell, 'Canadian veterans of People's Liberation Army form association, sing of China's martial glory', *National Post*, 30 October 2019.

31 <https://archive.today/wwuhs>. 聚澳现场丨军歌嘹亮唱响八一，澳中退役老兵俱乐/; <https://tinyurl.com/qom8evp>. See also Clive Hamilton, *Silent Invasion*, p. 248.

32 <https://twitter.com/Anne_MarieBrady/status/1116473692345786370>; <https://twitter.com/xmyhm/status/1115504141999022080>; <https://twitter.com/geoff_p_wade/status/1116480563613851648?lang=en>.

33 Cary Huang, '83 Chinese billionaires members of NPC and CPPCC: Hurun', *South China Morning Post*, 8 March 2013. A more up-to-date figure is not available.

34 Diamond and Schell, eds, *China's Influence & American Interests*, p. 34.

35 中国强大是侨胞心中最殷切的期盼; see 'Liexi jinnian quango zhengxie huiyi de 35 ming haiwai qiaobao dou you shei?' 列席今年全国政协会议的35名海外侨胞都有谁?, website of the Overseas Chinese Affairs Office, 3 March 2018, <http://web.archive.org/web/20190803225827/http://www.gqb.gov.cn/news/2018/0303/44447.shtml>.

36 John Dotson, 'The United Front Work Department goes global: the worldwide expansion of the Council for the Promotion of the Peaceful Reunification of China', *China Brief*, vol. 19, no. 9, 9 May 2019.

37 Dan Conifer and Stephanie Borys, 'Australia denies citizenship to Chinese political donor Huang Xiangmo and strips his permanent residency', *ABC News* online, 6 April 2019.

38 For example, Yang Wentian of the Phoenix CPPRC and Ma Ao of the New York City CPPRC. See 列席全国政协会议海外侨胞期望助力新时代 <http://web.archive.org/web/20190803232811/https://news.*sina*.com.cn/c/2019-03-02/doc-ihrfqzkc0514609.shtml> and 新机遇 海外侨胞展宏图 <https://tinyurl.com/vo9y8nm>.

39 'Ouzhou Zhongguo heping tongyi cujinhui zhi quanti lü'Ou qiaobao de huyushu' 欧洲中国和平统一促进会致全体旅欧侨胞的呼吁书 [A letter of appeal to all Chinese compatriots in Europe from the European Association for the Peaceful Reunification of China], *Qiaowang*, 14 May 2019, <http://www.chinaqw.com/hqhr/2019/05-14/222686.shtml>.

40 Mark Eades, 'Chinese government front groups act in violation of U.S. law', blog post, Foreign Policy Association, 9 May 2016.

41 Eades, 'Chinese government front groups act in violation of U.S. law'; <https://tinyurl.com/qrhw5et>.

42 Benjamin Haas, '"Think of your family": China threatens European citizens over Xinjiang protests', *The Guardian*, 18 October 2019.

43 Bethany Allen-Ebrahimian, 'Chinese police are demanding personal information from Uighurs in France', *Foreign Policy*, 2 March 2018. For Belgium, see Tim Nicholas Rühlig, Björn Jerdén, Frans-Paul van der Putten, John Seaman, Miguel Otero-Iglesias and Alice Ekman, eds, 'Political values in Europe-China relations', report by the European Think-tank Network on China (ETNC), December 2018, pp. 25–6.

44 <https://www.rfa.org/english/news/uyghur/threats-02272018150624.html>.

45 Paul Mooney and David Lague, 'The price of dissent: holding the fate of families in its hands, China controls refugees abroad', *Reuters*, 30 December 2015.

46 Steve Chao and Liz Gooch, 'No escape: the fearful life of China's exiled dissidents', *Al Jazeera*, 9 April 2018.

47 Chao and Gooch, 'No escape'.

48 <https://www.aljazeera.com/programmes/101east/2018/04/china-spies-lies-blackmail-180404145244034.html>.

49 <https://www.rfa.org/english/news/china/germany-agents-09132019142817.html>.

50 Didi Kirsten Tatlow, 'Datenkolonialismus. Chinas Angriff auf die offene Gesellschaft', *Zentrum Liberale Moderne*, 25 September 2018.

51 Camron Slessor, Claire Campbell and Daniel Keane, 'Fake Chinese police cars spotted in Perth and Adelaide amid pro-Hong Kong rallies', *ABC News* online, 19 August 2019.

52 In August 2004 the Chinese consulate in New York posted an article about *huaren canzheng* in the US, <http://archive.today/2019.09.21-073907/

https://www.fmprc.gov.cn/ce/cgny/chn/lsyw/qwgz/t147027.htm>. An article about *huaren canzheng* appeared in the same year in Canada, <http://archive.today/2019.09.21-074432/http://goabroad.xdf.cn/200406/18502.html>.

53 For Canada, see for example Tom Blackwell, 'MPP's ties to China raise questions about how close Canadian politicians should get to foreign powers', *National Post*, 6 September 2019. For New Zealand, see for example Tom Phillips, 'China-born New Zealand MP denies being a spy', *The Guardian*, 13 September 2017. For Australia, see Anon., 'ASIO identifies political candidates with links to China', *SBS News*, 9 December 2017; Wai Ling Yeung and Clive Hamilton, 'How Beijing is shaping politics in Western Australia', *China Brief*, vol. 19, no. 9, 9 May 2019; Clive Hamilton, 'Why Gladys Liu must answer to parliament about alleged links to the Chinese government', *The Conversation*, 11 September 2019. In the United States, the Coordination Council of Chinese America Associations has organised many *huaren canzheng* events. One example (in English) is at <https://web.archive.org/web/20171111051835/http://www.cccaa.org/ch/inusa/election_5.aspx>.

54 <https://tzb.jnu.edu.cn/f4/18/c5573a128024/page.htm>, Jinan University United Front Department, 5 May 2010.

55 Xue Qingchao 薛庆超, 'Di jiu zhang: Mao Zedong "shuai shitou", "can shazi", "wa qiangjiao"' 第九章：毛泽东"甩石头"，"掺沙子"，"挖墙脚", *People's Daily Online*, 29 October 2013, part 1, <https://tinyurl.com/vgufwzw> and part 3, <https://tinyurl.com/tdac338>.

56 The claim that it is most advanced in Canada is our judgement, based on close study.

57 Tom Igguldon, 'Questions raised about Liberal MP Gladys Liu amid claims of links to Chinese political influence operations', *ABC News* online, 9 September 2019; Hamilton, 'Why Gladys Liu must answer to parliament about alleged links to the Chinese government'.

58 Dan Oakes, 'Gladys Liu's Liberal Party branch called to relax foreign investment laws before she became federal MP', *ABC News* online, 14 September 2019.

59 Rob Harris, 'Morrison defends "great Australian" Gladys Liu against "smear"', *The Sydney Morning Herald*, 12 September 2019.

60 Nick McKenzie, Paul Sakkal and Grace Tobin, 'China tried to plant its candidate in federal parliament, authorities believe', *The Age*, 24 November 2019.

61 Yeung and Hamilton, 'How Beijing is shaping politics in Western Australia'.

62 <https://web.archive.org/web/20190921222515/https://world.huanqiu.com/article/9CaKrnK5dp9>, Association des Chinois Residant en France 法国华侨华人会主席任俐敏.

63 <http://archive.today/2019.09.21-225007/http://news.66wz.com/system/2018/09/06/105111657.shtml>.

64 The COEA's member organisations/provincial chapters are listed on its website: <https://web.archive.org/web/20190115003915/http://www.coea.org.cn/xhgg/xhgg.d.html?nid=19>.

65 <http://archive.today/2019.04.06-004152/http://www.gqb.gov.cn/news/2018/0504/44842.shtml>.

66 <https://web.archive.org/web/20161203100337/http://www.bcproject.org/about/#history>, Christine Lee 李贞驹.

67 Hamilton and Joske, 'Submission to the Parliamentary Joint Committee on Intelligence and Security', p. 27.

68 Lee's website: <https://tinyurl.com/s5neovh>. See also bio at <https://tinyurl.com/vcze47o>. Christine Lee on YouTube (in English), <https://www.youtube.com/watch?v=piezUzwS3Hk>.

69 <https://web.archive.org/web/20171009000710/http://uk.people.com.cn/GB/370630/370680/index.html>.

70 Hannah McGrath and Oliver Wright, 'Money, influence and the Beijing connection', *The Times*, 4 February 2017.

71 <https://web.archive.org/web/20190405083748/http://www.bcproject.org/michael-wilkes/>. Michael Wilkes on YouTube: <https://www.youtube.com/watch?v=GEDeOioavdE>. This news story details Michael Wilkes's involvement in the British Chinese Project: <http://qwgzyj.gqb.gov.cn/qjxy/187/2742.shtml>.

72 McGrath and Wright, 'Money, influence and the Beijing connection'.

73 <https://web.archive.org/web/20181211111940/https://www.chineseforlabour.org/executive_committee>.

74 Hu Yang, 'UK law firm opens office in Beijing', *China Daily*, 19 November 2011. Also, according to *China Daily*: 'Lee, an influential and active figure in the Chinese community in the UK, is chief legal advisor to the Chinese Embassy in the United Kingdom. Working with Chinese government departments, she has made great efforts in promoting the rights of Chinese in the UK.' The firm is also one of the legal experts recommended to overseas enterprises by the UK Trade and Investment government agency. In 2001, *China Daily* announced the opening of an office of Lee's law firm in Beijing. On Lee's legal services for the OCAO and her meeting with senior OCAO officials, see <http://archive.today/MMJSa> and <https://tinyurl.com/v8tvjss>.

75 <http://archive.today/2019.09.21-113520/http://www.ihuawen.com/article/index/id/42470/cid/45>.

76 <https://web.archive.org/web/20190921124029/http://paper.people.com.cn/rmrbhwb/html/2016-02/19/content_1654994.htm>.

77 <https://web.archive.org/web/20190711081020/http://www.christine-lee.com.cn/nd.jsp?id=108>.

78 <http://archive.today/i0wS8>; <https://tinyurl.com/wqbutsq>.

79 <https://tinyurl.com/w86f3e8>. Also, 'The British Chinese Project will open the door to politics for young ethnic Chinese. It will help them see politics

can start with small things around them. It will help them master rules of the game to better protect their rights and interests.'

80 <http://archive.today/dYWvh>. On Points of Light Awards, see <https://www.pointsoflight.gov.uk/> and Lee's citation at <https://www.pointsoflight.gov.uk/british-chinese-project/>.

81 <https://tinyurl.com/vqquzjo>; <https://tinyurl.com/vy3wmvm>; <https://tinyurl.com/sm8huhk>. Other founders were Dr Stephen Ng MBE and Dr Mee Ling Ng OBE.

82 <https://tinyurl.com/ue37f89>.

83 <https://tinyurl.com/ue37f89>.

84 <https://tinyurl.com/tkdjx23>.

85 <https://tinyurl.com/qk2vbrp>.

86 <https://tinyurl.com/tp3cxsd>.

87 <https://tinyurl.com/uj2oenu>; <https://tinyurl.com/s57cyu3>.

88 <https://tinyurl.com/v6as2v2>; <https://tinyurl.com/uggbtwg>; <https://tinyurl.com/rzzc96s>.

89 <http://archive.today/2019.07.07-113849/http://zjuka.blogspot.com/2009/12/>.

90 <http://archive.today/2019.07.07-113529/http://zjuka.org.uk/old/Visiting%20Qiao%20Lian%2002-07-10.pdf>.

91 <https://web.archive.org/web/20160421042133/http://qwgzyj.gqb.gov.cn/qjxy/181/2568.shtml>.

92 Anon., 'China, Britain to benefit from "golden era" in ties—Cameron', *Reuters*, 18 October 2015.

93 <https://tinyurl.com/scpdaf7>

94 <https://tinyurl.com/squysp4>.

95 <https://web.archive.org/web/20190630233450/http://wemedia.ifeng.com/89034940/wemedia.shtml>.

96 <https://tinyurl.com/t2yfcxr>.

97 <https://www.youtube.com/watch?v=sUgrj2r6FR8>.

98 <https://tinyurl.com/tso3r7x>.

99 <https://tinyurl.com/sbbxhbx>.

100 <http://www.channel4.com/news/boris-johnson-london-propery-deal-china-albert-dock>; <https://tinyurl.com/seffc8z>; <http://archive.today/qTqfr>.

101 <http://powerbase.info/index.php/Xuelin_Bates#Political_donations>.

102 Anon., 'Tory peer Bates failed to declare ZRG interests, paper reports', *Inside Croyden*, 12 April 2015.

103 Christian Eriksson and Tim Rayment, 'Minister faces quiz over link to new Crystal Palace', *Sunday Times*, 12 April 2015.

104 <http://powerbase.info/index.php/Xuelin_Bates#Political_donations>; <http://powerbase.info/index.php/The_Leader%27s_Group>.

105 <https://tinyurl.com/seffc8z>.

106 <https://tinyurl.com/wdcpdye>.

107 <https://tinyurl.com/uvomjuz>.
108 <https://tinyurl.com/vwcb6vj>.
109 <https://tinyurl.com/wlaunsu>, 6 February 2019.
110 <https://tinyurl.com/tfwtu9u>.
111 <https://tinyurl.com/rgqmdw6>; <https://mp.weixin.qq.com/s/G5XojgHiRyjn1G8A30GSJQ>.
112 <https://tinyurl.com/vqavhj8>.
113 Wang Yisan and Bai Tianxing, 'Lord Bates walks China: China contributes peace and prosperity to the world', *People's Daily*, 26 September 2019.
114 <https://tinyurl.com/tqljhn7>.
115 Anon., 'China interaction: stories of Zhejiang premiers in Beijing', *Beijing Review*, 11 October 2019.
116 <https://tinyurl.com/u46q5x7>; <https://tinyurl.com/yxytr5sj>; <https://www.walkforpeace.eu/mission-possible/>. The UK China Friendship Association was incorporated in November 2019, see <https://beta.companieshouse.gov.uk/company/12295975/officers>. A British-China Friendship Society was formed in 1949 but dissolved in 1965 when Maoists broke away to form the Society for Anglo-Chinese Understanding. See <https://tinyurl.com/yjqroghc>.
117 <https://tinyurl.com/t3b8t8m>.

Chapter 8 The ecology of espionage

1 A sample of reports on the scandal includes John Pomfret, 'China denies contribution charges', *The Washington Post*, 20 May 1998; David Jackson and Lena Sun, 'Liu's deals with Chung: an intercontinental puzzle', *The Washington Post*, 24 May 1998.
2 Agnès Andrésy quoted by Faligot, *Chinese Spies*, Melbourne: Scribe, 2019, pp. 204, 255–7.
3 As in the case of former Australia defence minister Joel Fitzgibbon. Before entering parliament, Fitzgibbon developed a close relationship with a Chinese businesswoman, Helen Liu, who also made large donations to his election fund and the Labor Party. It turned out that Helen Liu had close connections with China's intelligence agencies, and with top united front figures. She was a friend of Lieutenant-Colonel Liu Chaoying, the daughter of the Chinese general who donated $300,000 to the Clinton campaign. Helen Liu was also a good friend of Bob Carr, former premier of New South Wales and former foreign minister, and director of a think tank funded by a Chinese businessman who is now banned from Australia because he is believed by Australia's intelligence agency to be an agent of influence. See Hamilton, *Silent Invasion*, pp. 163–5. On Huang Xiangmo's exclusion, see Nick McKenzie and Chris Uhlmann, 'Canberra strands Beijing's man offshore, denies passport', *The Sydney Morning Herald*, 5 February 2019.

4 Dustin Volz and Aruna Viswanatha, 'FBI says Chinese espionage poses "most severe" threat to American security', *The Wall Street Journal*, 12 December 2018.
5 Cristina Maza, 'China involved in 90 percent of espionage and industrial secrets theft, Department of Justice reveals', *Newsweek*, 12 December 2018.
6 William Hannas, James Mulvenon and Anna Puglisi, *Chinese Industrial Espionage*, London: Routledge, 2013, pp. 204–7.
7 James To, *Qiaowu*, p. 43.
8 Anon., 'China is top espionage risk to Canada: CSIS', *CTV News*, 30 April 2007.
9 'The ideal spy is one who is a citizen or resident of the target country, has access to its sensitive decision-making portals, and/or is part of its government or industrial machinery'. Sreeram Chaulia, 'The age of the immigrant spy', *Asia Times*, 3 April 2008. 'Instead of the classical methods used by other great power intelligence services involving tight control over a few, deeply planted and valuable assets, Beijing employs an array of decentralized networks that thrive on the Chinese diaspora.'
10 Peter Mattis, '"Beyond spy versus spy": clarifying the analytic challenge of the Chinese intelligence services', *Studies in Intelligence*, vol. 56, no. 4, September 2012, pp. 47–57; Hannas, Mulvenon and Puglisi, *Chinese Industrial Espionage*, chapter 5.
11 Mattis, '"Beyond spy versus spy"'.
12 Hannas, Mulvenon and Puglisi, *Chinese Industrial Espionage*, chapter 8.
13 Robert Burnson, 'Accused Chinese spy pleads guilty in U.S. "dead-drop" sting', *Bloomberg*, 25 November 2019.
14 Faligot, *Chinese Spies*, p. 2.
15 Peter Mattis and Matthew Brazil, *Chinese Communist Espionage: An intelligence primer*, Annapolis: Naval Institute Press, 2019, pp. 55–6.
16 Mattis and Brazil, *Chinese Communist Espionage*, p. 55.
17 Mattis and Brazil, *Chinese Communist Espionage*, p. 239. According to Roger Faligot, whose information may be less up-to-date, the Shanghai State Security Bureau has responsibility for the United States and its main Western allies, including Canada, Australia and Western Europe; the Zhejiang office covers Northern Europe: the Qingdao office covers Japan and the Koreas; and the Beijing office covers Eastern Europe and Russia. Faligot, *Chinese Spies*, pp. 230–1.
18 Jay Solomon, 'FBI sees big threat from Chinese spies', *The Wall Street Journal*, 10 August 2005.
19 Faligot, *Chinese Spies*, p. 275. In the 1990s the MSS expanded its 'special section for broadcasting fake news' (p. 396). Faligot also refers to confidential economic reports produced by Xinhua news agency (p. 279).
20 Hannas, Mulvenon and Puglisi, *Chinese Industrial Espionage*, pp. 116–17.
21 Peter Mattis, 'China reorients strategic military intelligence', *Janes*, 2017. See the chart on p. 6.

22 Mattis and Brazil, *Chinese Communist Espionage*, p. 52.
23 James Scott and Drew Spaniel, *China's Espionage Dynasty*, Washington, D.C.: Institute for Critical Infrastructure Technology, 2016, p. 10. No source is given for these numbers, so they should be treated with caution.
24 Mattis, 'China reorients strategic military intelligence', p. 8, table. See also Faligot, *Chinese Spies*, p. 248.
25 Mattis, 'China reorients strategic military intelligence', p. 3.
26 Mattis, 'China reorients strategic military intelligence', p. 3.
27 Faligot, *Chinese Spies*, pp. 206, 247. SASTIND was previously the Commission for Science, Technology and Industry for National Defence (COSTIND).
28 <http://www.xinhuanet.com//politics/2017-08/26/c_1121545221.htm>.
29 Anon., 'Survey of Chinese-linked espionage in the United States since 2000', Center for Strategic and International Studies, 2019, <https://www.csis.org/programs/technology-policy-program/survey-chinese-linked-espionage-united-states-2000>.
30 Or at least had Chinese names. Andrew Chongseh Kim, 'Prosecuting Chinese "spies": an empirical analysis of the Economic Espionage Act', *Cardozo Law Review*, vol. 40, no. 2, 2019.
31 Anti-Chinese racism but not anti-Asian racism because the share of indictments for 'other Asians' remained constant between the two periods at nine per cent.
32 Nate Rayond and Brendan Pierson, 'FBI employee gets two years in prison for acting as Chinese agent', *Reuters*, 20 January 2017.
33 Zach Dorfman, 'How Silicon Valley became a den of spies', *Politico*, 27 July 2018; Trevor Loudon, 'Feinstein's spy: Russell Lowe and San Francisco's pro-China left', *Epoch Times*, 20 August 2018.
34 It was set up by the Chinese Progressive Association, known to be a united front group (Loudon, 'Feinstein's spy').
35 Glenn Bunting, 'Feinstein, husband hold strong China connections', *Los Angeles Times*, 28 March 1997. Feinstein seems to have had early sympathies for the CCP government and by the time she became mayor of San Francisco was a friend of China. Her election to the US Senate in 1992 was perhaps a pay-off for the CCP's 'surround the city' tactic.
36 <https://www.justice.gov/opa/press-release/file/953321/download>.
37 Faligot, *Chinese Spies*, p. 273.
38 Garrett Graff, 'China's 5 steps for recruiting spies', *Wired*, 31 October 2018.
39 <https://www.justice.gov/opa/pr/chinese-national-arrested-allegedly-acting-within-united-states-illegal-agent-people-s>.
40 Kate Mansey, 'Boris Johnson's deputy: "I had sex with a Chinese spy": Beauty lures politician to bed then drugs him to take secrets', *The Mirror*, 29 November 2009.
41 Andrew Porter, 'Downing Street aide in Chinese "honeytrap" sting', *The Telegraph*, 20 July 2008.

42 Mattis and Brazil, *Chinese Communist Espionage*, p. 255. For useful references, see the glossary of Chinese espionage and security terms in the appendix.

43 See references 65–69 in glossary, Mattis and Brazil, *Chinese Communist Espionage*.

44 Nigel Inkster, 'China's draft intelligence law', International Institute for Strategic Studies, blog post, 26 May 2017.

45 Peter Cluskey, 'Dutch ambassador to Beijing suspended over affair amid honeytrap fears', *Irish Times*, 17 October 2016.

46 Faligot, *China's Spies*, p. 394. See also: <https://tinyurl.com/y9d4o836>

47 Mike Giglio, 'China's spies are on the offensive', *The Atlantic*, 26 August 2019.

48 Anon., 'German spy agency warns of Chinese LinkedIn espionage', *BBC News* online, 10 December 2017; Jeff Stone, 'LinkedIn is becoming China's go-to platform for recruiting foreign spies', *Cyberscoop*, 26 March 2019.

49 Christoph Giesen and Ronen Steinke, 'Wie chinesische Agenten den Bundestag ausspionieren', *Süddeutsche*, 6 July 2018; Anon., 'Chinese spy on Bundestag through social media info purchased from German politicians: report', *The Local.de*, 6 July 2018.

50 Jodi Xu Klein, 'Fear mounts that Chinese-American scientists are being targeted amid US national security crackdown', *South China Morning Post*, 3 July 2019.

51 US counterintelligence chief William Evanina said that the PRC's intelligence agencies 'bring ungodly resources that we can't handle right now'. Quoted by Olivia Gazis, 'U.S. top spy-catcher: China brings "ungodly resources" to espionage', *CBS News* online, 5 September 2018.

52 Faligot, *China's Spies*, p. 215.

53 CICIR is listed on official Chinese website as one of the top think tanks in China, <https://web.archive.org/web/20190106155604/http://www.china.org.cn/top10/2011-09/26/content_23491278_5.htm>. Although now dated, a good source on CICIR is Anon., 'Profile of MSS-affiliated PRC foreign policy think tank', Open Source Center, 25 August 2011. See also Peter Mattis, 'Five ways China spies', *The National Interest*, 6 March 2014.

54 Anon., 'Profile of MSS-affiliated PRC foreign policy think tank'. On the 11th Bureau, see Mattis and Brazil, *Chinese Communist Espionage*, p. 56. See also Anon., 'China's Ministry of State Security', StratFor, 1 June 2012, <https://worldview.stratfor.com/article/chinas-ministry-state-security>.

55 Peter Mattis, 'Assessing the foreign policy influence of the Ministry of State Security', *China Brief (Jamestown Foundation)*, vol. 11, no. 1, 14 January 2011; <http://www.chinavitae.com/biography/3969>.

56 David Shambaugh, 'China's international relations think tanks: evolving structure and process', *China Quarterly*, vol. 171, September 2002, pp. 575–96.

57 Anon., 'Profile of MSS-affiliated PRC foreign policy think tank'.

58 Faligot, *Chinese Spies*, p. 218.

59 'EU-China Strategic Dialogue 2015', website of the EU Institute for Security Studies, 13 March 2015, <https://www.iss.europa.eu/content/eu-china-strategic-dialogue-2015>; '9th Meeting of the CSIS-CICIR Cybersecurity Dialogue', CSIS website, 2–3 February 2015, <https://www.csis.org/events/9th-meeting-csis-cicir-cybersecurity-dialogue>.

60 As an instance of China's intellectuals using the weaknesses of democracy to justify the one-party state, CICIR experts, responding to Russian meddling in the US presidential election, argued 'that the pervasive influx of fake news affecting the US election is clear precedent for why the Chinese government regulates the internet, to "insure that information online is true"', <https://tinyurl.com/vvjkp79>.

61 <https://www.twai.it/journals/orizzonte-cina/>; <https://tinyurl.com/rwpwzbt>.

62 For the link between the CIISS and PLA intelligence, see Peter Mattis, 'China's military intelligence system is changing', *War on the Rocks*, 29 December 2015.

63 Faligot, *Chinese Spies*, pp. 218–19.

64 The affidavit can be found at <https://www.justice.gov/opa/press-release/file/975671/download>, p. 5.

65 Nate Thayer, 'How the Chinese recruit American journalists as spies', *Asia Sentinel*, 4 July 2017.

66 <https://www.justice.gov/opa/press-release/file/975671/download>; Brandi Buchman, 'Bond revoked for ex-CIA agent charged with spying for China', *Courthouse News*, 10 July 2017.

67 Garrett Graff, 'China's 5 steps for recruiting spies', *Wired*, 31 October 2018.

68 Graff, 'China's 5 steps for recruiting spies'.

69 To, *Qiaowu*, p. 42

70 To, *Qiaowu*, pp. 45–6.

71 To, *Qiaowu*, p. 46.

72 Anon., 'Threats to the U.S. research enterprise: China's talent recruitment plans', staff report, United States Senate Permanent Subcommittee on Investigations, 2019.

73 Stephen Chen, 'America's hidden role in Chinese weapons research', *South China Morning Post*, 29 March 2017.

74 To, *Qiaowu*, pp. 43–4.

75 Jeffrey Mervis, 'NIH letters asking about undisclosed foreign ties rattle U.S. universities', *Science Mag*, 1 March 2019; Jocelyn Kaiser and David Malakoff, 'NIH investigating whether U.S. scientists are sharing ideas with foreign governments', *Science Mag*, 27 August 2018.

76 Todd Ackerman, 'MD Anderson ousts 3 scientists over concerns about Chinese conflicts of interest', *Houston Chronicle*, 19 April 2019.

77 Hvistendahl, 'Major U.S. cancer center ousts "Asian" researchers after NIH flags their foreign ties'.

78 < https://www.justice.gov/opa/press-release/file/1239796/download>

79 Douglas Belkin, 'Harvard chemistry chairman under investigation is a giant of his field', *Wall Street Journal*, 29 January 2020.

80 <https://archive.fo/7Htz#selection-2341.363-2341.497>.

81 Bill Wallace, 'Cox Report links S.F. association to spy network / Chinese exchange group accused of stealing U.S. weapons secrets', *SFGate*, 28 May 1999.

82 <https://www.justice.gov/usao-sdny/press-release/file/1203021/download>.

83 Hannas, Mulvenon and Puglisi, *Chinese Industrial Espionage*, pp. 78–80.

84 Hannas, Mulvenon and Puglisi, *Chinese Industrial Espionage*, p. 96.

85 For the case of Noshir Gowadia, see <web.archive.org/web/20070523175209/>; <honolulu.fbi.gov/dojpressrel/pressrel06/defensesecrets110906.htm>; <www.justice.gov/opa/pr/hawaii-man-sentenced-32-years-prison-providing-defense-information-and-services-people-s>.

86 In 2015 China's ambassador, Luo Zhaohui, briefed the chief representative of the China Association for International Exchange of Personnel (CAIEP) Canada, Lyu Ge, on the latest developments in China–Canada relations. 'He encouraged CAIEP Canada Ltd to break new ground in introducing Canadian talent to China', <http://ca.china-embassy.org/eng/gdxw/t1325872.htm>. In 2007 the Canadian government signed a cooperation agreement on science and technology with CAIEP and other agencies. The Canadian government has been promoting and facilitating joint projects, workshops etc. and removing barriers for the exchange of talent, <http://www.ec.gc.ca/international/default.asp?lang=En&n=BF139207-1&pedisable=true>.

87 Hannas, Mulvenon and Puglisi, *Chinese Industrial Espionage*, pp. 79–80.

88 Hannas, Mulvenon and Puglisi, *Chinese Industrial Espionage*, p. 110.

89 <http://www.cast-usa.net/>, see News section. For a more detailed discussion of CAST-USA's origins, organisational structure and operations, see <https://books.openedition.org/irdeditions/2642?lang=en>.

90 <http://www.cast-usa.net/>.

91 <http://www.cast-usa.net/>, see News section.

92 Hannas, Mulvenon and Puglisi, *Chinese Industrial Espionage*, p. 113; <http://www.castdc.org/cast_web_2006/network.htm>.

93 Hannas, Mulvenon and Puglisi, *Chinese Industrial Espionage*, p. 107

94 Hannas, Mulvenon and Puglisi, *Chinese Industrial Espionage*, chapter 5.

95 The following text is modified from Hamilton, *Silent Invasion*, pp. 184–6.

96 'Quan Ao Huaren zhuanjia xuezhe lianhehui chengli' 全澳华人专家学者联合会成立 [All-China Association of Chinese Experts and Scholars established], *People's Daily Online*, 11 October 2004, <https://tinyurl.com/r4cd9qj>.

97 <www.chinaql.org/c/2015-12-14/485805.shtml>. See also <https://tinyurl.com/rjkes3v>.

98 Interview 1 February 2017 with Chinese defector Chen Yonglin, who says some scientists are given very large bonuses for supplying information to the PRC.

99 Hannas, Mulvenon and Puglisi, *Chinese Industrial Espionage*, p. 114.

100 Hannas, Mulvenon and Puglisi, *Chinese Industrial Espionage*, pp. 122–3.

101 Quoted by Diamond and Schell, eds, *China's Influence & American Interests*, p. 124.

102 Quoted by Hannas, Mulvenon and Puglisi, *Chinese Industrial Espionage*, p. 126.

103 Hong Xiao, 'It's all about the people's exchanges: official', *China Daily*, 16 December 2017.

104 Note this similar organisation, related to CAIEP and also overseen by SAFEA—China Society for Research on International Exchange and Personnel Development: <https://web.archive.org/web/20190917013413/http://yjh.caiep.net/index_en.php>.

105 <http://ianharvey-ip.com/china/safea-caiep-china-and-ip-myth-and-reality/>.

106 Hong Xiao, 'Academia feeling heat of trade conflict', *China Daily*, 1 July 2019.

107 Bill Bishop, *Sinocism newsletter*, 12 June 2019.

108 Alex Joske, *Picking Flowers, Making Honey*, report by Australian Strategic Policy Institute, Canberra, 2019. See also Alex Joske, 'The China defence universities tracker', Australian Strategic Policy Institute, Canberra, 2019.

109 PLAIEU was merged with a few other institutes and universities in 2017. The current full name is 中国人民解放军战略支援部队信息工程大学. It was also transferred to the supervision of the PLA's new Strategic Support Force.

110 Clive Hamilton and Alex Joske, 'China's ghost university haunts U.S. campuses', unpublished paper, November 2017. See also Joske, *Picking Flowers*.

111 Clive Hamilton and Alex Joske, 'Australian universities are helping China's military surpass the United States', *The Sydney Morning Herald*, 27 October 2017. The text that follows borrows from this article by Joske and one of the authors of this book.

112 He was an alternate member from 2012 to 2017.

113 Ben Packham, 'Professor, Chinese generals co-authored defence research', *The Australian*, 31 July 2019.

114 Clive Hamilton and Alex Joske, 'Australian taxes may help finance Chinese military capability', *The Australian*, 10 June 2017. With thanks to Alex Joske for permission to reproduce and paraphrase sentences from this article. CETC's investment arm also holds the controlling share of Hikvision, <https://ipvm.com/reports/cetc-increase>.

115 Matthew Luce, 'A model company: CETC celebrates 10 years of civil-military integration', *China Brief (Jamestown Foundation)*, vol. 12, no. 4, 2012.

116 Anon., 'Woman sentenced for U.S. military sales to China', *Reuters*, 29 January 2011.

117 Matthew Godsey and Valerie Lincy, 'Gradual signs of change: proliferation to and from China over decades', *Strategic Trade Review*, vol. 5, no. 8, winter/spring 2019.

118 Anon., *Threats to the U.S. Research Enterprise*, p. 44.

119 Laurens Cerulus, 'Europe raises flags on China's cyber espionage', *Politico*, 10 April 2018.

120 Stephanie Borys, 'Inside a massive cyber hack that risks compromising leaders across the globe', *ABC News* online, 2 October 2019.

121 Anon., 'Singapore health database hack steals personal information of 1.5 million people, including PM', *ABC News* online, 20 July 2018.

122 A few months earlier, it was reported that Chinese hackers, probably the notorious APT10 group, had been targeting Japan's healthcare companies, although in that case the intention appeared to be theft of proprietary information on their products. Anon., 'China hackers accused of attacking Japanese defence firms', *South China Morning Post*, 23 April 2013.

123 <https://www.cnet.com/news/justice-department-indicts-chinese-hackers-allegedly-behind-anthem-breach/>.

124 Scott and Spaniel, *China's Espionage Dynasty*, p. 15.

125 Nicole Perlroth, 'Hack of community health systems affects 4.5 million patients', *The New York Times*, 18 August 2014.

126 David Wroe, 'Defence medical records sent to China in security breach', *The Sydney Morning Herald*, 7 July 2015.

127 Hacking into medical records may not be necessary in Australia; there has been a boom in Chinese investment in healthcare, a trend that seems to have attracted no official interest despite the security risks. Mergers and acquisitions totalling $5.5 billion took place over the three years 2015–17, the same amount as in the vastly larger US market. Anon., *Demystifying Chinese Investment in Australian Healthcare*, a report by KPMG and the University of Sydney, January 2018.

128 US House of Representatives Permanent Select Committee of Intelligence, 'Investigative report on the US national security issues posed by Chinese telecommunications companies Huawei and ZTE', 8 October 2012, <http://tinyurl.com/qrm3hc3> But see Elsa Kania, 'Much ado about Huawei (part 1)', *The Strategist*, ASPI, 27 March 2018.

129 Evan S. Medeiros, Roger Cliff, Keith Crane and James C. Mulvenon, 'A new direction for China's defense industry', RAND Corporation, 2005, p. 218.

130 Bryan Krekel, Patton Adams and George Bakos, *Occupying the Information High Ground: Chinese capabilities for computer network operations and cyber espionage*, report prepared for the U.S.-China Economic and Security Review Commission by Northrop Grumman Corp, 2012, p. 75.

131 John Aglionby, Emily Feng and Yuan Yang, 'African Union accuses China of hacking headquarters', *Financial Times*, 30 January 2018; Danielle Cave,

'The African Union headquarters hack and Australia's 5G network', *ASPI Strategist*, 13 July 2018.

132 Norman Pearlstine et al., 'The man behind Huawei', *Los Angeles Times*, 10 April 2019. In May 2019 it was reported that the Dutch intelligence agency AIVD believes Huawei equipment used in the network of a major Dutch telecommunication network has a hidden 'backdoor' installed that allows access to customer data. Anon., 'Dutch spy agency investigating alleged Huawei "backdoor": *Volkskrant*', *Reuters*, 16 May 2019.

133 Pearlstine et al., 'The man behind Huawei'.

134 Joanna Plucinska, Koh Gui Qing, Alicja Ptak and Steve Strecklow, 'How Poland became a front in the cold war between the U.S. and China', *Reuters*, 2 July 2019.

135 See for example, Wayne Ma, 'How Huawei targets Apple trade secrets', *The Information*, 18 February 2019.

136 Tripto Lahiri, 'The US says Huawei had a bonus program for employees who stole trade secrets', *Quartz*, 30 January 2019.

137 Elsa Kania, 'Much ado about Huawei', *ASPI Strategist*, Part 1, 27 March 2018, Part 2, 28 March 2018.

138 David Shepardson and Karen Freifeld, 'China's Huawei, 70 affiliates on U.S. trade blacklist', *Reuters*, 16 May 2019.

139 Dan Sabbagh and Jon Henley, 'Huawei poses security threat to UK, says former MI6 chief', *The Guardian*, 16 May 2019.

140 Christopher Hope, 'Chinese firm Huawei spends tens of thousands lobbying British politicians', *The Telegraph*, 30 November 2012.

141 Hope, 'Chinese firm Huawei spends tens of thousands lobbying British politicians'.

142 Adam Satariano and Raymond Zhong, 'How Huawei wooed Europe with sponsorships, investments and promises', *The New York Times*, 22 January 2019.

143 Robert Fife and Stephen Chase, 'Goodale says decision on Huawei 5G network to come before election', *The Globe and Mail*, 1 May 2019; Erin Dunne, 'Huawei's latest advocate? An Obama cybersecurity official', *Washington Examiner*, 12 April 2019. Donald Trump tweeted: 'This is not good, or acceptable.'

144 'Huawei Deutschland—Deutschland besser verbinden', Huawei website, not dated, <https://web.archive.org/web/20200112210508/http://huawei-dialog.de/mission-statement/>.

145 Satariano and Zhong, 'How Huawei wooed Europe with sponsorships, investments and promises'.

146 Limin Zhou and Omid Ghoreishi, 'The man behind McCallum's controversial press conference that led to his removal as Canada's ambassador to China', *Epoch Times*, 28 January 2019.

147 Tom Blackwell, 'A curious mirroring of Beijing's official line', *Windsor Star*, 23 February 2019.

148 Anon., 'Chinese-Canadian group defends detained Huawei CFO', CBC, 11 December 2018.

149 Bob Mackin, 'Richmond mayoral candidate says "there is no human rights abuse in China"', *The Breaker*, 3 October 2018.

150 Hamilton, *Silent Invasion*, pp. 158–9.

151 Harrison Christian, 'Huawei piles pressure on Govt with ads and sponsorship, security experts say', *Stuff.com*, 18 April 2019.

152 Kelvin Chan and Rob Gillies, 'Huawei night in Canada: inside tech giant's push to burnish its brand', *Toronto Star*, 13 February 2019.

153 Elizabeth Gibney, 'Berkeley bans new research funding from Huawei', *Nature*, no. 566, 7 February 2019, pp. 16–17.

154 Satariano and Zhong, 'How Huawei wooed Europe with sponsorships, investments and promises'.

155 Robert Delaney, 'Shutting the gates of academia: American universities cut ties to Huawei and Confucius Institute', *South China Morning Post*, 19 March 2019.

156 Ilaria Maria Sala, 'Chinese tech firm Huawei's bullying attitude fails to win over hearts and minds', *Hong Kong Free Press*, 15 December 2019.

Chapter 9 Media: 'Our surname is Party'

1 Anon., 'China's Xi urges state media to boost global influence', *Reuters*, 19 February 2016; 'Xi Jinping: jianchi zhengque fangxiang chuangxin fangfa shouduan tigao xinwen yulun chuanboli yindaoli' 习近平:坚持正确方向创新方法手段 提高新闻舆论传播力引导力 [Uphold the correct direction and innovate methods to raise communication power and guidance of news and public opinion]; *People's Daily Online*, 19 February 2016; <https://tinyurl.com/u7utsnr>.

2 David Shambaugh, 'China's soft power push: the search for respect', *Foreign Affairs*, July/August 2015.

3 Li Congjun, 'Toward a new world media order', *The Wall Street Journal*, 1 June 2011.

4 Didi Kirsten Tatlow, 'Mapping China-in-Germany', *Sinopsis*, 2 October 2019.

5 See for example David Bandurski, 'Journalism denied: how China views the news', *China Media Project*, 1 February 2018.

6 Anon., 'Document 9: a *ChinaFile* translation', *ChinaFile*, 8 November 2013, <http://www.chinafile.com/document-9-chinafile-translation>.

7 David Bandurski, 'The spirit of control', *Medium*, 25 February 2016. We are indebted to John Fitzgerald for highlighting the difference in connotation between '*xing*' and 'surname'.

8 For a practical example, see 'Chengdu wanbao yin kandeng you yanzhong zhengzhi cuowo de zhaopian shoudao weigui weiji jinggao' 《成都晚报》因刊 登有严重政治错误的照片受到违规违纪警告 [*Chengdu Evening Times* receives a warning of violation of regulations and discipline because of publishing a photo containing a serious political mistake], *Neibu tongxin*, no. 7, 2000, p. 12.

9 Lizzie Dearden, 'Chinese journalists punished for wrongly reporting Xi Jinping's "resignation" in state media spelling mistake', *The Independent*, 7 December 2015.

10 Tom Phillips, 'Chinese reporter makes on-air "confession" after market chaos', *The Guardian*, 31 August 2015.

11 See *China Daily* job ads: 'Zhongguo ribao she gongkai zhaopin gangwei xuqiu' 中国日报社公开招聘岗位需求 [*China Daily* public recruitment positions], *China Daily* online, 27 November 2017, <https://tinyurl.com/yx7a6hzj>.

12 Lily Kuo, 'Chinese journalists to be tested on loyalty to Xi Jinping', *The Guardian*, 20 September 2019.

13 For instance, the China Public Diplomacy Association offers ten-month courses to journalists from Africa, South Asia and Southeast Asia. See Ros Chanveasna, 'China training journalists from 44 countries', *Khmer Times*, 6 March 2018.

14 Anon., 'China's pursuit of a new world media order', Reporters Without Borders, 22 March 2019, <https://rsf.org/en/reports/rsf-report-chinas-pursuit-new-world-media-order>.

15 Anon., 'China's pursuit of a new world media order'; Anon., '*New York Times* hosts 3rd World Media Summit', *China Daily*, 10 October 2013.

16 Nadège Rolland, 'Mapping the footprint of Belt and Road influence operations', *Sinopsis*, 12 August 2019.

17 'Media Cooperation Forum on B&R; held in Hainan', *Xinhua Silk Road Information Service*, 31 October 2018, <https://tinyurl.com/rzoju5j>.

18 See for example 'Jointly build a bridge of friendship and mutual understanding—address by HE Ambassador Ma Zhaoxu at the 3rd China-Australia Forum', website of the Chinese embassy in Australia, 26 August 2014, <https://web.archive.org/web/20191130181921/http://au.china-embassy.org/eng/sgjs/Topics123/t1185770.htm>.

19 'Xinhuashe juxing jinian Yingyu duiwai xinwen kaibo liushi zhounian zuotanhui' 新华社举行纪念英语对外新闻传播六十周年座谈会 [Xinhua news agency holds symposium to commemorate the 60th anniversary of external news dissemination], *Duiwai xuanchuan cankao*, no. 10, 2004, p. 6.

20 Xi Shaoying 习少颖, *1949–1966 nian Zhongguo duiwai xuanchuan shi yanjiu* 1949–1966 年中国对外宣传史研究 [Research on China's external propaganda history from 1949 to 1966], Wuhan: Huazhong keji daxue chubanshe, 2010, p. 28.

21 Louisa Lim and Julia Bergin, 'Inside China's audacious global propaganda campaign', *The Guardian*, 7 December 2018.

22 Vivian Wu and Adam Chen, 'Beijing in 45b yuan global media drive', *South China Morning Post*, 13 January 2009. According to Reporters Without Borders, the sum was meant to cover a period of ten years and was later increased to 10 billion RMB per year. Reporters without Borders, 'China's pursuit of a new world media order', p. 29.

23 Wang Guoqing 王国庆, 'Jianchi "ruan", "ying" liang shou qi zhua, nuli tigao woguo meiti guoji chuanbo nengli' 坚持'软'、'硬'两手齐抓 努力提高我国媒体国际传播能力 [Adhere to grasp with 'soft' and 'hard' hands together, to make an effort to improve China's media international dissemination capabilities], *Zhongguo guangbo dianshi xuekan*, no. 10, 2010, p. 1.

24 See the graphic in 'Dang Xinwen lianbo yu shang Zhongguo zhi sheng' 当'新闻联播'遇上'中国之声', 1 April 2018, website of the *Nordic Chinese Times*, <https://web.archive.org/web/20191018121009/http://nordicapd.com/content.asp?pid=31&cid=4162>. The term used is 业务领导, 'professional guidance', which describes a relationship in which one entity can issue binding orders to another in the Chinese bureaucracy.

25 'Who we are', website of CGTN, not dated, <https://tinyurl.com/vc3d6ev>.

26 Reporters Without Borders, 'China's pursuit of a new world media order', p. 4.

27 'About China Radio International', website of CRI, not dated, <http://english.cri.cn/11114/2012/09/20/1261s723239.htm>.

28 See also David Bandurski, 'Xinhua News Agency steps out into the world', *China Media Project*, 22 October 2009, <http://chinamediaproject.org/2009/10/22/xinhua-news-agency-steps-out-into-the-world/>.

29 'Guanyu Xinhuashe' 关于新华社 [About Xinhua News Agency], website of *Xinhua*, not dated, <https://web.archive.org/web/20190827153150/http://203.192.6.89/xhs/>.

30 'About CNC', website of *CNC*, not dated, <https://web.archive.org/web/20190827153236/http://en.cncnews.cn/e_about_cnc/about.html>.

31 Kirsty Needham, 'How Australians set up Communist China's official propaganda tool', *The Sydney Morning Herald*, 5 December 2018.

32 Annual Report of the *China Daily* for 2018 on Service Units Online (gjsy.gov.cn), the official website for China's 'Service units' (事业单位).

33 'About China Daily Group', website of *China Daily*, not dated, <https://web.archive.org/web/20190827153657/http://www.chinadaily.com.cn/static_e/2011about.html>.

34 Annual Report of the *China Daily* for 2018 on Service Units Online (gjsy.gov.cn), the official website for China's 'Service units' (事业单位).

35 Chinese observers have long admired what they consider the United States' ability to let 'different voices sing the same tune'. By this they mean that different actors take on different roles when criticising China, doing so with

different degrees of intensity and in different words while relaying the same message. See Liu Yaming 刘雅鸣 and Li Pei 李珮, 'Quanqiu chuanbo shidai wo guo duiwai xuanchuan xin chulu (er)—Di yi shijian fachu shengyin waixuan bixu xian fa zhi ren' 全球传播时代我国对外宣传新出路（二—第一次发出声音外宣必须先发制人 [A new way out for China's external propaganda in the era of global communication—Starting with the first sound, external propaganda needs to gain the upper hand by releasing news first], *Duiwai xuanchuan cankao*, no. 12, 2003, p. 18.

36 特别是与外国合作以商业面貌出现 Benkan teyue jizhe 本刊特约记者, 'Tixian shidaixing, bawo guilüxing, fuyu chuangzaoxing: Ji 2003 nian quanguo waixuan gongzuo huiyi' 体现时代性 把握规律性 富于创造性—记 2003 年全国外宣工作会议 [Embody the characteristics of the times, grasp the rules, be rich in innovation—Notes from the nationwide work meeting for external propaganda in 2003], *Duiwai xuanchuan cankao*, no. 2, 2003, p. 3.

37 Paul Mozur, 'Live from America's capital, a TV station run by China's Communist Party', *The New York Times*, 28 February 2019.

38 Mozur, 'Live from America's capital, a TV station run by China's Communist Party'.

39 Lim and Bergin, 'Inside China's audacious global propaganda campaign'.

40 Lim and Bergin, 'Inside China's audacious global propaganda campaign'.

41 He Qinglian, 'The fog of censorship: media control in China', Human Rights in China, 2008, <https://www.hrichina.org/sites/default/files/PDFs/Reports/HRIC-Fog-of-Censorship.pdf, pp. 71ff>.

42 Known as 本土化 in Chinese. See Brady, *Magic Weapons*, p. 10.

43 For example, Sean Callebs, <https://tinyurl.com/tj3l5yw>; Jeff Moody, <https://tinyurl.com/wd8vlqb>; Elaine Reyes, <https://tinyurl.com/r6ft56m>; Jim Spellman, <https://tinyurl.com/u4sf7ga>; Brian Salter, <https://tinyurl.com/uyv2qkx>.

44 'Hiring Chinese citizens to do auxiliary work', International Press Center, not dated, <https://web.archive.org/web/20191130184313/http://ipc.fmprc.gov.cn/eng/wgjzzhzn/t716850.htm>.

45 Reprinted in Henansheng geming weiyuanhui banshizu 河南省革命委员会办事组 [Office of the revolutionary committee of Henan province], *Mao Zedong guanyu duiwai xuanchuan de zhishi* 毛泽东关于对外宣传的指示 [Directives from Chairman Mao about external propaganda work], 1 August 1972.

46 John F. Copper, 'Western media reveal China bias', *China Daily*, 5 February 2018, <https://web.archive.org/web/20191018124935/http://www.chinadaily.com.cn/a/201802/05/WS5a779716a3106e7dcc13aa92.html>.

47 New China TV (TV channel run by Xinhua), <https://www.youtube.com/watch?v=aaAW1RVE9mM>.

48 CGTN America, 'The heat: author Martin Jacques discusses China & global issues Pt 1', CGTN YouTube channel, 19 October 2017, <https://www.youtube.com/watch?v=cOs4T0mEzA0>.

49 Diamond and Schell, eds, *China's Influence & American Interests*, p. 70. The scholar reported she was paid US$150 per interview.

50 'History and milestones', website of CRI, not dated, <https://archive.is/20131116074500/http://english.cri.cn/about/history.htm>.

51 'CWI and Xinhuanet sign cooperation agreement', website of CWI, 4 November 2014, <https://web.archive.org/web/20190829153344/https://www.cwi.nl/news/2014/cwi-and-xinhuanet-sign-cooperation-agreement>.

52 'China Media Centre (CMC) hosts roundtable discussions with leading UK specialists on China and senior Chinese officials', 6 November 2018, <https://tinyurl.com/snc5hqv>.

53 <https://www.westminster.ac.uk/research/groups-and-centres/china-media-centre>; 'China Media Centre (CMC) hosts roundtable discussions with leading UK specialists on China and senior Chinese officials', 6 November 2018, <https://tinyurl.com/snc5hqv>.

54 'Professional exchange: the China Professional Leadership Programme', website of University of Westminster, <https://tinyurl.com/vfnbuo8>.

55 'Professor Hugo de Burgh', website of University of Westminster, <https://tinyurl.com/td22euk>.

56 Bill Kenber, 'Hugo de Burgh, professor who has pushed for closer ties with China,' *The Times*, 24 August 2019.

57 'Professional exchange: the China Professional Leadership Programme', website of the University of Westminster, <https://tinyurl.com/vfnbuo8>.

58 'China's international relations and economic strategies: perceptions of the UK and China', China Media Center, 31 October 2018, <https://tinyurl.com/uw74p93>.

59 <https://tinyurl.com/r9vdl72>.

60 <https://tinyurl.com/r9vdl72>.

61 'CMC's courses for media handlers: the practical elements', website of the China Media Centre, 16 October 2019, <https://tinyurl.com/tktfph7>.

62 'Professional exchange: the China Professional Leadership Programme', website of University of Westminster, <https://tinyurl.com/vfnbuo8>.

63 Viola Zhou, 'Why is LinkedIn so big in China? Because it censors', *Inkstone*, 4 January 2019.

64 Erin Dunne, 'LinkedIn's China compromise shows price of market access', *Washington Examiner*, 3 January 2019.

65 Megha Rajagopalan, 'LinkedIn censored the profile of another critic of the Chinese government', *Buzzfeed News*, 8 January 2019.

66 'Xinhuashe haiwai shejiao meiti tongyi zhanghao "New China" zhengshi yunxing' 新华社海外社交媒体统一账号"New China"正式运行 [Xinhua's

unified account for overseas social media 'New China' officially launched], *People's Daily Online*, 1 March 2015, <https://tinyurl.com/yx4w76sx>.

67 Steven Jiang, 'Taiwan furious after China attempts to take credit for LGBT marriage win', *CNN*, 20 May 2019.

68 Ben Blanchard, 'China's parliament rules out allowing same-sex marriage', *Reuters*, 21 August 2019.

69 Layla Mashkoor and Kassy Cho, 'Chinese state media and others are spreading false information about the protests in Hong Kong', *Buzzfeed News*, 14 June 2019.

70 'Zui "zhencheng" de daoqian'最真诚的道歉 [The most 'sincere' apology], Xinhua Xianggang on Facebook, 15 August 2019, <https://tinyurl.com/s4fjktr>.

71 Chen Weihua, Twitter, 1 September 2019, <https://tinyurl.com/sahdtnm>.

72 Screenshots on file with the authors.

73 Twitter Inc., 'Updating our advertising policies on state media', Twitter blog, 19 August 2019, <https://blog.twitter.com/en_us/topics/company/2019/advertising_policies_on_state_media.html>.

74 CCTV, 'Lingdaoren shi zenme liancheng de?' 领导人是怎样炼成的? [How leaders are made], CCTV channel on YouTube, <https://www.youtube.com/watch?v=eGX2kMUWvIo>. For an English version of the same clip, see <https://www.youtube.com/watch?v=M734o_17H_A>. 'How leaders are made' was produced by Studio on Fuxing Road, which some media reports have linked to the CCP's International Liaison Department. See Chun Han Wong, 'Chinese president Xi Jinping's extreme makeover', *The Wall Street Journal*, 12 May 2016.

75 For example, Agence France Presse in Beijing, 'China turns to psychedelic David Bowie lookalike to push "five-year plan"', *The Guardian*, 27 October 2015.

76 Julia Hollingsworth, 'Australian politicians are targeting voters on WeChat. But fake content could end up costing them', *CNN*, 15 May 2019.

77 Joel Harding, 'The Chinese government fakes nearly 450 million social media comments a year. This is why', *The Washington Post*, 19 May 2019.

78 See Zheping Huang, 'Chinese trolls jumped the firewall to attack Taiwan's president and military on Facebook', *Quartz*, 3 January 2017.

79 Zhang Han, 'Patriotic posts flood East Turkestan pages to fight untrue reports on Xinjiang', *Global Times*, 10 April 2019.

80 Maggie Miller, 'Twitter, Facebook accuse China of misinformation targeting Hong Kong protests', *The Hill*, 19 August 2019.

81 Jake Wallis, 'China's information warfare darkens the doorstep of Twitter and Facebook', *ASPI Strategist*, 21 August 2019, <https://www.aspistrategist.org.au/chinas-information-warfare-darkens-the-doorstep-of-twitter-and-facebook/>.

82 Amar Toor, 'Zuckerberg meets with China's propaganda chief', *The Verge*, 21 March 2016; Loulla-Mae Eleftheriou-Smith, 'China's President Xi Jinping

"turns down Mark Zuckerberg's request to name his unborn child" at White House dinner', *The Independent*, 4 October 2015.

83 Will Oremus, 'Why YouTube keeps demonetizing videos of the Hong Kong protests', *OneZero*, 8 July 2019, <https://onezero.medium.com/why-youtube-keeps-demonetizing-videos-of-the-hong-kong-protests-460da6b6cb2b>.

84 Personal experience while following the protests on Twitter, also noted by a number of other users.

85 借船出海; See Brady, *Magic Weapons*, p. 10.

86 For example, 'Für eine bessere Welt—Ein Gastbeitrag des Staatspräsidenten Xi Jinping anlässlich seines Besuches in Deutschland' [For a better world —a guest comment by president Xi Jinping during his visit in Germany], website of the Chinese embassy in Germany, 4 July 2017, <https://web.archive.org/web/20191130192124/http://de.china-embassy.org/det/sgyw/t1475300.htm>.

87 Jichang Lulu, 'China's state media and the outsourcing of soft power', *Asia Dialogue*, 15 July 2015, <https://theasiadialogue.com/2015/07/15/chinas-state-media-and-the-outsourcing-of-soft-power/>.

88 Koh Gui Qing and John Shiffman, 'Beijing's covert radio network airs China-friendly news across Washington, and the world', *Reuters*, 2 November 2015.

89 Diamond and Schell, eds, *China's Influence & American Interests*, p. 82. See also 'Gongsi gaikuang', 公司概况 [Company overview], website of EDI media, not dated, <https://web.archive.org/web/20190827155315/http://www.edimediainc.com/zh/%e5%85%ac%e5%8f%b8%e6%a6%82%e6%b3%81/>. EDI Media Inc 鹰龙传媒有限公司 Qing and Shiffman, 'Beijing's covert radio network airs China-friendly news across Washington, and the world'.

90 James Su (Su Yantao 苏彦韬), 'Team', website of EDI Media, not dated, <https://web.archive.org/web/20190827155537/https://www.edimediainc.com/en/team/>.

91 'About us', website of *GBTimes*, not dated, <https://web.archive.org/web/20190827155713/https://gbtimes.com/page/about-us>.

92 'GBTimes', Media Bias/Fact Check, not dated, <https://mediabiasfactcheck.com/gbtimes/>; according to the company's self-presentation, it jointly belongs to Guoguang and Finnish company FutuVision. See <https://tinyurl.com/sbmpgkk>. However, FutuVision is simply an earlier name of the Zhao's company GBTimes. See 'About us', website of GBTimes; Koh Gui Qing and Jane Wardell, 'Chinese radio broadcaster taps front men in Finland and Australia', *Reuters*, 2 November 2015.

93 Zhao Yinong does not deny receiving funds from CRI. See Qing and Shiffman, 'Beijing's covert radio network airs China-friendly news across Washington, and the world'.

94 'Zhongxinshe daibiaotuan canfang Fenlan Huanqiu shidai chuanmei gongsi' 中新社代表团参访芬兰环球时代传媒公司 [Delegation from China

News Service visits GBTimes media company in Finland], *China News Service*, 6 September 2016, <https://tinyurl.com/urszvmz>.

95 Jichang Lulu, 'China's state media and the outsourcing of soft power', *Asia Dialogue*, 15 July 2015, <https://theasiadialogue.com/2015/07/15/chinas-state-media-and-the-outsourcing-of-soft-power/>.

96 Lim and Bergin, 'Inside China's audacious global propaganda campaign'.

97 'About us', *ChinaWatch* website, not dated, <https://tinyurl.com/thlo2xh>; Vanessa Steinmetz, 'Anmerkung: Dieser Ausgabe kann Propaganda beiliegen', *Der Spiegel*, 25 August 2016; <https://www.nytimes.com/paidpost/china-daily/china-watch.html>; <https://tinyurl.com/vwg3ac6>.

98 Jack Hazlewood, 'China spends big on propaganda in Britain ... but returns are low', *Hong Kong Free Press*, 3 April 2016. According to estimates published in the Hoover Institute report on Chinese influence, inserts would cost around US$250,000 per year in US media. Diamond and Schell, eds, *China's Influence & American Interests*, pp. 83–4.

99 'Ambassador Liu Xiaoming holds talks with the *Daily Telegraph* editors and gives an interview', website of the Chinese embassy in the UK, 23 January 2019, <https://tinyurl.com/yx5f4vtp>.

100 'Minister Ma Hui visits Telegraph Media Group and holds talks with the editors', website of the Chinese Ministry of Foreign Affairs, 21 June 2019, <http://archive.is/20egn>.

101 'The Chinese embassy holds symposium on "Xi Jinping Thought on Diplomacy"', website of the Chinese MFA, 10 April 2019, <http://archive.is/5Pud6>.

102 Lim and Bergin, 'Inside China's audacious global propaganda campaign'.

103 'Xinhua, AP sign MOU to enhance cooperation', *Xinhua*, 25 November 2018, <https://web.archive.org/web/20190827160133/http://www.xinhuanet.com/english/2018-11/25/c_137630583.htm>; Josh Rogin, 'Congress demands answers on AP's relationship with Chinese state media', *The Washington Post*, 24 December 2018.

104 AP and Xinhua had previously signed an MoU in 2011. 李从军同美联社社长签署合作谅解备忘录, *Xinhua*, 19 December 2011, <https://web.archive.org/web/20191130194357/http://www.xinhuanet.com//ziliao/xhsld/2011-12/19/c_122447652.htm>.

105 'Xinhuashe yu Lutoushe qingzhu hezuo 60 zhounian' 新华社与路透社庆祝合作６０周年 [Xinhua and Reuters celebrate 60 years of cooperation], *Xinhua*, 30 June 2017, <http://www.xinhuanet.com/xhsld/2017-06/30/c_1121241072.htm>.

106 'Fu Ying visited headquarters of Reuters Group', website of the Chinese Embassy in the UK, 4 July 2007, <https://tinyurl.com/wrpmqwa>. According to the report published by the Chinese embassy, 'the two parties also exchanged opinions on feasibility of Reuters being listed in Shanghai Stock

Exchange and the ways to strengthen communications between Chinese and British online news media.'

107 Anon., 'Exclusive Q&A with Chinese President Xi Jinping', *Reuters*, 18 October 2015.

108 Anon., 'Xinhua launches Belt and Road info partnership with European media, think-tanks', *Xinhua*, 2 December 2017, <https://tinyurl.com/rwrh5bn>.

109 'China, Portugal ink cooperation agreement on media exchange under BRI', *Xinhua Silk Road Information Service*, 27 February 2019, <https://tinyurl.com/v3rwv3f>.

110 'Xinhua CEIS, DPA ink agreement to promote information exchanges', *Xinhua Silk Road Information Service*, 15 May 2018, <https://tinyurl.com/s79wj2d>; 'Athens Macedonian News Agency: News in English', Hellenic Resources Institute, 17 May 2012, <http://www.hri.org/news/greek/apeen/2017/17-05-12_1.apeen.html>; 'Xinhua, AAP sign new agreement for closer cooperation', 12 September 2018, <https://tinyurl.com/swndpot>; 'Italy-China: cooperation agreement between ANSA and Xinhua', Ansamed, 17 May 2016, <https://tinyurl.com/tt48dm5>.

111 'Cooperation agreement between Class Editori and China Media Group', *Xinhua Silk Road Information Service*, 2 July 2019, <https://tinyurl.com/r3kovfm>.

112 'Xinhua, AP sign MOU to enhance cooperation', *Xinhua*, 25 November 2018, <https://web.archive.org/web/20190827160133/http://www.xinhuanet.com/english/2018-11/25/c_137630583.htm>; Josh Rogin, 'Congress demands answers on AP's relationship with Chinese state media', *The Washington Post*, 24 December 2018.

113 Ruptly, 'Australia: Chinese protesters rally against South China Sea ruling in Melbourne', Ruptly YouTube channel, 23 July 2016, <https://www.youtube.com/watch?v=jSeaPFxRyxA>.

114 To, *Qiaowu*, pp. 179–80.

115 Alex Joske, 'Reorganizing the United Front Work Department: new structures for a new era of diaspora and religious affairs work', *China Brief (Jamestown Foundation)*, vol. 19, no. 9, 9 May 2019, <https://jamestown.org/program/reorganizing-the-united-front-work-department-new-structures-for-a-new-era-of-diaspora-and-religious-affairs-work/>. Nick McKenzie, Richard Baker, Sashka Koloff and Chris Uhlmann, 'The Chinese Communist Party's power and influence in Australia', *ABC News* online, 29 March 2018.

116 To, *Qiaowu*, pp. 176–8.

117 Diamond and Schell, eds, *China's Influence & American Interests*, p. 85.

118 John Fitzgerald, 'Beijing's *guoqing* versus Australia's way of life', *Inside Story*, 27 September 2016.

119 Hamilton, *Silent Invasion*, p. 41.

120 Dan Levin, 'Chinese-Canadians fear China's rising clout is muzzling them', *The New York Times*, 27 August 2016.

121 Tom Blackwell, 'Host on Chinese-language station in Toronto says he was fired for criticizing Beijing', *The County Weekly News*, 8 October 2019.

122 Blackwell, 'Hoston on Chinese-language station'.

123 '"Jiang hao Zhongguo gushi, chuanbo hao Zhongguo shengyin" luntan Beijing juxing' '讲好中国故事、传播好中国声音'论坛北京举行 ['Tell China's story well, spread China's voice well' forum held (in) Beijing], *Ouzhou Shibao*, 28 September 2016, <https://web.archive.org/web/20191130195737/http://www.oushinet.com/qj/qjnews/20160928/243581.html>. See also Hamilton, *Silent Invasion*, pp. 42–3.

124 'Xiehui jianjie' 协会简介 [Introduction to the Association], website of the Association of Overseas Chinese Media in Europe, not dated, <https://tinyurl.com/uuwrom9>.

125 'Ouzhou shibao wenhua chuanmei jituan' 欧洲时报文化传媒集团 [Guang Hua Cultures et Media], website of *Ouzhou Shibao*, not dated, <https://tinyurl.com/rqucaen>.

126 'Ouzhou shibao wenhua chuanmei jituan', <https://tinyurl.com/rqucaen>.

127 '"Oushidai" shequ yonghu xieyi' "欧时代"社区用户协议 [Nouvelles d'Europe community user agreement], website of *Ouzhou Shibao*, not dated, <https://web.archive.org/web/20190818202416/http://www.oushidai.com/intro/agreement?local=eu>.

128 See the bottom of their homepage at <https://web.archive.org/web/20190801163031/http://www.eztvnet.com/>.

129 'Guanyu women: gongsi jianjie' 关于我们⊠公司简介 [About us: introduction to the company], website of the *Nordic Chinese Times*, <http://archive.today/2019.10.18-162821/http://nordicapd.com/content.asp?pid=22>.

130 'Shanghui jieshao' 商会简介 [Introduction to the Chamber of Commerce], <http://web.archive.org/web/20190801204004/http://acec.org.es/language/zh/about-4/>.

131 'Zhengxie gongzuo baogao jiedu: yi fen yangyi minzhu fazhi jingshen de baogao' 政协工作报告解读：一份洋溢民主法制精神的报告 [Interpretation of the work report of the CPPCC: a report filled with the spirit of democracy and rule of law], China.org.cn, 4 March 2008, <https://tinyurl.com/sso2uxu>.

132 'Xibanya Ouhua chuanmei jituan jianjie' 西班牙欧华传媒集团简介 [Introduction the Spanish Ouhua Media Group], <https://web.archive.org/web/20190801150949/http://www.ouhua.info/2016/0527/7269.html>.

133 For example, Wu Zuolai 吴祚来, 'Duiwai chuanbo yu wenhua jiaolü' 对外传播与文化焦虑 [External communication and cultural anxiety], *Duiwai chuanbo*, no. 9, 2009, pp. 14–15.

134 Andre Tartar, Mira Rojanasakul and Jeremy Scott Diamond, 'How China is buying its way into Europe', *Bloomberg*, 23 April 2018.

135 Philippe Le Corre, 'This is China's plan to dominate Southern Europe', Carnegie Endowment for International Peace, 30 October 2018, <https://carnegieendowment.org/2018/10/30/this-is-china-s-plan-to-dominate-southern-europe-pub-77621>.

136 Website of Propeller TV, <https://web.archive.org/web/20190827155110/https://www.propellertv.co.uk/>.

137 'China-UK media roundtable held in London', CRIEnglish, 24 November 2015, <https://web.archive.org/web/20191130200506/http://english.cri.cn/12394/2015/11/24/53s905534.htm>.

138 Ben Kwok, 'Meet Yam Tak-cheung, the new Forbes owner', *ejinsight*, 21 July 2014, <http://www.ejinsight.com/20140721-yam-tak-cheung-new-forbes-owner/>.

139 Kris Cheng, 'Forbes terminates contract with writer after deleting article critical of Asia Society tycoon', *Hong Kong Free Press*, 30 July 2017.

140 Adam Jourdan and John Ruwitch, 'Alibaba's Jack Ma is a Communist Party member, China state paper reveals', *Reuters*, 27 November 2018.

141 <https://tinyurl.com/s69hmq2>.

142 Phila Siu, 'Sweden "using me as chess piece" says detained Hong Kong bookseller Gui Minhai in government-arranged interview', *South China Morning Post*, 9 February 2018.

143 PEN America, *Darkened Screen: Constraints on foreign journalists in China*, PEN America, 22 September 2016, p. 7.

144 Joshua Keating, 'Bloomberg suspends China reporter amid censorship scandal', *Slate*, 18 November 2013.

145 Diamond and Schell, eds, *China's Influence & American Interests*, p. 93; PEN America, *Darkened Screen*, pp. 13–14.

146 'US Journalists' visit to China in October 2018', website of CUSEF, 2 November 2018, <https://tinyurl.com/vwvdr35>.

147 Hamilton, *Silent Invasion*, pp. 104–7.

148 'Sverige har varit som en sömngångare om Kina' [Sweden has been like a sleepwalker on China], *Expressen*, 23 February 2019, <https://www.expressen.se/ledare/ledarsnack/sverige-har-varit-som-en-somngangare-om-kina/>.

149 Melissa Chan, 'Goodbye to China, country of contradictions', *Al Jazeera*, 13 May 2012, <https://tinyurl.com/ckko84e>; Tom Phillips, 'French journalist accuses China of intimidating foreign press', *The Guardian*, 26 December 2015; Foreign Correspondents Club of China, *Under watch: reporting in China's surveillance state*, Foreign Correspondents Club of China, 2018, p. 10; Anon., 'China denies credentials to *Wall Street Journal* reporter', *Reuters*, 30 August 2019.

150 Foreign Correspondents Club of China, *Under Watch*, p. 12. The FCCC report only speaks of 'French media'.

151 Alvin Lum, '*Financial Times* journalist Victor Mallet about to leave Hong Kong after visa denial', *South China Morning Post*, 12 October 2018.
152 PEN America, *Darkened Screen*, p. 11.
153 Anon., 'China seeks to shape Hong Kong narrative with letter to media', *Bloomberg*, 21 August 2019; Catherine Wong, 'China urges foreign media to "help right public opinion wrongs" on Hong Kong protests', *South China Morning Post*, 22 August 2019.
154 PEN America, *Darkened Screen*, p. 7.
155 Personal conversation, 25 February 2019, Berlin; email conversation, 10 January 2020.
156 PEN America, *Darkened Screen*, p. 16.

Chapter 10 Culture as battleground

1 Janette Jaiwen Ai, 'The political use of China's traditions in contemporary China', PhD thesis, School of Social and Political Sciences, the University of Melbourne, 2012.
2 Anon., 'The CCP's "Cultural Leadership" history since the founding of the PRC', *People's Daily*, 10 November 2009.
3 Liu Runwei 刘润为, 'Hongse wenhua yu wenhua zixin' 红色文化与文化自信 [Red culture and cultural confidence], *Qiushi*, 23 June 2017, <http://www.qstheory.cn/dukan/hqwg/2017-06/23/c_1121197124.htm. Liu's bio is here: <https://web.archive.org/web/20191004045738/http://m.hswh.org.cn/column/120.html>.
4 Yang Lin 杨林, 'Yi wenhua rentong shixian tongyi zhanxian de zui da dongyuan' 以文化认同实现统一战线的最大动员 [Achieving the greatest united front mobilisation through cultural identity], *Qiushi*, 17 January 2017, <https://tinyurl.com/rlkgzjl>; Anon., 'Xi's article on dialectical materialism to be published', *China Daily*, 2 January 2019.
5 Lin Jian 林坚, 'Zhonghua wenhua haiwai chuanbo ren zhong dao yuan' 中华文化海外传播任重道远, originally published in *Huanqiu Shibao*, 20 April 2019, republished on the website of the Jiangsu Institute of Socialism, 23 April 2019, <https://tinyurl.com/vcuhhx3>.
6 <https://tinyurl.com/tc2uzjx>.
7 <https://tinyurl.com/vk3yman>.
8 <https://www.londondesignbiennale.com/supporters>.
9 'Jituan jianjie' 集团简介 [Introduction to the group], website of China Poly Group (中国保利集团公司), <https://tinyurl.com/rxez766>.
10 <https://www.globalsecurity.org/military/world/china/poly.htm>; Barbara Demick, 'In China, "red nobility" trumps egalitarian ideals', *Los Angeles Times*, 4 March 2013.
11 'Jituan jianjie' 集团简介 [Introduction to the group], website of China Poly Group, <https://tinyurl.com/rxez766>.

12 <https://fortune.com/global500/2018/china-poly-group/>. For its corporate structure, see <https://www.globalsecurity.org/military/world/china/poly.htm>.
13 'About us: introduction', <https://tinyurl.com/rjlgvuu>.
14 'Clifford Chance advises Poly Culture Group on HK$2.57 billion IPO', website of Clifford Chance, 7 March 2014, <https://tinyurl.com/wvqpyz9>.
15 <https://www.globalsecurity.org/military/world/china/poly.htm>. Cain Nunns, 'China's Poly Group: the most important company you've never heard of', Public Radio International, 25 February 2013.
16 He Ping's (贺平) bio on CAIFC website, <http://archive.today/2019.10.04-080431/http://www.caifc.org.cn/content.aspx?id=4267>. See also Bo Zhiyue, 'Who are China's princelings?', *The Diplomat*, 24 November 2015.
17 Anon., 'Mapping China's red nobility', *Bloomberg*, 26 December 2012.
18 Sam Cooper and Doug Quan, 'How a murky company with ties to the People's Liberation Army set up shop in B.C.', *Vancouver Sun*, 26 August 2017. See also <https://www.weforum.org/people/xu-niansha>.
19 'Chairman XU Niansha was awarded Great Officials of Star of Italy', website of Poly Culture Group, 28 July 2017, <https://tinyurl.com/qk6httf>.
20 Jiang Yingchun 蒋迎春, *China Daily*, 12 September 2018, <https://tinyurl.com/uxkjh4k>.
21 Zheng Xin, 'Poly Group set to boost ties with global partners', *China Daily*, 21 September 2018.
22 Zheng Xin, 'Poly Group set to boost ties with global partners'.
23 'China-Germany friendship concert successfully held in Cologne Cathedral by Poly WeDo', website of Poly Culture Group, 19 July 2017, <https://tinyurl.com/s257rzn>.
24 'About us: introduction', <https://tinyurl.com/rjlgvuu>; Cooper and Quan, 'How a murky company with ties to the People's Liberation Army set up shop in B.C.'.
25 <http://beijing.lps-china.com/partners/poly-art/>.
26 Cooper and Quan, 'How a murky company with ties to the People's Liberation Army set up shop in B.C.'.
27 Anon., 'U.S. lists new Iran sanctions on several Chinese firms', *Reuters*, 12 February 2013.
28 Bob Mackin, 'Hard currency, soft power: Poly Culture rolls into British Columbia', *South China Morning Post*, 7 December 2016.
29 <https://tinyurl.com/ttvf3kf>; see also <https://twitter.com/geoff_p_wade/status/1084683664380768256>. Poly Culture North America's interim 2018 report noted that it had held 'three high-end thematic exhibitions and 32 cultural exchange events', <https://tinyurl.com/yx3t3xhp>.
30 'Wengehua Zhonghua wenhua cujinhui jiepai chengli' 温哥华中华文化促进会揭牌成立 [Vancouver Chinese Culture Promotion Association

inaugurated], *Dahuawang*, 17 July 2019, <http://dawanews.com/dawa/node3/n5/n18/u1ai26835.html>.

31 Sam Cooper and Brian Hill, 'Alleged gang kingpin may have used Liberal MP's law firm to launder money through B.C. condo deal', *Global News*, 11 June 2019.

32 <https://tinyurl.com/r2ceb84>.

33 Zak Vescera, 'Local Chinese groups take out pro-Communist Party ads amidst Hong Kong protests', *Vancouver Sun*, 26 June 2019. Note too that in 2016 George Chow was appointed an honorary adviser to the Teo Chew Society of Vancouver, <https://tinyurl.com/vydwptb>. The current president of this group is Feng Rujie (冯汝洁), who in 2018 was appointed an overseas council member of the 10th Committee of the All-China Federation of Returned Overseas Chinese, <https://tinyurl.com/tn9obxe>.

34 Douglas Quan, 'Defence minister ripped for attending gala honouring Chinese Communist Party anniversary', *National Post*, 30 September 2019.

35 Bob Mackin, 'B.C.'s Premier and L-G to skip Communist China's 70th birthday parties', *The Breaker*, 28 August 2019. Chow's trip to Guangzhou was also reported by the OCAO Guangzhou, see <https://tinyurl.com/sbh8kxq>.

36 Sean Brady, 'Kamloops' Chinese community provides input on museum project', *Kamloops This Week*, 19 January 2019.

37 Brady, 'Kamloops' Chinese community provides input on museum project'.

38 Geoff Wade, 'Spying beyond the façade', *The Strategist*, Australian Strategic Policy Institute, 13 November 2013. The names used by Wade differ because this was written prior to China's major military reform in 2015–16.

39 <http://www.caifc.org.cn/en/jgsz_l.aspx?cid=28>; <http://www.caifc.org.cn/en/content.aspx?id=1083>.

40 Mark Stokes and Russell Hsiao, 'The People's Liberation Army General Political Department: political warfare with Chinese characteristics', Project 2049 Institute, 14 October, 2013.

41 Stokes and Hsiao, 'The People's Liberation Army General Political Department', p. 25.

42 Wade, 'Spying beyond the façade'.

43 Wade, 'Spying beyond the façade'.

44 Andy Kroll and Russ Choma, 'Businesswoman who bought Trump penthouse is connected to Chinese Intelligence Front Group', *Mother Jones*, 15 March 2017.

45 China Arts Foundation (北京中国艺术基金会), <https://tinyurl.com/stlxdro>; <https://tinyurl.com/tz5tm43>.

46 Zheping Huang, 'An intricate web ties the woman who paid $16 million for Trump's condo to China's power elite', *Quartz*, 17 March 2017.

47 Anthony Tommasini, 'Let it rain! (After the music, of course)', *The New York Times*, 14 July 2010. Photos of the concert are featured on the *NYT*'s

Facebook page. Chinese websites announcing it: <http://ent.sina.com.cn/y/2011-08-08/11063380366.shtml> and <https://tinyurl.com/sb8f6bv>.

48 Anon., 'Was Lang Lang's propaganda song a jab at White House?', *CBS News*, 24 January 2011.

49 <https://tinyurl.com/rol7pdp>.

50 <http://blacktiemagazine.com/International_Society/Shanghai.htm>.

51 <https://tinyurl.com/uxs4tor>.

52 <https://www.guidestar.org/profile/33-1156962>.

53 <http://gaa.lucita.org/about_who_angela.shtml>; Anon., 'New York Philharmonic forms international advisory board', *Broadway World*, 29 October 2014.

54 Anon., 'New York Philharmonic forms international advisory board'.

55 Andy Kroll and Russ Choma, 'Trump just sold a $15.8 million condo to a consultant who peddles access to powerful people', *Mother Jones*, 27 February 2017.

56 Kroll and Choma, 'Businesswoman who bought Trump penthouse is connected to Chinese intelligence front group'.

57 <https://twitter.com/chinaartsintl/status/604404511197827072/photo/1>; <https://twitter.com/chinaartsintl/status/604405504643862529/photo/1>.

58 Anon., 'New York Philharmonic forms international advisory board'.

59 Kroll and Choma, 'Businesswoman who bought Trump penthouse is connected to Chinese intelligence front group'.

60 <https://www.thequestforit.com/photos/it_charity_invites/china-arts-foundation_ballet_tiffany-event.html>.

61 <https://tinyurl.com/tl8j59j>; <https://tinyurl.com/revjsda>; <https://twitter.com/chinaartsintl?lang=en>; <https://tinyurl.com/wmm2bwl>.

62 Huang, 'An intricate web ties the woman who paid $16 million for Trump's condo to China's power elite'.

63 <https://tinyurl.com/vqwt2bb>, Huaxing Art Troupe (华星艺术团).

64 Another project is Chinese Mutual Aid Centers. See 'Qiu Yuanping wei xin yi pi "Huaxing yishutuan" jie pai' 裘援平为新一批"华星艺术团"揭牌 [Qiu Yuanping unveils plates for new batch of Huaxing Arts Troupes], *Qiaowang*, 28 September 2016, <https://tinyurl.com/stwvanl>.

65 <https://tinyurl.com/wb3wzrj>; Chongyi Feng, 'How the Chinese Communist Party exerts its influence in Australia: detained professor', *ABC News* online, 6 June 2017.

66 'Deguo Falankefu Huaxing yishutuan chenggong ban chunwan' 德国法兰克福 华星艺术团成功办春晚 [Frankfurt Huaxing Arts Troupe successfully organises Spring Festival gala], *Global Times online*, 7 February 2018; <https://tinyurl.com/t7zahaj>.

67 <http://www.chinaconsulatechicago.org/eng/lghd/t1547374.htm>.

68 <https://tinyurl.com/yxq9zxgx>. '建立了与政要、主要华人社团、社会名流以及艺术家联系资料档案库'.

69 Nick McKenzie, Nick Toscano and Grace Tobin, 'Crown's unsavoury business links: how Australia's casino got tied up with criminals', *The Age*, 28 July 2019.
70 <https://tinyurl.com/uhz76hf>.
71 Jeff Yang, 'The shocking viral reaction to a prom dress', *CNN* online, 3 May 2018.
72 Joyce Siu, 'Vintage in vogue: patriotic ladies revive "Qipao" dress', *Sixth Tone*, 4 January 2018.
73 Anon., 'Qipao fans step out worldwide', *China Daily*, 18 May 2015.
74 Anon., 'Qipao fans step out worldwide'.
75 <https://tinyurl.com/r8qxjbj>; <https://tinyurl.com/u3sd4ww>.
76 <https://tinyurl.com/uqhdt7k>.
77 <https://tinyurl.com/ru889ws>.
78 <https://tinyurl.com/sogu336>.
79 <https://tinyurl.com/vlseqh5>. There seems to have been an internal dispute in 2017. From 28 April 2017, Wang Quan is no longer 'chairman' of the Chinese Cheongsam Association. In the same year, Wang set up the China Qipao Society Global Alliance, <https://tinyurl.com/s5ywoe6>; <https://tinyurl.com/r4gwmy8>. The China Qipao Association more recently translates its name as the Chinese Cheongsam Association. There are a number of other societies celebrating the qipao, <https://tinyurl.com/uxz6lbo>.
80 <https://tinyurl.com/wbvgofd>.
81 Anon., 'Chinese Qipao Federation lands in Germany', *People's Daily*, 23 January 2018.
82 <https://tinyurl.com/ujhwanb>; <https://tinyurl.com/sfcdb3s>.
83 <https://tinyurl.com/wp69pyc>.
84 <https://tinyurl.com/uz2f5mz>.
85 <https://tinyurl.com/unz5f7c>; <https://tinyurl.com/tw2xk5m>.
86 In the words of the director of the United Front Theory Department at the Liaoning party school, Shen Yan, 'Use culture to carry out cultural united front work in the new era' (以文化之做好新时代文化统战工作) <https://tinyurl.com/sb3nbt5>.
87 Shan Renping, 'Canadian Miss World contestant misguided by her values', *Global Times*, 29 November 2015.
88 Anon., 'Canada's Miss World finalist Anastasia Lin comes out as a Falun Gong practitioner', *South China Morning Post*, 28 August 2015.
89 Anon., 'Canada's Miss World finalist Anastasia Lin comes out as a Falun Gong practitioner'.
90 Tom Blackwell, 'Ottawa man says Dragon-boat festival CEO ordered him to remove Falun Gong shirt, citing Chinese sponsorship', *National Post*, 16 July 2019.
91 Anon., 'US town arts center removes paintings depicting President Xi Jinping', Radio Free Asia, 4 February 2019.

92 Anon., 'US town arts center removes paintings depicting President Xi Jinping'.
93 Anon., 'Zhang Yimou's "One Second" abruptly pulled from Berlinale', *Asia in Cinema*, 11 February 2019.
94 Patrick Frater, 'Banned in Berlin: why China said no go to Zhang Yimou', *Variety*, 11 February 2019.
95 Anon., 'Ai Weiwei hits out at self-censorship by Western organizations after film is cut', Radio Free Asia, 21 February 2019.
96 <https://audi-konfuzius-institut-ingolstadt.de/en/institut/ueber-uns.html>.
97 Anon., 'Ai Weiwei hits out'.
98 Amy Qin, 'Dissident artist Ai Weiwei is cut from film; producer cites "fear of China"', *The New York Times*, 19 February 2019.
99 Anon., 'Ai Weiwei hits out'.
100 Qin, 'Dissident artist Ai Weiwei is cut from film'.
101 Tim Winter, 'One Belt, One Road, One Heritage: cultural diplomacy and the Silk Road', *The Diplomat*, 29 March 2016; Zhang Xinjiang, '"Belt and Road" boosts Chinese cultural industry', *China Daily*, 2 May 2018.
102 <http://www.xinhuanet.com/ent/2016-11/17/c_1119928799.htm>. Full text in Chinese at <http://archive.today/2019.10.05-001738/https://www.scio.gov.cn/xwfbh/xwbfbh/wqfbh/37601/38866/xgzc38872/Document/1636159/1636159.htm>.
103 At least according to this article: <http://archive.today/2019.10.05-002647/https://www.yidaiyilu.gov.cn/xwzx/gnxw/13841.htm>. Others give different numbers.
104 Diana Yeh, 'The cultural politics of invisibility', in Ashley Thorpe and Diana Yeh, eds, *Contesting British Chinese Culture*, London: Palgrave, 2018, p. 49.
105 Yeh, 'The cultural politics of invisibility'.
106 The League of Theatres is headquartered in Beijing's Xicheng district. The *People's Daily* wrote that the decision to establish the Silk Road International League of Theatres was an extension of the strategic partnership between the China Arts and Entertainment Group, the government of the Xicheng district, and Beijing Tianqiao Zenith Investment Group (a state-owned local company specialising in cultural performances, established in 2014), <https://web.archive.org/web/20190208040104/http://ydyl.people.com.cn/n1/2018/0402/c411837-29901477.html>. Beijing Tianqiao Zenith Investment Group is a large company 'committed to build a comprehensive production chain of culture and performing arts', <https://web.archive.org/web/20190208041156/http:/www.bjtqss.com/index.php?m=content&c=index&a=lists&catid=7>.
107 <http://www.xinhuanet.com/ent/2016-11/17/c_1119928799.htm>. 'China's Minister of Culture Luo Shugang said the establishment of the Silk Road International League of Theatres was a creative achievement under the

framework of the Belt and Road Initiative', Anon., 'Silk Road International League of Theaters launched in Beijing', *China Daily*, 24 October 2016.

108 National Development and Reform Commission, 'Ministry of Culture "One Belt, One Road" Cultural Development Action Plan (2016–2020)', website 2016 <http://www.ndrc.gov.cn/fzgggz/fzgh/ghwb/gjjgh/201707/t20170720_855005.html>.

109 <https://web.archive.org/web/20180822192043/http://srilt.org/en/members/>; <http://www.xinhuanet.com/ent/2016-11/17/c_1119928799.htm>.

110 Jia Tolentino, 'Stepping into the uncanny, unsettling world of Shen Yun', *The New Yorker*, 19 March 2019.

111 <http://leeshailemish.com/on-shen-yun/whos-afraid-of-shen-yun/>.

112 Frank Fang, 'Document reveals Beijing pressured UN diplomats to boycott Shen Yun performances', *Epoch Times*, 21 February 2019.

113 Juan Pablo Cardenal and Heriberto Araujo, 'China quiso prohibir el estreno de una obra de teatro en Barcelona', *El Mundo*, 6 April 2014.

114 <http://leeshailemish.com/on-shen-yun/2014/03/30/chinese-embassy-epic-fail-in-berlin/>.

115 Copy of email in possession of authors. On 20 July 2019 Stacy Lyon was emailed and offered an opportunity to comment or explain. She did not reply.

116 Andreas Bøje Forsby, 'Diplomacy with Chinese characteristics: the case of Denmark', *Asia Dialogue*, 18 December 2018. In 2012 Danish police forces 'systematically prevented peaceful pro-Tibet demonstrators from exercising their constitutionally guaranteed right to freedom of speech when Hu's motorcade toured the streets of Copenhagen'.

117 Anon, 'Xi urges Spanish enterprises to make best use of CIIE platform', *China Daily*, 29 November 2018.

118 Janita Kan, 'Chinese embassy pressured theatre to cancel Shen Yun performances in Spain, investigation reveals', *Epoch Times*, 29 January 2019.

119 Anon., 'El Teatro Real acercará al público chino su contenido a través de la plataforma cultural online Palco Digital', *Europa Press*, 1 April 2019. The report does not appear to be an April Fools' Day spoof.

120 Amy Qin and Audrey Carlsen, 'How China is rewriting its own script', *The New York Times*, 18 November 2018.

121 Qin and Carlsen, 'How China is rewriting its own script'.

122 <https://twitter.com/markmackinnon/status/1152241649893945346>.

123 Pradeep Taneja, 'China-India bilateral economic relations', in Kanti Bajpai, Selina Ho and Manjari Chatterjee, eds, *Routledge Handbook on China–India Relations*, London: Routledge, forthcoming.

124 Anon., 'Xi sends letter to congratulate 70th anniversary of national writer, artist groups', *China Daily*, 16 July 2019.

125 Patrick Boehler and Vanessa Piao, 'Xi Jinping's speech on the arts is released, one year later', *The New York Times*, 15 October 2015.

126 Joel Martinsen, 'The Chinese Writers' Association: what good is it?', blog post, *Danwei*, 17 November 2006. In his history of Chinese literature, Hong Zicheng wrote that the more important functions of the CWA 'were to exercise political and artistic leadership and control of a writer's literary activities, and to guarantee that literary norms were implemented', Hong Zicheng, *A History of Contemporary Chinese Literature*, Leiden: Brill, 2007, p. 27. Deng Xiaoping's daughter Deng Rong is a member of the Chinese Writers' Association, see <https://web.archive.org/web/20150322033230/http://www.chinaartsfoundation.org/cn/leadership.html>.

127 Oiwan Lam, 'Two writers publicly resign amid the Chinese Communist Party's tightening grip on culture', *Hong Kong Free Press*, 20 March 2016.

128 On University of Waterloo, see Anon., 'Our quilts: one world same dream', *China Daily*, 2 May 2014; <https://www.writersunion.ca/member/yan-li>. On Melbourne Writers Festival, see Hamilton, *Silent Invasion*, pp. 239–42. On University of Iowa, see <https://iwp.uiowa.edu/programs/life-of-discovery/2012>.

129 Alex Joske, 'Reorganizing the United Front Work Department: new structures for a new era of diaspora and religious affairs work', *China Brief*, vol. 19, no. 9, 9 May 2019.

130 Adrian Zenz, 'You can't force people to assimilate. So why is China at it again?', *The New York Times*, 16 July 2019.

131 Anon., 'Chinese Catholic bishop ordained with Pope's approval', *BBC News* online, 28 August 2019.

132 See Hamilton, *Silent Invasion*, pp. 243–4.

133 Julia Bowie and David Gitter, 'The CCP's plan to "Sinicize" religions', *The Diplomat*, 14 June 2018; Laurie Chen, 'Red flag for Buddhists? Shaolin Temple "takes the lead" in Chinese patriotism push', *South China Morning Post*, 28 August 2018.

134 Geoff Wade, tweet, 2 August 2018, <https://twitter.com/geoff_p_wade/status/1024960867778093056>.

135 <https://www.dpmchina.org/directors-blog/chinas-plan-to-sinicize-religions>.

136 Rhiana Whitson, 'Communist Party-linked group holds event at Hobart's Parliament House, Tasmanian politicians attend', *ABC News* online, 5 December 2017.

137 <https://tinyurl.com/qsup4cp>.

138 <https://twitter.com/alexjoske/status/1161052811334828032?lang=en>.

139 Reported in David Gitter et al., *Party Watch*, Centre for Advanced China Research, Weekly report 3/1, 28 September 2019.

140 Lauren Teixeira, 'He never intended to become a political dissident, but then he started beating up Tai Chi masters', *Deadspin*, 3 October 2019.

Chapter 11 Think tanks and thought leaders

1 Quoted in Bethany Allen-Ebrahimian, 'This Beijing-linked billionaire is funding policy research at Washington's most influential institutions', *Foreign Policy*, 28 November 2017.

2 绝对不允许吃共产党的饭，砸共产党的锅。 Quoted in「绝不容吃饭砸锅」习近平批示讲硬话, *Mingpao*, 27 October 2014, <https://www.mingpaocanada.com/van/htm/News/20141027/tcbf1_r.htm>.

3 <https://tinyurl.com/wy8bj7x>.

4 'Professor John L. Thornton Honored Friendship Award', Tsinghua SEM, 13 October 2008, <https://tinyurl.com/v3zb7yf>.

5 'About us', <http://www.silkroad-finance.com/en/about/>; 'John Thornton: Chairman of the Board', <http://www.silkroad-finance.com/en/our-team/>. The SRFC has its own think tank, the Silk Road Research Center, whose executive vice chairman is princeling Li Xiaolin, daughter of former premier Li Peng, <https://twitter.com/geoff_p_wade/status/1067775094875799562?lang=en>. Speaking to partners at Renmin University, Li Xiaolin said that the centre is 'a new type of think tank with Chinese characteristics established to serve the "One Belt, One Road" initiative'. See 'Executive Vice Chairman of the Silk Road Planning Research Center LI Xiaolin visits RUC', website of Renmin University, 7 May 2018, <https://www.ruc.edu.cn/archives/32079>.

6 'John Thornton: Chairman of the Board', website of Silk Road Finance Corporation, not dated, <https://web.archive.org/web/20190606092335/http://www.silkroad-finance.com/en/our-team/>; 'Li Shan: huiguo chuangye bi zheng qian geng you xingfu gan' 李山：回国创业比挣钱更有幸福感 [Li Shan: returning to China and starting a business makes me happier than earning money], *Sina*, 1 November 2011, <https://web.archive.org/web/20150921232843/http://news.sina.com.cn/c/2006-11-01/102911389539.shtml>.

7 Rachelle Younglai, 'The man with the key to China: Barrick Gold's quest to open new doors', *The Globe and Mail*, 6 December 2013, <https://tinyurl.com/whrndx6>.

8 'Professor John L. Thornton Honored Friendship Award', Tsinghua SEM, 13 October 2008, <https://tinyurl.com/v3zb7yf>.

9 'About the Brookings-Tsinghua Center for Public Policy', website of the Brookings Institution, not dated, <https://www.brookings.edu/about-the-brookings-tsinghua-center-for-public-policy/>.

10 'Brookings China Council launches on the eve of Obama-Xi Summit', website of the Brookings Institution, 22 September 2015, <https://www.brookings.edu/news-releases/brookings-china-council-launches-on-the-eve-of-obama-xi-summit/>.

11 <https://twitter.com/PekingMike/status/1071441574528192512>; <https://threadreaderapp.com/thread/1084191340232142849.html>; Edward Wong

and Michael Forsythe, 'China's tactic to catch a fugitive official: hold his two American children', *The New York Times*, 25 November 2018.

12 Isaac Stone-Fish, 'Huawei's surprising ties to the Brookings Institution', *The Washington Post*, 7 December 2018.

13 'Donors to Chatham House', website of Chatham House, <https://www.chathamhouse.org/about/our-funding/donors-chatham-house>.

14 'H.E. Ambassador Liu Xiaoming meets with director of Chatham House Dr Robin Niblett CMG', website of the Chinese embassy to the UK, 6 January 2017, <https://web.archive.org/web/20190823174422/http://www.chinese-embassy.org.uk/eng/tpxw/t1429999.htm>.

15 Robin Niblett, 'What the world can expect from the Boris Johnson government', *The Hill*, 30 July 2019.

16 Yu Jie, 'Britain needs to decide what it wants from China', Chatham House, 26 February 2019, <https://www.chathamhouse.org/expert/comment/britain-needs-decide-what-it-wants-china>.

17 'Spotlight: overseas experts laud Xi's speech on China's foreign policy', *Xinhua*, 24 June 2018, <https://tinyurl.com/vdpkss5>.

18 'Ambassador Liu Xiaoming attends "Vision China" hosted by *China Daily* and delivers a keynote speech', website of the Chinese embassy to the UK, 15 September 2018, <https://tinyurl.com/u2qmg8e>; <https://tinyurl.com/v72jauj>.

19 'Interview: consumers to underpin Chinese growth in coming years, says Jim O'Neill', *Xinhua*, 13 September 2019, <https://tinyurl.com/woj965n>.

20 Lei Xiaoxun and Wang Minglei, 'Analysts agree that vision puts China on right track', *China Daily*, 21 October 2017.

21 'Lord Browne of Madingley', website of Chatham House, not dated, <https://www.chathamhouse.org/about/governance/panel-senior-advisers>.

22 'EU–China economic relations to 2025: building a common future', a joint report by Bruegel, Chatham House, China Center for International Economic Exchanges, and the Chinese University of Hong Kong', September 2017, <https://www.chathamhouse.org/publication/eu-china-economic-relations-2025-building-common-future>.

23 'Next steps in renminbi internationalization', Chatham House, not dated, <https://tinyurl.com/umd56fr>.

24 'About the Paulson Institute', website of the Paulson Institute, not dated, <http://www.paulsoninstitute.org/about/about-overview/>.

25 'A first gathering for implementation of the Green Investment Principles for the Belt and Road', 26 September 2019, <https://tinyurl.com/vgtbxyu>.

26 See for example articles filed under Macro Outlook, <https://macropolo.org/analysis_category/macro-outlook/>. Neil Thomas, 'Matters of record: relitigating engagement with China', *Macro Polo*, 3 September 2018.

27 'Vice-premier meets former US treasury secretary Henry Paulson', website of the Chinese government, 11 April 2019, <https://tinyurl.com/tuknw6a>.

28 'Chen Jining meets with Chairman of Paulson Institute', website of Beijing government, 15 April 2019, <http://www.ebeijing.gov.cn/Government/Mayor_office/OfficialActivities/t1583250.htm>.

29 'Chen Jining meets with Chairman of Paulson Institute', website of Beijing government, 15 April 2019, <http://www.ebeijing.gov.cn/Government/Mayor_office/OfficialActivities/t1583250.htm>. The report does not mention what the MoU was on, much less provide the full text of the document. Based on the Paulson Institute's previous work with Chinese partners, it may have been about green finance.

30 'China issues first certificates for overseas NGOs', *China Daily*, 21 January 2017, <https://web.archive.org/web/20191201150112/http://www.chinadaily.com.cn/china/2017-01/24/content_28041563.htm>.

31 CGTN America, 'Authors say Western-style democracy won't work in Hong Kong', CGTN America YouTube channel, 17 October 2014, <https://www.youtube.com/watch?v=nrhANAmPOxg>. See also CGTN America, 'Nicolas Berggruen on "Giving Pledge" and think tanks', CGTN America YouTube channel, 21 April 2015, <https://www.youtube.com/watch?v=FAUNOL_d8YM>.

32 CGTN America, 'Authors say Western-style democracy won't work in Hong Kong'.

33 Zhang Weiwei, 'For China's one-party rulers, legitimacy flows from prosperity and competence', Berggruen Institute, 1 March 2017, <https://www.berggruen.org/ideas/articles/for-china-s-one-party-rulers-legitimacy-flows-from-prosperity-and-competence/>.

34 On Zheng Bijian, see <https://web.archive.org/web/20191029020838/http://www.ciids.cn/content/2016-04/19/content_12581303.htm>. On Understanding China conferences, see <https://web.archive.org/web/20190821155415/https://www.berggruen.org/people/group/21st-century-council/>; Rachel S. Bauch, 'Berggruen Institute and Peking University announce new hub for research and dialogue on global transformations affecting humanity', Berggruen Institute, 6 June 2018, <https://tinyurl.com/vxglz3t>. See also Nathan Gardels, 'Chinese President Xi Jinping meets the 21st Century Council in Beijing', Berggruen Institute, 3 November 2015, <https://tinyurl.com/s5frygq>.

35 'CIIDS Chairman Zheng Bijian met with Berggruen Institute co-founder Nathan Gardels last weekend to discuss globalization and China', Berggruen Institute on Twitter, 18 July 2017, <https://twitter.com/berggruenInst/status/887342354700541952>.

36 'The 3rd "Understanding China" conference', <https://web.archive.org/web/20190921003945/http://img.cyol.com/img/news/ddzg.pdf>.

37 '*The Washington Post* and Berggruen Institute partner to publish *The WorldPost*', *The Washington Post*, 6 February 2018, <https://www.washingtonpost.com/

pr/wp/2018/02/06/the-washington-post-and-the-berggruen-institute-partner-to-publish-the-worldpost/>.

38 The *Huffington Post* runs many articles under the *WorldPost* label and republished Zhang Weiwei's praise of China's political model. See 'In China, unlike Trump's America, political legitimacy is built on competence and experience', *Huffington Post*, 3 March 2017.

39 Tiffany Li, 'China's influence on digital privacy could be global', *The Washington Post*, 7 August 2018.

40 Song Bing, 'China's social credit system may be misunderstood', *The Washington Post*, 29 November 2018; 'Song Bing', <https://www.berggruen.org/people/bing-song/>. Hat tip to Mike Forsythe on Twitter. The argument that the social credit system has not been portrayed accurately in the media has merit, but Song Bing's article portrays the system much too positively.

41 'Daniel Bell', <https://www.berggruen.org/people/daniel-bell/>; <https://chinamatters.blogspot.com/2012/11/its-not-freedom-vs-truth-its-daniel.html>.

42 Mark Mackinnon, 'Canadian iconoclast Daniel A. Bell praises China's one-party system as a meritocracy', *The Globe and Mail*, 24 November 2012.

43 Andrew Nathan does a brilliant deconstruction of Bell in 'The problem with the China model', *Chinafile*, 5 November 2015.

44 'Gaoju dangmei qizhi, lüxing zhize shiming' 高举党媒旗帜 履行职责使命 [Holding high the banner of Party media and performing the duties of the mission], website of the Cyberspace Administration of China, 26 April 2017, <https://tinyurl.com/vn39gs8>.

45 'Gaoju dangmei qizhi, lüxing zhize shiming' 高举党媒旗帜 履行职责使命 [Holding high the banner of Party media and performing the duties of the mission].

46 Mark Stokes and Russell Hsiao, 'The People's Liberation Army General Political Department: Political warfare with Chinese characteristics', Project 2049 Institute, October 2013, p. 25; Bethany Allen-Ebrahimian, 'This Beijing-linked billionaire is funding policy research at Washington's most influential institutions', *Foreign Policy*, 28 November 2017.

47 For example, <https://web.archive.org/web/20190914172232/https://www.eastwest.ngo/sites/default/files/us-china-sanya-initiative-dialogue-10th-meeting.pdf>: 'The EastWest Institute (EWI) convened the 10th anniversary of the U.S.-China Sanya Initiative from October 27 to 29, 2018. The dialogue was made possible through the generous support of the China-United States Exchange Foundation (CUSEF) and other private donors and was organized in close partnership with the China Association for International Friendly Contact (CAIFC).' See also Michael Raska, 'China and the "three warfares"', *The Diplomat*, 18 December 2015.

48 Tony Cheung, 'Former Hong Kong leader Tung Chee-hwa accuses the United States and Taiwan of orchestrating "well-organised" recent protests', *South China Morning Post*, 31 July 2019.

49 'Our founders', <https://www.fungfoundation.org/our-founders/>; <https://www.cusef.org.hk/dr-victor-k-fung/>.

50 The full name of this foundation is 'The Victor and William Fung Foundation'. See <https://www.fungscholars.org/about/>.

51 'Mission', AmericaChina Public Affairs Institute, not dated, <https://www.americachina.us/mission>.

52 'Goals', AmericaChina Public Affairs Institute, not dated, <https://www.americachina.us/goals>.

53 <https://efile.fara.gov/docs/5875-Short-Form-20150204-162.pdf>; 'About', website of BLJ Worldwide, not dated, <http://www.bljworldwide.com/about-us/>.

54 'Podesta, Tony, lobbyist profile: summary 2017', Center for Responsive Politics, <https://www.opensecrets.org/lobby/lobbyist.php?id=Y0000046505L&year=2017>.

55 Richard Pollock, 'Tony Podesta made $500k lobbying for Chinese firm convicted of illegal sales to Iran', *Daily Caller*, 27 March 2017.

56 'Center For American Progress Visit 2016', website of CUSEF, 23 June 2016, <https://www.cusef.org.hk/high-level-dialogues/center-for-american-progress-visit-2016/>.

57 Robert Henderson, 'China: Great power rising', in B. McKercher (ed.), Routledge Handbook of Diplomacy and Statecraft, London: Routledge, 2021, p. 70.

58 Center for American Progress, 'U.S.-China high level dialogue', <https://wikileaks.org/podesta-emails/fileid/9612/2554>.

59 Bethany Allen-Ebrahimian, 'This Beijing-linked billionaire is funding policy research at Washington's most influential institutions', *Foreign Policy*, 28 November 2017.

60 François Godement and Abigaël Vasselier, *China at the Gates. A new power audit of EU-China relations*, London: European Council on Foreign Relations, 2017, p. 78.

61 Jonathan Oliver, 'Which way will Nick Clegg turn?', *Sunday Times*, 25 April 2010.

62 Pierre Defraigne, letter to *Politico* in response to its article 'China-backed think tank exits Brussels', <https://www.coleurope.eu/system/tdf/uploads/page/madariaga*politico*en.pdf?file=1&type=node&id=9804&force>.

63 James Panichi, 'China-backed think tank exits Brussels', *Politico*, 23 July 2015.

64 'Dewinter werkte voor Chinese "spion": "Als hij een spion was, was ik James Bond"', *Gazet van Antwerpen*, 12 November 2018, <https://www.gva.be/cnt/dmf20181112_03935995/filip-dewinter-werkte-voor-chinese-spion>.

65 Anon, 'Sichou zhi lu hepingjiang jijinhui zhuxi, heping zhi lü lishizhang Shao Changchun kan sichou zhi lu renwen hezuojiang huodezhe Weikeduo Youxianke boshi' 丝绸之路和平奖基金会主席、和平之旅理事长邵常淳看望丝绸之路人文合作奖获得者维克多 尤先科博士 [Shao Changchun, Chairman of Silk Road Peace Prize Foundation and Chairman of Peace Journey visits Dr. Victor Yushchenko, winner of the Silk Road Humanities Cooperation award], website of Beijing Peace Tour Cultural Exchange Center, 21 March 2018, <https://web.archive.org/web/20190823180811/http://www.peace-art.org/detail/602.html>.

66 Pierre Defraigne, letter to *Politico* in response to its article 'China-backed think tank exits Brussels', <https://www.coleurope.eu/system/tdf/uploads/page/madariaga*politico*en.pdf?file=1&type=node&id=9804&force>.

67 For example, 'EU-China relations seminar for the students of the College of Europe (17/01)', College of Europe, <https://web.archive.org/web/20190920155437/https://www.coleurope.eu/news/eu-china-relations-seminar-students-college-europe-17/01>; 'International conference: "a new order or no order? Continuity and discontinuity in the EU-China-US relationship"', College of Europe, <https://tinyurl.com/see2o4w>.

68 'China-EU human rights seminar emphasizes diversity', *China Daily*, 29 June 2018.

69 Euractiv, 'EU-China: mending differences', special report, 29 May–2 June 2017.

70 'Luigi Gambardella: Eu-China should move beyond stereotypes', in Euractiv, 'EU-China: mending differences', special report, 29 May–2 June 2017, pp. 10–12.

71 'Mission', ChinaEU, <http://www.chinaeu.eu/mission/>.

72 Nicholas Hirst, 'Europe's Mr. China', *Politico*, 31 May 2017.

73 Reported meetings have taken place with Federica Mogherini, Andrus Ansip, Jyrki Katainen, Eric Peters, Mariya Gabriel, Edward Bannerman, Carlos Moedas, Aare Järvan and Hanna Hinrikus, <https://www.integritywatch.eu/>.

74 Chen Yingqun, 'ChinaEU chief responds to Xi speech', *China Daily*, 16 November 2016.

75 'Europe-China forum: cooperation, competition and the search for common ground', event held on 28 November 2018, <https://web.archive.org/web/20190914160202/https://www.friendsofeurope.org/events/europe-china-forum-cooperation-competition-and-the-search-for-common-ground/>; 'Europe-China policy & practice roundtable', event held on 18 November 2019, <https://web.archive.org/web/20190914160854/https://www.friendsofeurope.org/events/europe-china-policy-practice-roundtable-2/>.

76 'Zhu Oumeng shituan tuanzhang Zhang Ming dashi chuxi di ershiyi ci Zhong Ou lingdaoren huiwu zhengce chuifenghui bing fabian zhuzhi yanjiang' 驻欧盟使团团长张明大使出席第二十一次中欧领导人会晤政策吹风会

并发表主旨演讲, Foreign Ministry of the PRC, 20 March 2019, <https://www.fmprc.gov.cn/web/wjdt_674879/zwbd_674895/t1647463.shtml>.

77 For example, Federico Grandesso, 'Interview: China will remain top priority for EU foreign policy, says EU expert', *Xinhua*, 25 July 2019, <http://www.xinhuanet.com/english/2019-07/25/c_138256727.htm>; 'G20 summit displays China's ability in chairing global governance forum', *Xinhua*, 1 September 2016, <http://m.chinadaily.com.cn/en/2016-09/01/content_26666969.htm>.

78 'Partners', website of EU-Asia Center, not dated, <https://web.archive.org/web/20200103170646/http://www.eu-asiacentre.eu/sponsors.php?cat_id=3>.

79 Fraser Cameron, 'EU can now move forward with China', *China Daily*, 9 May 2017.

80 Vincent Metten, 'The ambivalent attitude of the Brussels based European Institute for Asian Studies on Tibet', Save Tibet, 8 December 2015, <https://weblog.savetibet.org/2015/12/the-ambivalent-attitude-of-the-brussels-based-european-institute-for-asian-studies-on-tibet/>.

81 Chen Jia, 'Associating the "Davos Spirit" with China's rising economy', *New York Times* advertisement created by *China Daily*, not dated, <https://web.archive.org/web/20191201130912/https://www.nytimes.com/paidpost/china-daily/associating-the-davos-spirit-with-chinas-rising-economy.html>.

82 Chen Jia, 'Associating the "Davos Spirit" with China's rising economy'.

83 Isaac Stone-Fish, 'What China experts have to do to get on Beijing's visa "whitelist"', *The Washington Post*, 5 September 2019.

84 Diamond and Schell, eds, *China's Influence & American Interests*, p. 68.

85 Jennifer Duke, 'Huawei heaps pressure on Telstra, Google over think tank funding', *The Sydney Morning Herald*, 14 February 2019.

86 David Bandurski, 'The "misguided academics" of Europe', *China Media Project*, 6 February 2018; see also Matthias Müller and Nina Belz, 'Wie China seinen Einfluss in Europa ausbaut', NZZ, 5 February 2018.

87 Frank Pieke, 'Why the West should stop projecting its fears onto China and cultivate a more mature relationship', *South China Morning Post*, 30 September 2019.

88 Frank Pieke, 'How misconceptions brought China-West relations to the breaking point', *The Diplomat*, 22 August 2019.

89 'Hanxuejia Peng Ke: wo de gongzuo shi jiekai renmen dui Zhongguo keban yinxiang de miansha' 汉学家彭轲：我的工作是揭开人们对中国刻板印象的面纱 [Sinologist Pieke: my job is to lift the veil on people's stereotypes on China], *Jiemian*, 14 August 2018, <https://www.jiemian.com/article/2383387.html>.

90 'Open letter by MERICS director and CEO Frank N. Pieke', MERICS, 1 October 2019, <https://web.archive.org/web/20191201153357/https://www.merics.org/en/china-flash/open-letter-merics-director-and-ceo-frank-n-pieke>.

91 'Press release: leadership change at MERICS', MERICS website, 22 January 2020, <https://www.merics.org/en/china-flash/press-release-leadership-change-merics>.

92 Tom Plate, 'The world can think its way out of a US-China deadlock, starting by reading Singapore's Kishore Mahbubani', *South China Morning Post*, 22 April 2019.

93 'Remarks by Ambassador Lu Shaye at the Seminar on China-Canada Relations', website of the Chinese embassy in Canada, 24 May 2019, <https://web.archive.org/web/20191201161606/http://ca.china-embassy.org/eng/gdxw/t1666127.htm>.

94 Jeffrey Sachs, 'The war on Huawei', *Project Syndicate*, 11 December 2018.

95 For a commentary on the affair, see Jichang Lulu, 'Huawei's Christmas battle for Central Europe', *Sinopsis*, 28 December 2018.

96 'Digital nation: stronger economy, better society, adept governance', Huawei position paper, November 2018, p. 2, <https://tinyurl.com/ubatdru>.

97 Sachs has also dismissed concerns when asked about tech theft. See Cristina Maza, 'China is using cyberespionage against U.S. to gain military and technology advantages, report reveals', *Newsweek*, 9 May 2018.

98 Matthew Russell Lee, 'UN @JeffDSachs fled Twitter after shown as CEFC adviser by Inner City Press Now Roanoke Cyprus', Inner City Press, 20 February 2019.

99 Jichang Lulu uncovered and documented some of these functions on Twitter, <https://web.archive.org/web/20191201163721/https://twitter.com/jichanglulu/status/1076864146707283968>.

100 Kristie Lu Stout, 'Jeffrey Sachs: Trump's war on Huawei is "a danger to the world"', YouTube, 12 December 2018, <https://www.youtube.com/watch?v=N5Ta_RhsXYY>; CBC News, 'Canada doing U.S. bidding in Huawei case, economist says', YouTube, 15 December 2018, <https://www.youtube.com/watch?v=NKX0tGG80SU>.

101 Li Qingqing, 'Is neo-McCarthyism what US elites want to see?', *Global Times*, 17 December 2018.

102 Yen Nee Lee, 'Trump's "economic illiteracy" caused the US-China trade war, says professor', *CNBC*, 23 March 2019.

103 'Mission & History', website of the Committee of 100, <https://web.archive.org/web/20190921013849/https://www.committee100.org/mission-history/>. A 2013 mission statement, now taken down, explained that C100's stance 'does not align with any political party in the United States or with any government in Asia', 'Mission & History', website of the Committee of 100, archived version from 30 December 2013, <https://web.archive.org/web/20190921013849/https://www.committee100.org/mission-history/>.

104 'Mission & History', website of the Committee of 100, archived version from 30 December 2013, <https://web.archive.org/web/20131230025620/https://www.committee100.org/mission-history/>.

105 'Mission & History', website of the Committee of 100, <https://web.archive.org/web/20190921013849/https://www.committee100.org/mission-history/>.

106 See for example Deirdre Shesgreen, 'Trapped, alone and "desperate to come home". American siblings barred from leaving China', *US Today*, 14 September 2019.

107 See Mark Simon, 'How the "Committee of 100" is doing Beijing's bidding in the US', *Hong Kong Free Press*, 1 May 2019. 'The Committee of 100 is a pro-Beijing group, concerned almost exclusively with the interests aligned with those of the Chinese Communist Party.'

108 <https://tinyurl.com/spehtk9>.

109 For example, 'Guowuyuan Qiaoban zhuren Qiu Yuanping huijian Meiguo "Bairenhui" huizhang' 国务院侨办主任裘援平会见美国"百人会"会长 [Qiu Yuanping, Director of the Overseas Chinese Affairs Office of the State Council, meets with the President of the U.S. Committee of 100], website of the Chinese government, 16 April 2013, <https://web.archive.org/web/20190907233857/http://www.gov.cn/govweb/gzdt/2013-04/16/content_2379247.htm>.

110 Liu Yandong huijian Meiguo "Beirenhui" daibiaotuan' 刘延东会见美国"百人会"代表团 [Liu Yandong meets delegation from U.S. 'Committee of 100'], *Hangzhou tongyi zhanxian*, 30 November 2007, <https://web.archive.org/web/20191201180958/http://www.hztyzx.org.cn/article/132.html>.

111 'Tongzhanbu fubuzhang pilu Dalai siren daibiao tijiao wenjian neirong' 统战部副部长披露达赖私人代表提交文件内容 [Deputy head of the United Front Work Department reveals content of documents provided by Dalai Lama's personal representative], *Sohu*, 7 December 2008, <https://web.archive.org/web/20190907230715/http://news.sohu.com/20081207/n261060735.shtml>.

112 'Mr. Ronnie C. Chan: governors', website of CUSEF, not dated, <https://www.cusef.org.hk/en/who-we-are/our-leadership/mr-ronnie-c-chan>; 'Chen Qizong' [Ronnie Chan], website of the Center for China and Globalization, not dated, <https://web.archive.org/web/20190824171418/http://www.ccg.org.cn/Director/Member.aspx?Id=969>.

113 Kris Cheng, '"Disappointed": Joshua Wong's party accuses Asia Society of self-censorship following "ban"', *Hong Kong Free Press*, 7 July 2017; Anon, 'Forbes deletes article on Asia Society billionaire Chairman Ronnie Chan', *BC Magazine*, 20 July, 2017; Tom Grundy, 'Deleted Forbes article criticising Asia Society tycoon resurfaces online amid accusations of censorship', *Hong Kong Free Press*, 20 July 2017.

114 Denise Tang, 'Ronnie Chan: philanthropist taking charity through the roof', *South China Morning Post*, 22 September 2014.

115 'Zhonghua Renmin Gongheguo guomin jingji he shehui fazhan di shisan ge wu nian (2016-2020 nian) guihua gangyao' 中华人民共和国国民经 济和社会发展第十三个五年 (2016–2020年) 规划纲要 [Outline of

the Thirteenth Five-Year Plan for the economic and social development of the People's Republic of China (2016-2020)], website of the government of China, 17 March 2016, <http://www.gov.cn/xinwen/2016-03/17/content_5054992.htm>.

116 'Zhonggong Zhongyang Bangongting, Guowuyuan Bangongting yin fa "Guanyu jiaqiang Zhongguo tese xinxing zhiku jianshe de yijian"' 中共中央办公厅、国务院办公厅印发《关于加强中国特色新型智库建设的意见》[The General Office of the Central Committee of the CCP and the General Office of the State Council issue the 'Opinion on strengthening the construction of new type think tanks with Chinese characteristics'], website of the Chinese government, 20 January 2015, <https://web.archive.org/web/20190824162259/http://www.gov.cn/xinwen/2015-01/20/content_2807126.htm>. See also 'Liu Qibao zap guojia gaoduan zhiku lishihui kuoda huiyi shang qiangdiao tuidong gaoduan zhiku jianshe shixian lianghao kaiju' 刘奇葆在国家高端智库理事会扩大会议上强调 推动高端智库建设实现良好开局, *Xinhua*, 22 January 2016, <http://www.xinhuanet.com/politics/2016-01/22/c_1117867512.htm>.

117 'Huang Kunming: dazao shiying xin shidai xin yaoqiu de gao shuiping zhiku' 黄坤明：打造适应新时代新要求的高水平智库 [Huang Kunming: creating high-level think tanks that meet the new requirements of the new era], *People's Daily Online*, 21 March 2019, <http://politics.people.com.cn/n1/2019/0321/c1001-30988496.html>.

118 'About us: who we are', website of the Charhar Institute, not dated, <https://web.archive.org/web/20191201184548/http://en.charhar.org.cn/index.php?a=lists&catid=9>.

119 'Dr. Han Fangming, founding chairman', website of the Charhar Institute, <https://web.archive.org/web/20191201184657/http://en.charhar.org.cn/index.php?a=lists&catid=11>.

120 坚持党的领导，把握正确导向。坚持党管智库，坚持中国特色社会主义方向.

121 Anon., 'China to introduce dual-management on think tanks', *Xinhua*, 4 May 2017.

122 Chun Han Wong, 'A rare champion of pro-market policies to close in China', *The Wall Street Journal*, 27 August 2019; Nectar Gan, 'Chinese government pressured property agent into welding iron gates to liberal think tank office doors, penning in workers, director says', *South China Morning Post*, 11 July 2018.

123 'Geren jianjie' 个人简介 [Self-introduction], personal website of Wang Huiyao, <https://web.archive.org/web/20190825160957/http://scgti.org/wanghuiyao/plus/list.php?tid=11>.

124 '2019 Munihei Anquan Huiyi zhuanti yantaohui chenggong juban, chongjian xin duobian zhixu cheng guoji jiaodian' 2019慕尼黑安全会议专题研讨会成功举办 重建新多边秩序成国际焦点 [2019 Munich

Security Conference successfully held; building a new multilateral order becomes international focus], personal website of Wang Huiyao, 18 February 2019, <https://web.archive.org/web/20190825161859/http://scgti.org/wanghuiyao/a/dongtai/2019/0218/1899.html>.

125 'Zhongguo zhiku shouci zai Munihei Anquan Huiyi juban guanfang bianhui huiju guoji shengyin gongyi "yi dai yi lu" xin juhui' 中国智库首次在慕尼黑安全会议举办官方边会 汇聚国际声音共议"一带一路"新机遇" [Chinese think tank holds official side event at Munich Security Conference for the first time bringing together international voices to discuss new opportunities of the 'Belt and Road'], personal website of Wang Huiyao, 18 February 2019, <https://web.archive.org/web/20190825162042/http://scgti.org/wanghuiyao/a/dongtai/2019/0218/1901.html>.

126 'Huiyao (Henry) WANG', Paris Peace Forum, <https://parispeaceforum.org/place/huiyao-henry-wang/>.

127 Hou Lei, 'Top level think tank set up for policymaking', website of the Permanent Mission of the People's Republic of China to the UN, 3 April 2009, <www.china-un.org/eng/gyzg/t555926.htm>.

128 'Zhongguo guoji jingji jiaoliu zhongxin jianjie'中国国际经济交流中心简介 [Introduction to the China Center for International Economic Exchanges], website of CCIEE, not dated, <https://web.archive.org/web/20190803152321/http://www.cciee.org.cn/list.aspx?clmId=18>.

129 'Zhongguo guoji jingji jiaoliu zhongxin neishe jigou zhuyao yewu jigou shezhi ji zhuyao zhize' 中国国际经济交流中心内设机构主要业务机构设置及主要职责 [Main professional institutional arrangements and main responsibilities of institutions inside the CCIEE], website of CCIEE, not dated, <https://web.archive.org/web/20190803153132/http://www.cciee.org.cn/list.aspx?clmId=635>.

130 Li and Xu, 'Chinese think tanks'.

131 <https://tinyurl.com/yd92dkhp>.

132 <https://tinyurl.com/yd92dkhp>.

133 East Asian Bureau of Economic Research and China Center for International Economic Exchanges, *Partnership for Change*, Australia-China joint economic report, Canberra: ANU Press, 2016.

134 'EU–China economic relations to 2025: building a common future', a joint report by Bruegel, Chatham House, China Center for International Economic Exchanges, and the Chinese University of Hong Kong, September 2017, <http://bruegel.org/wp-content/uploads/2017/09/CHHJ5627_China_EU_Report_170913_WEB.pdf>.

135 'About us', website of the Taihe Institute, not dated, <https://web.archive.org/web/20181109140630/http://www.taiheglobal.org/en/gywm/index.html>.

136 Nadège Rolland, 'Mapping the footprint of Belt and Road influence operations', *Sinopsis*, 12 August 2019; '"Yi dai yi lu" guoji zhiku luntan jijiang zai Dunhuang juban' "一带一路"国际智库论坛即将在敦煌举办,

Center for China and Contemporary World Studies, 14 September 2018, <https://web.archive.org/web/20190825154017/http://www.cccws.org.cn/Detail.aspx?newsId=4800&TId=103>; 'Belt and Road Studies Network inaugurated', Belt and Road Studies Network, 24 April 2019, <https://tinyurl.com/vplnujy>.

137 Rolland, 'Mapping the footprint of Belt and Road influence operations'.

138 'Silk Road Think Tank Network declaration on joint action', website of the Silk Road Think Tank Network, 16 May 2017, <https://web.archive.org/web/20190920203610/http://www.esilks.org/about/declaration>.

139 Isaac Stone Fish, 'Beijing establishes a D.C. think tank, and no one notices', *Foreign Policy*, 7 July 2016.

140 See Jonas Parello-Plesner and Belinda Li, 'The Chinese Communist Party's foreign interference operations: how the U.S. and other democracies should respond', Hudson Institute, June 2018, p. 38.

141 Anon., 'Making waves: China tries to strengthen its hand in a dangerous dispute', *The Economist*, 2 May 2015.

142 Author interviews, April 2019.

143 'Advisory board', website of ICAS, not dated, <http://chinaus-icas.org/about-icas/advisory-board/>; Myron Nordquist, 'UNCLOS Article 121 and Itu Aba in the South China Sea Final Award: a correct interpretation?', in S. Jayakumar, T. Koh, R. Beckman, T. Davenport and Hao Duy Phan, eds, *The South China Sea Arbitration: The legal dimension*, Edward Elgar, 2018.

144 'Bateman, Sam S.', website of the University of Wollongong Australia, not dated, <https://scholars.uow.edu.au/display/sam_bateman>.

145 Sam Bateman, 'Rethinking Australia's plan B', *ASPI Strategist*, 29 October 2018.

146 Sam Bateman, 'The South China Sea arbitration ruling—two months on', *ASPI Strategist*, 21 September 2016. He did not note his link to ICAS.

147 Gordon Houlden, 'Opinion: why the South China Sea decision matters to Canada', *Edmonton Journal*, 15 July 2016.

148 ICAS, 'Panel 1: risk of U.S.-China strategic competition', ICAS YouTube channel, 28 May 2019, <https://www.youtube.com/watch?v=F1LNEyzeHzA>; ICAS, 'Luncheon speech: Ms. Susan Thornton', ICAS YouTube channel, 28 May 2019, <https://www.youtube.com/watch?v=z8_K5Im_Hm8>; ICAS, 'Panel 1: China-U.S. relations at a time of flux', ICAS YouTube Channel, 8 July 2018, <https://www.youtube.com/watch?v=NrgRvMACpxk>; ICAS, 'ICAS Interview with Michael Swaine', ICAS YouTube channel, 1 August 2016, <https://www.youtube.com/watch?v=Yx3OnYKPr7M&t=551s>; Duncan DeAeth, '"China's actions consistent with status-quo in Taiwan Strait" says ex-US State Dept. official', *Taiwannews*, 26 April 2019.

149 'China-CEE Institute', website of the China-CEE Institute, not dated, <https://web.archive.org/web/20190419075129/https://china-cee.eu/structure/>.

150 'News and events', website of the China-CEE Institute, not dated, <https://archive.is/EB8MN>.

151 'Introduction of the World Forum on China Studies', website of the China-CEE Institute, not dated, <https://web.archive.org/web/20190921182720/http://www.chinastudies.org.cn/zgxlte1/1.htm>.

152 'China's reforms help deepen common interests of US, China', World Forum on China Studies, 25 May 2015, <https://web.archive.org/web/20190921183120/http://www.chinastudies.org.cn/e/967.htm>.

153 'European symposium of World Forum on China Studies held in Berlin', World Forum on China Studies, 13 July 2017, <https://web.archive.org/web/20190921183615/http://www.chinastudies.org.cn/e/1517.htm>.

Chapter 12 Thought management: CCP influence in Western academia

1 These are three out of the four confidences that have been promoted under Xi Jinping. The fourth is confidence in Chinese culture.

2 Liu Jianming, 刘建明, *Deng Xiaoping xuanchuan sixiang yanjiu* 邓小平宣传思想研究 [Research on the propaganda thought of Deng Xiaoping], Shenyang: Liaoning renmin chubanshe, 1990, pp. 164–5.

3 Liu Jianming, 刘建明, *Deng Xiaoping xuanchuan sixiang yanjiu* 邓小平宣传思想研究 [Research on the propaganda thought of Deng Xiaoping].

4 Hao Yongping 郝永平 and Huang Xianghuai 黄相怀, 'Renmin Ribao renmin yaolun: zengqiang xueshu zixin jiangqing Zhongguo daolu' 人民日报人民要论：增强学术自信 讲清中国道路 [*People's Daily* people's essential theory: increase academic confidence to clearly explain the Chinese path], *People's Daily* online, 23 February 2018.

5 'Jigou zhineng' 机构职能 [Institutional functions], website of the National Office for Philosophy and Social Sciences, 19 September 2018, <https://web.archive.org/web/20190802154705/http://www.npopss-cn.gov.cn/n1/2018/0919/c220819-30302949.html>.

6 Chen Zhuanghai 沈壮海, 'Jianshe juyou ziti tese he youshi de xueshu huayu tixi' 建设具有自己特色和优势的学术话语体系 [Establishing an academic discourse system with our own characteristics and strengths], *People's Daily* online, 23 May 2016, <http://theory.people.com.cn/n1/2016/0523/c49157-28370464.html>.

7 See 'Putong gaozhong Yingyu kecheng biaozhun (2017)' 普通高中英语课程标准 (2017). 'Putong gaozhong Deyu kecheng biaozhun (2017)' 普通高中德语课程标准 (2017). We are indebted to Katja Drinhausen for bringing this to our attention.

8 Ingrid d'Hooghe, Annemarie Montulet, Marijn de Wolff and Frank N. Pieke, *Assessing Europe–China Collaboration in Higher Education and Research*, Leiden: LeidenAsiaCentre, 2018, p. 11.

9 Editorial board, 'A professor at China's premier university questioned Xi Jinping. Then he was suspended', *The Washington Post*, 28 March 2019; Didi

Tang, 'Professor Zheng Wenfeng suspended for saying Chinese history is overrated', *The Times*, 22 August 2019.

10 Quoted in Anon., 'A message from Confucius', *The Economist*, 22 October 2009.

11 David Shambaugh, 'China's propaganda system: institutions, processes and efficacy', *China Journal*, no. 57, January 2007, p. 50.

12 'How many Confucius Institutes are in the United States?', National Association of Scholars, 9 April 2018, last updated 15 July 2019, <https://www.nas.org/blogs/dicta/how_many_confucius_institutes_are_in_the_united_states>.

13 Benedict Rogers, 'How China's overseas Confucius Institutes pose a powerful threat to academic freedom', *Hong Kong Free Press*, 5 May 2019.

14 This has not always been the case, but some institutions that did not follow this arrangement have faced problems for precisely this reason. For instance, the Confucius Institute Lyon was founded as an independent, not-for-profit organisation in 2009. However, three years later, Hanban began demanding the CI be integrated into the University of Lyon, suspending its annual subsidy for the institute without warning. The institute was closed in 2013 after the two sides failed to find a solution. 'Lyon Confucius Institute closure', personal website of Gregory Lee, the former director, <https://www.gregorylee.net>.

15 Alexander Bowe, *China's Overseas United Front Work: Background and implications for the United States*, U.S.-China Economic and Security Review Commission, August 2018, p. 13.

16 Rachelle Petersen, *Outsourced to China: Confucius Institutes and soft power in American higher education*, New York: National Association of Scholars, 2017.

17 Petersen, *Outsourced to China*, p. 88.

18 Geoff Wade, 'Confucius Institutes and Chinese soft power in Australia', Canberra: Parliamentary Library, 24 November 2014; Hamilton, *Silent Invasion*, p. 218.

19 Anon, 'Dalian Waiguoyu Xueyuan fahui waiyu yuanxiao youshi tuidong Gang Ao Tai haiwai tongzhan gongzuo "wu xin" fazhan' 大连外国语学院发挥外语院校优势 推动港澳台海外统战工作"五新"发展 [Dalian Foreign Studies University gives full play to the advantages of foreign language colleges and promotes 'five new' developments in united front work in Hong Kong, Macau, Taiwan and overseas], website of the UFWD, 12 July 2018, <http://archive.ph/2019.03.18-053516/http://www.zytzb.gov.cn/tzcx/291691.jhtml#selection-217.0-226.0>.

20 Robert Burton-Bradley, 'China's Confucius Institutes have spy agencies and governments increasingly alarmed', *ABC News* online, 10 March 2019.

21 'Letter of protest at interference in EACS Conference in Portugal, July 2014', European Association of Chinese Studies, <https://web.archive.org/web/20140809004832/http://www.chinesestudies.eu/index.php/433-letter-of-protest-at-interference-in-eacs-conference-in-portugal-july-2014>.

22 *China's Confucius Institutes: An inquiry by the Conservative Party Human Rights Commission*, February 2019, <http://conservativehumanrights.com/news/2019/CPHRC_Confucius_Institutes_report_FEBRUARY_2019.pdf>.

23 *China's Confucius Institutes: An inquiry by the Conservative Party Human Rights Commission.*

24 Henry Jom, 'Victoria Uni cancelled documentary due to Chinese consular pressure, documents reveal', *NTD*, 3 December 2018.

25 'Staff code of conduct', <https://policy.vu.edu.au/document/view.php?id=176&version=2>.

26 Anon., 'Sydney University criticised for blocking Dalai Lama visit', *The Guardian*, 18 April 2013.

27 Adam Harvey, 'Uni under fire for pulling pin on Dalai Lama event', *ABC News* online, 18 April 2013.

28 Jordan Baker, 'China debate raises spectre of White Australia Policy, says uni chief', *The Sydney Morning Herald*, 23 August 2019.

29 Fergus Hunter, 'Foreign influence showdown as universities decline to register China-funded Confucius Institutes', *The Sydney Morning Herald*, 21 March 2019.

30 Diamond and Schell, eds, *China's Influence & American Interests*, p. 41. In an interview with the BBC, Madam Xu Lin also confirms this when she claims that the teachers that are sent are Chinese citizens and therefore must obey Chinese law (1:12–1:28). John Sudworth, 'Confucius Institute: the hard side of China's soft power', *BBC*, 22 December 2014.

31 Daniel Sanderson, 'Universities "sign Chinese gagging clause"', *The Times*, 5 September 2018.

32 Daniel Golden, 'China says no talking Tibet as Confucius funds U.S. universities', *Bloomberg*, 2 November 2011; Hannah Knowles and Berber Jin, 'Warnings of Chinese government "influence" on campuses divide Stanford community', *Stanford Daily*, 30 May 2019.

33 Shiany Perez-Cheng, 'La embajada de China en España coaccionó a la Universidad de Salamanca para cancelar eventos culturales de Taiwán' [The Chinese embassy in Spain coerced the University of Salamanca to cancel cultural events of Taiwan], *Sociopolítica de Asia Pacífico*, 25 August 2018, <https://deasiapacifico.wordpress.com/2018/08/25/la-embajada-de-china-en-espana-coacciono-a-la-universidad-de-salamanca-para-cancelar-eventos-culturales-de-taiwan/>.

34 Elaine Hou and Chung Yu-chen, 'MOFA condemns attempted exclusion of Taiwan students in Hungary', *Focus Taiwan*, 4 May 2019.

35 Vanessa Frangville @VanessaFrangvi, Twitter status, <https://twitter.com/VanessaFrangvi1/status/1112417710355431426>.

36 Anastasya Lloyd-Damnjanovic, *A Preliminary Study of PRC Political Influence and Interference Activities in American Higher Education*, Washington D.C.: Wilson Center, 2018, p. 74.

37 Peter Mattis and Alex Joske, 'The third magic weapon: reforming China's united front', *War in the Rocks*, 24 June 2019.

38 'Guanyu xuelian' 关于学联 [About the Association], website of the Chinese Students and Scholars Association UK, <https://tinyurl.com/trz6gh5>.

39 'BUCSSA 波士顿大学中国学生学者联合会 是波士顿大学唯一在纽约总领馆注册的华人组织。我们致力于贴心高效地服务于波士顿大学华人'. See 'BUCSSA jieshao' BUCSSA 介绍 [Introduction to BUCSSA], website of Boston University's Chinese Students and Scholars Association, not dated, <https://web.archive.org/web/20190802154850/http://www.bucssa.net/portal.php>; 'Guanyu women' 关于我们 [About us], website of Vanderbilt University Chinese Students and Scholars Association, <https://web.archive.org/web/20190802154939/https://studentorg.vanderbilt.edu/vucssa/?page_id=14>.

40 Lloyd-Damnjanovic, *A Preliminary Study of PRC Political Influence and Interference Activities in American Higher Education*; Diamond and Schell, eds, *China's Influence & American Interests*, pp. 180–1.

41 See '2005 nian Kunshilanzhou Zhongguo xuesheng xuezhe lianyihui gongzuo huiyi shunli zhaokai' 2005年昆士兰州中国学生学者联谊会工作会议顺利召开 [2005 Queensland Chinese Students and Scholars Association work conference held successfully], website of the Chinese embassy in Australia, 11 May 2005, <http://archive.ph/2019.08.27-232636/http://au.china-embassy.org/chn/zagx/jyjl/t195066.htm#selection-287.0-287.26>. According to the article, the Education Division of the consulate funded 'meaningful activities, with a focus on large-scale events with over 200 participants'.

42 Hooghe, Montulet, de Wolff and Pieke, *Assessing Europe-China collaboration in higher education and research*, p. 27.

43 Ben Packham, 'China diplomat slapped down over uni protest', *The Australian*, 27 July 2019. The student who was assaulted, Drew Pavlou, sought a court order restraining the consul-general. The court action was unresolved at the time of writing.

44 Jennifer Creery, 'Don't mind the haters: Tibetan-Canadian student Chemi Lhamo brushes off pro-China cyberbullying campaign', *Hong Kong Free Press*, 31 March 2019.

45 Jennifer Creery, 'Don't mind the haters'; L. Kennedy, 'Update on petition', <https://www.change.org/p/update-on-petition>. The original text of the petition seems to be no longer available, only an update, added after the cyberbullying received a backlash. The quotes and content cited here are from the updated (and presumably watered down) text of the petition.

46 Gerry Shih and Emily Rauhala, 'Angry over campus speech by Uighur activist, Chinese students in Canada contact their consulate, film presentation', *The Washington Post*, 14 February 2019.

47 Justin Mowat, 'McMaster student government bans Chinese students' group from campus', *CBC*, 26 September 2019.

48 Shih and Rauhala, 'Angry over campus speech by Uighur activist'.
49 Lloyd-Damnjanovic, *A Preliminary Study of PRC Political Influence and Interference Activities in American Higher Education*, pp. 76–7.
50 Hooghe, Montulet, de Wolff and Pieke, *Assessing Europe-China Collaboration in Higher Education and Research*, p. 27.
51 Personal communication, February 2019.
52 Perry Link, 'China: the anaconda in the chandelier', *ChinaFile*, 11 April 2002.
53 Sheena Chestnut Greitens and Rory Truex, 'Repressive experiences among China scholars: new evidence from survey data', *China Quarterly*, 1 August 2018, p. 18; Lloyd-Damnjanovic, *A Preliminary Study of PRC Political Influence and Interference Activities in American Higher Education*, pp. 56, 64–5.
54 Greitens and Truex, 'Repressive experiences among China scholars', p. 3.
55 Lloyd-Damnjanovic, *A Preliminary Study of PRC Political Influence and Interference Activities in American Higher Education*, p. 45.
56 'The debate over Confucius Institutes: a *ChinaFile* conversation', *ChinaFile*, 23 June 2014, <http://www.chinafile.com/conversation/debate-over-confucius-institutes>.
57 See for example Edward Wong, 'China denies entry to American scholar who spoke up for a Uighur colleague', *The New York Times*, 7 July 2014; Perry Link, 'The long shadow of Chinese blacklists on American Academe', *Chronicle of Higher Education*, 22 November 2013.
58 See Greitens and Truex, 'Repressive experiences among China scholars'.
59 Personal experience, December 2017. The pattern was the same for others the authors know who didn't get a visa.
60 Concerned scholars of China, 'An open letter from concerned scholars of China and the Chinese diaspora: Australia's debate on "Chinese influence"', *Policy Forum*, 26 March 2018.
61 Anon., 'Shifou tingzhi "Zhongguo shentoulun" Aodaliya liang pai xuezhe zhenfengxiangdui' 是否停止“中国渗透论” 澳大利亚两派学者针锋相对 [Two scholarly factions in Australia clash on whether or not to stop the 'Chinese infiltration debate'], *Global Times* online, 29 March 2018.
62 See testimony of Prof. Christopher Hughes (LSE) at the UK House of Commons Foreign Affairs Committee on 'Autocracies and UK Foreign Policies', 3 September 2019, <https://tinyurl.com/wwhv9ch>.
63 See Christopher Hughes, 'Confucius Institutes and the university: distinguishing the political mission from the cultural', *Issues & Studies*, vol. 50, no. 4, December 2014, pp. 49–50.
64 See testimony of Prof. Christopher Hughes (LSE) at the UK House of Commons Foreign Affairs Committee on 'Autocracies and UK Foreign Policies', 3 September 2019, <https://tinyurl.com/wwhv9ch>.
65 Paul Musgrave, 'Universities aren't ready for trade war casualties', *Foreign Policy*, 19 May 2019.

66 'Canada's foreign student enrolment took another big jump in 2018', *ICEF Monitor*, 20 February 2019, <https://monitor.icef.com/2019/02/canadas-foreign-student-enrolment-took-another-big-jump-2018/>.

67 'International student statistics in UK 2019', Studying-in-UK.org, <https://www.studying-in-uk.org/international-student-statistics-in-uk/>. Students from India and the United States, the next two countries after China, are under 20,000 each.

68 Hazel Ferguson and Henry Sherrell, 'Overseas students in Australian higher education: a quick guide', website of the Parliament of Australia, 20 June 2019, <https://www.aph.gov.au/About_Parliament/Parliamentary_Departments/Parliamentary_Library/pubs/rp/rp1819/Quick_Guides/OverseasStudents>.

69 Josh Rudolph, 'UCSD stands by Dalai Lama invite despite protest', *China Digital Times*, 17 February 2017.

70 Lloyd-Damnjanovic, *A Preliminary Study of PRC Political Influence and Interference Activities in American Higher Education*, p. 62.

71 'Introduction of the World Forum on China Studies', website of the World Forum on China Studies, <https://web.archive.org/web/20190802155359/http://www.chinastudies.org.cn/zgxlte1/1.htm>.

72 Liu Xiangrui, 'Sinologists gets a look at local culture', *China Watch*, 17 July 2018, <https://www.telegraph.co.uk/china-watch/culture/sinology-programme-beijing/>. Going by the URL, this article looks like it's from *The Telegraph*, but it's not. It's one of the many *China Watch* articles prepared by the *China Daily*.

73 'Rang waiguo xuezhe jiang hao Zhongguo gushi 2019 qingnian Hanxuejia yanxiu jihua Shanghai ban kaiban' 让外国学者讲好中国故事 2019青年汉学家研修计划上海班开班 [Let foreign scholars tell China's story well—2019 Young Sinologist Training plan Shanghai class begins], *Dongfangwang*, 17 June 2019, <https://web.archive.org/web/20191128022003/http://www.gxnews.com.cn/staticpages/20190617/newgx5d072662-18423310.shtml>.

74 'Chinese government special scholarship—CEE special scholarship', website of China's University and College Admission System, <https://web.archive.org/web/20190802155554/https://scholarship.cucas.edu.cn/China_Youth_University_for_Political_Sciences_scholarships/Chinese_Government_Scholarships_scholarship/Chinese_Government_Special_Scholarship___CEE_Special_Scholarship_scholarship_1884.html>.

75 Lloyd-Damnjanovic, *A Preliminary Study of PRC Political Influence and Interference Activities in American Higher Education*, p. 58.

76 '"Waiguoren xiezuo Zhongguo jihua" di si qi zhengji zhiyin fabu' "外国人写作中国计划"第四期征集指引发布 [Guidelines for fourth call of 'Foreigners Writing on China Project' published], website of the Chinese Culture and Translation Studies Support Research Center, 22 August 2019, <https://web.archive.org/web/20191128025551/http://www.cctss.org/article/headlines/5386>.

77 Malcolm Moore, 'Cambridge University under fresh scrutiny over Chinese government-linked donation', *The Telegraph*, 8 October 2014.

78 Tarak Barkawi, 'Power, knowledge and the universities', *Al Jazeera*, 9 February 2012, <https://www.aljazeera.com/indepth/opinion/2012/02/2012269402871736.html>.

79 'China Executive Leadership Program', website of the China Development Research Foundation, <https://web.archive.org/web/20190802155639/http://cdrf-en.cdrf.org.cn/qgb/index.jhtml>.

80 Bethany Allen-Ebrahimian, 'This Beijing-linked billionaire is funding policy research at Washington's most influential institutions', *Foreign Policy*, 28 November 2017.

81 Elizabeth Redden, 'Thanks, but no, thanks', *Inside Higher Ed*, 16 January 2018.

82 Primrose Riordan, 'London School of Economics academics outraged by proposed China programme', *Financial Times*, 27 October 2019.

83 Mike Gow, 'Sino-foreign joint venture universities: an introduction', *The Newsletter*, no. 77, summer 2017, International Institute for Asian Studies.

84 Gow, 'Sino-foreign joint venture universities'.

85 See in particular article 5 of the Regulations of the People's Republic of China on Sino-Foreign Cooperative Education, <https://web.archive.org/web/20190610164330/http://www.fdi.gov.cn/1800000121_39_1937_0_7.html>.

86 Zhuang Pinghui, 'Cambridge and Peking universities in talks about partnership plan for "role model" Shenzhen', *South China Morning Post*, 7 September 2019.

87 'History', website of Sias University, not dated, <https://web.archive.org/web/20190802155723/http://en.sias.edu.cn/AboutSias/168/894.html>.

88 Yojana Sharma, 'Ministry ends hundreds of Sino-foreign HE partnerships', *University World News*, 6 July 2018.

89 Marjorie Heins, 'Trading academic freedom for foreign markets', National Coalition against Censorship, 30 July 2012, <https://ncac.org/fepp-articles/trading-academic-freedom-for-foreign-markets>.

90 Diamond and Schell, eds, *China's Influence & American Interests*, p. 181.

91 John Levine, 'NYU Shanghai campus "self-censoring, politically neutral" on Hong Kong: faculty', *New York Post*, 19 October 2019.

92 Cited in Levine, 'NYU Shanghai campus "self-censoring, politically neutral" on Hong Kong'.

93 Marjorie Heins, 'Trading academic freedom for foreign markets'; Daniel Golden, 'China halts U.S. academic freedom at classroom door for colleges', *Bloomberg*, 28 November 2011.

94 Some insight into Party-building activities on joint campuses can be gained from Chinese reports. See 'Quanguo Zhong wai hezuo banxue dangjian gongzuo tuijinhui zai Chengdu juban' 全国中外合作办学党建工作推进

会在成都举办 [National Conference on promoting Party building in Sino-foreign jointly run schools takes place in Chengdu], originally published on Renmin zhengxie wang, 24 May 2018, <http://archive.ph/2019.11.28-110411/https://cfcrs.xmu.edu.cn/2018/0601/c4034a344069/page.htm#selection-1235.0-1235.20>.

95 Emily Feng, 'China tightens grip on foreign university joint ventures', *Financial Times*, 7 August 2018.

96 Zheping Huang, 'A Dutch university has canceled plans to offer degrees at its China campus', *Quartz*, 30 January 2018.

97 Example from a study session at the Sino-Dutch Biomedical and Information Engineering School: Anon., 'Xueyuan danwei juxing dang zhibu shuji niandu shuzhi dahui' 学院党委举行党支部书记年度述职大会 [Party Committee of the school holds annual debriefing of party branch secretaries], website of the College of Medicine and Biological Information Engineering, 6 June 2019, <https://web.archive.org/web/20190802155816/http://www.bmie.neu.edu.cn/2019/0606/c576a129912/page.htm>; example from Bangor College at the Central South University of Forestry and Technology: Anon., 'Bangge xueyuan dang zongzhi zhongxinzu 2019 nian di er ci lilun xuexi' 班戈学院党总支中心组2019年第二次理论学习 [Second theoretical study (session) of Bangor Party Branch Center in 2019], website of Bangor College, <https://web.archive.org/web/20190802155855/http://bangor.csuft.edu.cn/djgz/201903/t20190319_84465.html>; example from Leeds-SWJTU: 'ASO', 'Lizi xueyuan kaizhan benzhou yewu xuexi huiyi' 利兹学院开展本周业务学习会议 [Leeds College conducts this week's professional study session], website of Southwest Jiaotong University–Leeds Joint School, 3 June 2019, <https://web.archive.org/web/20190802155934/https://leeds.swjtu.edu.cn/info/1041/2034.htm>.

98 'Lizi xueyuan kaizhan benzhou yewu xuexi huiyi' 利兹学院开展本周业务学习会议 [Leeds College conducts this week's professional study session], website of Southwest Jiaotong University–Leeds Joint School, 3 June 2019, <https://web.archive.org/web/20190802155934/https://leeds.swjtu.edu.cn/info/1041/2034.htm>.

99 Zuo Qian 左倩, 'Wo xiao kaizhan qingzhu Zhongguo Gongchandang chengli 98 zhounian "bu wang chuxin laoji shiming" chongwen rudang shici zhuti dangri huodong' 我校开展庆祝中国共产党成立98周年"不忘初心牢记使命"重温入党誓词主题党日活动 [Our school held a Party day event for the 98th anniversary of the founding of the Communist Party with the theme 'Don't forget the origins, remember the mission' renewing the Party oath], <https://web.archive.org/web/20190802160503/http://news.sias.edu.cn/contents/309/29795.html>.

100 Levine, 'NYU Shanghai campus "self-censoring, politically neutral" on Hong Kong'.

101 Colleen O'Dea, 'Chinese government to control Kean U faculty in Wenzhou? Union up in arms', *NJ Spotlight*, 16 November 2018, <https://www.njspotlight.com/stories/18/11/15/chinese-government-to-control-kean-u-faculty-in-wenzhou-union-asks-nj-to-investigate/>.

102 'Mission statement', website of Duke University, approved by the Duke University Board of Trustees 1 October 1994, and revised 23 February 2001, <https://trustees.duke.edu/governing-documents/mission-statement>.

103 Joanna Gagis, 'Teachers union critical of Kean ceding control of China campus', *NJTV News*, 13 December 2018, <https://www.njtvonline.org/news/video/teachers-union-critical-of-kean-ceding-control-of-china-campus/>; Donna M. Chiera, 'Op-ed: Kean University's China fiasco illustrates need for state oversight', 13 February 2019, <https://www.njspotlight.com/stories/19/02/12/op-ed-kean-universitys-china-fiasco-illustrates-need-for-state-oversight/>.

104 Elizabeth Redden, 'Is Kean giving control of its overseas faculty to Chinese government?', *Inside Higher Ed*, 16 November 2018; Kelly Heyboer, 'Communist Party members "preferred" for jobs on Kean U.'s new China campus, ad says', *NJ.com*, 23 July 2015.

105 'About us: leadership', website of Wenzhou-Kean University, not dated, <https://web.archive.org/web/20190802160618/http://www.wku.edu.cn/en/org/>.

106 'Introduction to Asia Europe Business School (AEBS)', China Admissions, not dated, <https://web.archive.org/web/20191201225457/https://www.china-admissions.com/asia-europe-business-school-aebs/>.

107 Friedman quoted in Jessica Chen Weiss, 'Cornell University suspended two exchange programs with China's Renmin University: here's why', *The Washington Post*, 1 November 2018.

108 'Fudan-European China Forum 2017 successfully held', website of the Fudan-European Centre for China Studies, 8 May 2017, <https://web.archive.org/web/20190802160731/https://www.fudancentre.eu/news/2017/5/26/fudan-european-china-forum-2017>.

109 'About', website of Brussels Academy for China-European Studies, not dated, <http://www.baces.be/about/>.

110 Bruno Struys, 'Waarom de Chinese directeur van het Confuciusinstitut aan de VUB ons land niet meer binnen mag', *DeMorgan*, 29 October 2019.

111 Du Xiaoying, 'Peking University opens UK campus', *China Daily* online, 26 March 2018.

112 'UC is home to the first CASS Chinese Studies Centre in Portugal', University of Coimbra, <https://web.archive.org/web/20190825011406/http://www.uc.pt/en/iii/initiatives/china/2018_12_05_CASS>.

113 'Guojia sheke jijin Zhonghua xueshu wai yi xiangmu jianjie' 国家社科基金中华学术外译项目简介[Brief introduction to the Chinese Academic Foreign Language Translation Project of the National Social Science

Fund], website of the National Office for Philosophy and Social Science, 7 September 2011, <https://web.archive.org/web/20190802160848/http://www.npopss-cn.gov.cn/GB/230094/231486/15611673.html>.

114 Javier C. Hernández, 'Leading Western publisher bows to Chinese censorship', *The New York Times*, 1 November 2017.

115 'Peer review boycott of Springer Nature publishing company', change.org petition started by Charlene Makley, Change.org, 1 November 2017, <https://web.archive.org/web/20190802160927/https://www.change.org/p/peer-review-boycott-of-academic-publications-that-censor-content-in-china/u/21865528>.

116 Elizabeth Redden, 'An unacceptable breach of trust', *Inside Higher Ed*, 3 October 2018.

117 'Taylor & Francis Social Sciences and Humanities Library: statement', website of Taylor & Francis Group, 20 December 2018, <https://newsroom.taylorandfrancisgroup.com/taylor-francis-social-sciences-and-humanities-library/>.

118 Personal communication. See also 'Publishers pledge on Chinese censorship of translated works', <https://pen.org/sites/default/files/Publishers_Pledge_Chinese_Censorship_Translated_Works.pdf>.

119 Anon., 'Foreign authors warned about book censorship in China', *The Guardian*, 21 May 2015.

120 For the full lists, see <https://twitter.com/CliveCHamilton/status/1099454938453659649>.

121 Harrison Christian, 'Kiwi publishers face censorship demands from Chinese printers', Stuff.co.nz, 18 August 2019.

122 The book was Clive Hamilton's *Silent Invasion*. It was not the main concern cited. The main concern was lawfare, viz. the use of the legal system to impose an onerous financial burden on Allen & Unwin through vexatious defamation actions by pro-Beijing agents. A third reason given was the fear of Beijing-inspired cyber attacks closing down the company's website, which is crucial to its marketing. Nick McKenzie and Richard Baker, 'Free speech fears after book critical of China is pulled from publication', *The Sydney Morning Herald*, 12 November 2017.

123 Michael Bachelard, 'Chinese government censors ruling lines through Australian books', *The Sydney Morning Herald*, 23 February 2019.

124 'Zhong Mei hezuo chuban shi shang de kaituo xianfeng' 中美合作出版史上的开拓先锋, *People's Daily* online, 15 November 2006, <https://web.archive.org/web/20190824165314/http://book.people.com.cn/GB/69360/5045049.html>.

125 Ke Liming 可黎明, 'Zhongguo xueshu "zou chuqu": Zhongguo shehui kexue chubanshe Faguo fenshe zai Bo'erduo chengli' 中国学术"走出去"：中国社会科学出版社法国分社在波尔多成立 [Chinese academia 'going out': Chinese Social Sciences Press establishes French branch in Bordeaux], *People's*

Daily online, 11 April 2017, <http://archive.today/2019.11.28-100840/http://world.people.com.cn/n1/2017/0411/c1002-29201762.html>.

126 Martin Albrow, *China's Role in a Shared Human Future: Towards a theory for global leadership*, Global China Press, 2018. From the author bio: 'His first visit to China was in 1987 on an observational tour with the State Family Planning Commission and in recent years he has contributed to the annual Symposium on China Studies with the Academy of Social Sciences and the Ministry of Culture of the PRC.' See <https://www.amazon.com/Chinas-Role-Shared-Human-Future/dp/1910334340>.

127 Michael Bates and Xuelin Li Bates, *Walk for Peace: Transcultural experiences in China*, Global China Press, 2016.

128 'Belt and Road Initiative: Cutting-edge studies relating to China's massive BRI project', <https://tinyurl.com/radd58a>.

129 Cai Fang and Peter Nolan, eds, *Routledge Handbook of the Belt and Road*, Routledge, 2019.

130 'Science Bulletin', <https://www.journals.elsevier.com/science-bulletin>.

131 'Springer Nature partners with FLTRP in promoting Chinese thought and culture overseas', website of Springer Nature, 25 August 2016, <https://tinyurl.com/vv6fmpk>.

132 The four journals were *Frontiers of Literary Studies in China*, *Frontiers of History in China*, *Frontiers of Law in China* and *Frontiers of Philosophy in China*, published jointly with Higher Education Press, which belongs to the Chinese Ministry of Education. 'Brill has terminated its agreement with Higher Education Press in China', website of Brill, 25 April 2019, <https://brill.com/newsitem/126/brill-has-terminated-its-agreement-with-higher-education-press-in-china>.

133 Jacob Edmond, 'Three new essays on the Chinese script and a new twist to the old problem of censorship in Chinese studies', 18 April 2019, <https://tinyurl.com/yyexdqgf>.

134 Edmond, 'Three new essays on the Chinese script and a new twist to the old problem of censorship in Chinese studies'.

135 Edmond, 'Three new essays on the Chinese script and a new twist to the old problem of censorship in Chinese studies'. Another case that did go public was that of Timothy Groose, an assistant professor at the Rose-Hulman Institute of Technology in Indiana. Groose had prepared a book review by request on behalf of the new journal *China and Asia: A journal in historical studies*, also published by Brill. Due to the grave situation in Xinjiang, he had opened his review with a paragraph on the mass detainment of Uyghurs and other ethnic minorities in Xinjiang. A day after Groose submitted the review, he received an edited manuscript back in which the opening statement about Uyghurs had been crossed out. After Groose expressed his concern and followed up with the journal's editor-in-chief, Han Xiaorong, he received a response suggesting that his piece may not be published at all. When, after

several more months of silence, Groose went public with his story, Han Xiaorong responded publicly, claiming that the review had been excluded because it was 'not directly relevant to our journal's central theme, which is China's historical relations with other Asian countries'. He acknowledged requesting the deletion of the comments on mass internment in Xinjiang, saying they 'were primarily of a political nature and were about a current event that was still developing', but denied that this constituted a form of censorship. See Timothy Groose, 'How an academic journal censored my review on Xinjiang', *Los Angeles Review of Books China Channel*, 13 May 2019; Elizabeth Redden, 'X-ing out Xinjiang', *Inside Higher Ed*, 20 May 2019; 'My response to Timothy Groose's "How an academic journal censored my review on Xinjiang"', *MCLC Resource Center*, 16 May 2019.

136 Edmond, 'Three new essays on the Chinese script and a new twist to the old problem of censorship in Chinese studies'.

137 John Ross, 'Journal articles "tacitly support China territory grab"', *Times Higher Education*, 11 December 2019; Clive Hamilton, 'Scientific publishers disregard international law', *Journal of Political Risk*, vol. 7, no. 12, December 2019.

138 Hamilton, 'Scientific publishers disregard international law'.

Chapter 13 Reshaping global governance

1 Melanie Hart and Blaine Johnson, 'Mapping China's global governance ambitions', *Center for American Progress*, 28 February 2019; 'Xi urges breaking new ground in major country diplomacy with Chinese characteristics', *Xinhua*, 24 June 2018.

2 Hart and Johnson, 'Mapping China's global governance ambitions'.

3 Ariana King, 'China is "champion of multilateralism", foreign minister says', *Nikkei Asian Review*, 29 September 2018.

4 Yi Ling and Liu Tian, 'Xinhua headlines: at G20, Xi leads chorus for multilateralism', *China.org.cn*, 29 June 2019, <https://web.archive.org/web/20191202191647/http://www.china.org.cn/world/Off_the_Wire/2019-06/29/content_74935190.htm>.

5 Anon., 'China, EU vow to uphold multilateralism, facilitate bilateral trade, investment', *China.org.cn*, 10 April 2019, <https://web.archive.org/web/20190514153948/http://www.china.org.cn/world/2019-04/10/content_74664092.htm>.

6 Hart and Johnson, 'Mapping China's global governance ambitions'.

7 Maaike Okano-Heijmans and Frans-Paul van der Putten, *A United Nations with Chinese characteristics?*, Clingendael report, December 2018, p. 2, <https://www.clingendael.org/sites/default/files/2018-12/China_in_the_UN_1.pdf>.

8 Colum Lynch and Robbie Gramer, 'Outfoxed and outgunned: how China routed the U.S. in a U.N. agency', *Foreign Policy*, 23 October 2019.

9 'Mr. Liu Zhenmin, Under-Secretary-General', United Nations Department of Economic and Social Affairs, <https://www.un.org/development/desa/statements/usg-liu.html>. Liu's predecessor at the UN was Wu Hongbo 吴红波. For advising on internet governance, see Okano-Heijmans and van der Putten, *A United Nations with Chinese characteristics?*, p. 13.

10 Cited in Colum Lynch, 'China enlists U.N. to promote its Belt and Road project', *Foreign Policy*, 10 May 2018, <https://foreignpolicy.com/2018/05/10/china-enlists-u-n-to-promote-its-belt-and-road-project/>.

11 Okano-Heijmans and van der Putten, *A United Nations with Chinese characteristics?*, p. 13.

12 'Jointly building Belt and Road towards SDGS', United Nations Department of Economic and Social Affairs, <https://www.brisdgs.org/about-bri-sdgs>.

13 Okano-Heijmans and van der Putten, *A United Nations with Chinese characteristics?*, p. 4.

14 'UN agencies Belt and Road involvement', website of UN Environment Programme, undated, <https://tinyurl.com/w49oc8t>.

15 'Zhongguo zhengfu yu Lianheguo Kaifa jihua shu qianshu "Guanyu gongtong tuijin sichou zhi lu jingji dai he 21 shiji haishang sichou zhi lu jianshe de liangjie beiwanglu"'中国政府与联合国开发计划署签署《关于共同推进丝绸之路经济带和21世纪海上丝绸之路建设的谅解备忘录》[The Chinese government and the United Nations Development Programme sign Memorandum of Understanding on jointly promoting the Silk Road Economic Belt and the 21st Century Maritime Silk Road], website of the Chinese government, 19 September 2016, <https://tinyurl.com/yjjjskw4>.

16 'UNDP and China to cooperate on Belt and Road Initiative', United Nations Development Programme, 19 September 2016, <https://www.undp.org/content/undp/en/home/presscenter/pressreleases/2016/09/19/undp-and-china-to-cooperate-on-belt-and-road-initiative.html>. See also *Sinopsis* and Jichang Lulu, 'United Nations with Chinese characteristics: elite capture and discourse management on a global scale', *Sinopsis*, 25 June 2018.

17 'Cooperation for common prosperity', 14 May 2017, <https://tinyurl.com/tv9ukgf>. The UNDP's 2017 Governance Report focused on the BRI, analysing its potential contributions to sustainable development. 'A new means to transformative global governance towards sustainable development', 9 May 2017, <https://tinyurl.com/rztq9fq>.

18 'At China's Belt and Road Forum, Guterres calls for "inclusive, sustainable and durable" development', *UN News*, 26 April 2019, <https://news.un.org/en/story/2019/04/1037381>.

19 'United Nations poised to support alignment of China's Belt and Road Initiative with sustainable development goals, secretary-general says at opening ceremony', United Nations, 26 April 2019, <https://www.un.org/press/en/2019/sgsm19556.doc.htm>.

20 Human Rights Watch, 'The cost of international advocacy: China's interference in United Nations' human rights mechanisms', Human Rights Watch, 5 September 2017, <https://www.hrw.org/report/2017/09/05/costs-international-advocacy/chinas-interference-united-nations-human-rights>.

21 Ted Piccone, 'China's long game on human rights at the UN', Brookings, September 2018, p. 4, <https://www.brookings.edu/wp-content/uploads/2018/09/FP_20181009_china_human_rights.pdf>.

22 Human Rights Watch, 'The cost of international advocacy'.

23 Human Rights Watch, 'The cost of international advocacy'.

24 Human Rights Watch, 'The cost of international advocacy'.

25 'Chi wo huzhao wufa ru Lianheguo zongbu qiagong waijiaobu jiaoshe zhong' 持我护照无法入联合国总部洽公 外交部交涉中, *Apple Daily*, 20 October 2015, <https://tw.appledaily.com/new/realtime/20151020/715101/>.

26 Lu Yi-hsuan and Jake Chung, 'UN body turns away Taiwanese without Chinese IDs', *Taipei Times*, 17 June 2017, <http://www.taipeitimes.com/News/front/archives/2017/06/17/2003672712>.

27 Jennifer Creery, 'Taiwan lodges protest with the United Nations for denying entry to Taiwanese reporter', *Hong Kong Free Press*, 15 October 2018.

28 'In an interview with @CCTV, former UN Under-Secretary-General & head of @UNDESA Wu Hongbo said he represented Chinese national interests in his position as a UN official, saying he ordered that WUC President @Dolkun_Isa be expelled from the 2017 UN Indigenous Forum @UN4Indigenous', World Uyghur Congress on Twitter, 25 April 2019, <https://twitter.com/uyghurcongress/status/1121349082457485312?lang=de>; Human Rights Watch, 'The cost of international advocacy'.

29 Randy Mulyanto, 'Taiwan weighs options after diplomatic allies switch allegiance', *Al Jazeera*, 26 September 2019, <https://www.aljazeera.com/news/2019/09/taiwan-weighs-options-diplomatic-allies-switch-allegiance-190925070254771.html>.

30 Chen Shih-chung, 'Taiwan's participation vital to global influenza pandemic preparedness and response', *Voice Publishing*, 22 May 2017, <https://thevoiceslu.com/2017/05/taiwans-participation-vital-global-influenza-pandemic-preparedness-response/>.

31 Amir Attaran, 'Taiwan, China and the WHO: of pandas and pandemics', *Canadian Medical Association Journal*, vol. 180, 2009, <https://www.ncbi.nlm.nih.gov/pmc/articles/PMC2679814/>.

32 <https://tinyurl.com/u6bhadn>

33 Ben Blanchard, 'Taiwan calls China 'vile' for limiting WHO access during virus outbreak', Reuters, 4 February 2020.

34 Rintaro Hosukawa and Tsukasa Hadano, 'Did WHO's China ties slow decision to declare emergency?', *Nikkei Asian Review*, 1 February 2020.

35 Kimmy Chung, 'Beijing never pressured me in office, former WHO chief Margaret Chan says,' *South China Morning Post*, 7 July 2017.

36 'Taiwan accuses World Health Organization of bowing to Beijing over invitation to top health meeting', *South China Morning Post*, 8 May 2018: 'In Beijing on Monday, foreign ministry spokesman Geng Shuang said the island was only able to attend the assembly from 2009–2016 because the previous Taiwan government had a consensus with Beijing that there is only "one China"'; 'Taiwan: Ministry of *Foreign Affairs* urges WHO to issue invitation to annual assembly', Underrepresented Nations and Peoples Organization, 20 February 2019, <https://unpo.org/article/21384>.

37 Jennifer Creery, 'Watchdog urges United Nations to defy Chinese pressure and let Taiwanese journalists cover events', *Hong Kong Free Press*, 19 September 2018.

38 Sam Yeh, 'YAR: let's not abandon Taiwan on international stage', *Toronto Sun*, 3 May 2019.

39 'China: framework agreement aims to help enterprises reduce risks in overseas operations', website of the International Committee of the Red Cross, 27 March 2019, <https://www.icrc.org/en/document/icrc-cccmc-dcaf-sign-framework-agreement-in-responsible-business-conduct>.

40 'ICRC's special envoy to China Jacques Pellet speaks with CGTN', CGTN channel on YouTube, 23 April 2019, <https://www.youtube.com/watch?v=IgPN_RvuTGs>.

41 'China: livelihood project reduces poverty, changes mindset in Xinjiang', ICRC, 26 March 2019, >https://www.icrc.org/en/document/china-ecosec-xinjiang-livelihood-2019>.

42 Matt Schrader, '"Chinese Assistance Centers" grow United Front Work Department global presence', *Jamestown Foundation*, 5 January 2019.

43 '2018 "Hua zhu zhongxin" nianhui huimou: ning qiao xin qiao li gongxiang minzu fuxing meng' 2018 "华助中心"年会回眸：凝侨心侨力 共享民族复兴梦 [Looking back at the 2018 annual meeting of the 'Overseas Chinese help center': solidifying overseas Chinese hearts and overseas Chinese power, sharing the dream of national rejuvenation].

44 '2018 "Hua zhu zhongxin" nianhui huimou: ning qiao xin qiao li gongxiang minzu fuxing meng' 2018 "华助中心"年会回眸：凝侨心侨力 共享民族复兴梦 [Looking back at the 2018 annual meeting of the 'Overseas Chinese help center': solidifying overseas Chinese hearts and overseas Chinese power, sharing the dream of national rejuvenation].

45 Frank Chung, '"It's a police station honouring a police state": outrage as Melbourne cop shop raises Chinese Communist flag', *News.com.au*, 3 October 2019.

46 Thomas Eder, Bertram Lang and Moritz Rudolf, 'China's global law enforcement drive: the need for a European response', *MERICS China Monitor*, 18 January 2017, <https://web.archive.org/web/20191011035019/https://

www.merics.org/sites/default/files/2018-05/Merics_China-Monitor_36_Law-Enforcement.pdf>.

47 'Europol and the People's Republic of China join forces to fight transnational crime', Europol, 19 April 2017, <https://www.europol.europa.eu/newsroom/news/europol-and-people's-republic-of-china-join-forces-to-fight-transnational-crime>.

48 'Europol executive director receives the vice minister of China at agency's headquarters', Europol, 19 January 2018, <https://www.europol.europa.eu/*newsroom*/news/europol-executive-director-receives-vice-minister-of-china-agency's-headquarters>.

49 Michael Martina, Philip Wen and Ben Blanchard, 'Exiled Uighur group condemns Italy's detention of its general secretary', *Reuters*, 28 July 2017.

50 Ben Blanchard, 'China upset as Interpol removes wanted alert for exiled Uighur leader', *Reuters*, 24 February 2018.

51 Bethany Allen-Ebrahimian, 'Can the Chinese be trusted to lead global institutions?', *Foreign Policy*, 11 October 2018.

52 Chris Buckley, 'Ex-president of Interpol is sent to prison for bribery in China', *The New York Times*, 21 January 2020.

53 Eder, Lang and Rudolf, 'China's global law enforcement drive'.

54 Michael Laha, 'Taking the anti-corruption campaign abroad: China's quest for extradition treaties', *CCP Watch*, 13 March 2019, <https://www.ccpwatch.org/single-post/2019/03/13/Taking-the-Anti-Corruption-Campaign-Abroad-Chinas-Quest-for-Extradition-Treaties>.

55 Kevin Ponniah, 'Why is Spain in the middle of a spat between China and Taiwan?', *BBC*, 23 March 2017.

56 Anon., 'Spain deports 94 Taiwanese to Beijing for telecom fraud', *Reuters*, 7 June 2019.

57 'Zhongguo jingyuan jiangshu shouci Zhong Yi jingwu lianhe xunluo jingli' 中国警员讲述首次中意警务联合巡逻经历 [Chinese police officer recounts first Sino-Italian police patrol experience], *Xinhua*, 18 May 2015, <https://web.archive.org/web/20191011034150/http://www.xinhuanet.com/world/2016-05/18/c_1118891085.htm>.

58 Eder, Lang and Rudolf, 'China's global law enforcement drive'.

59 Eder, Lang and Rudolf, 'China's global law enforcement drive'.

60 Emma Graham-Harrison, 'China suspends cooperation with France on police affairs, says report', *The Guardian*, 3 August 2019.

61 Anon., 'China says its police brought graft suspect back from France', *Reuters*, 13 March 2017; Harold Thibault and Brice Pedroletti, 'Quand la Chine vient récupérer ses fugitifs en France', *Le Monde*, 23 May 2017, <https://www.lemonde.fr/asie-pacifique/article/2017/05/23/quand-la-chine-vient-recuperer-ses-fugitifs-en-france_5132103_3216.html>.

62 Anon., 'China says its police brought graft suspect back from France'.

63 Philip Wen, 'Operation Fox Hunt: Melbourne grandmother Zhou Shiqin returns to China', *The Sydney Morning Herald*, 26 October 2016.
64 Tim Nicholas Rühlig, Björn Jerdén, Frans-Paul van der Putten, John Seaman, Miguel Otero-Iglesias and Alice Ekman, 'Political values in Europe-China relations', European Think Tank Network on China Report 2018, pp. 25–6.
65 Kate O'Keeffe, Aruna Viswanatha and Cezary Podkul, 'China's pursuit of fugitive businessman Guo Wengui kicks off Manhattan caper worthy of spy thriller', *The Wall Street Journal*, 22 October 2017; Josh Rogin, 'Without Rex Tillerson's protection, a top State Department Asia nominee is in trouble', *The Washington Post*, 15 March 2018.
66 Peter Walker, 'Xi Jinping protesters arrested and homes searched over London demonstrations', *The Guardian*, 23 October 2015.
67 Rühlig et al., 'Political values in Europe-China relations', p. 25; 'Tibetan protest targeted in Belgium and Nepal', Free Tibet, 3 April 2014, <https://freetibet.org/news-media/na/tibetan-protest-targeted-belgium-and-nepal>.
68 Anon., 'Dozens arrested during Swiss protests against Chinese president's visit', *The Guardian*, 15 January 2017.
69 Cited in Peter Walker, 'Xi Jinping protesters arrested and homes searched over London demonstrations'.
70 Dou Kelin 窦克林, 'Guojia jiancha tizhi gaige zhuli fan fubai guoji zhuitao zhuizang' 国家监察体制改革助力反腐败国际追逃追赃 [Reform of national supervision system aids international pursuit in anti-corruption], *Zhongguo jijian jiancha zazhi*, no. 1, 2019, p. 1, <https://web.archive.org/web/20191202181143/http://zgjjjc.ccdi.gov.cn/bqml/bqxx/201901/t20190109_186640.html>.
71 'Swedish Supreme Court rules against extradition to China', Safeguard Defenders, <https://safeguardwdefenders.com/en/swedish-supreme-court-refuses-extradition-china>.
72 Anon., 'Kinas ambassadör: "Vi har hagelgevär för våra fiender"', *Expressen*, 2 December 2019; <https://twitter.com/jojjeols/status/1201376527713099776>.
73 Eder, Lang and Rudolf, 'China's global law enforcement drive'; Julie Boland, *Ten Years of the Shanghai Cooperation Organization: A lost decade? A partner for the U.S.?*, Washington D.C.: Brookings Institute, 20 June 2011, p. 8.
74 Peter Stubley, 'Uighur Muslims forbidden to pray or grow beards in China's "re-education" camps, former detainee reveals', *The Independent*, 22 March 2019.
75 Interpol SCO-RATS Memorandum of Understanding, 2014 <https://www.interpol.int/en/content/download/11136/file/21-%20SCO-RATS.pdf>.
76 'Guanyu Shanghai Hezuo Zuzhi Diqu Fankongbu jigou zhiweihui daibiaotuan canjia guoji xingjing zuzhi "Ka'erkan" xiaogmu gongzuo zu huiyi qingkuang' 关于上海合作组织地区反恐怖机构执委会代表团参加国际刑警组织"

卡尔坎"项目工作组会议情况 [About the participation of a delegation from the Executive Committee of the Shanghai Cooperation Organization's Regional Anti-Terrorism Structure in Interpol's project 'Kalkan' working group], website of SCO-RATS, 21 July 2017, <http://ecrats.org/cn/news/6915>.

77 'New framework for enhanced cooperation between RATS SCO and UN CTED', UN Security Council Counter-Terrorism Committee, 25 March 2019, <https://www.un.org/sc/ctc/news/2019/03/25/new-framework-enhanced-cooperation-rats-sco-un-cted/>.

78 Jan-Peter Westad, Richard Assheton and Peter Oborne, 'Campaigners against Uighur oppression blacklisted on terrorism database', *Middle Eastern Eye*, 16 April 2019, <https://www.middleeasteye.net/news/exclusive-campaigners-against-uighur-oppression-blacklisted-terrorism-database>.

79 Westad, Assheton and Oborne, 'Campaigners against Uighur oppression blacklisted on terrorism database'.

80 Winslow Robertson quoted in Lily Kuo and Niko Kommenda, 'What is China's Belt and Road Initiative?', *The Guardian*, 30 July 2018.

81 Alice Ekman, 'China's "new type of security partnership" in Asia and beyond: a challenge to the alliance system and the "Indo-pacific" strategy', Elcano Royal Institute, 25 March 2019.

82 Ekman, 'China's "new type of security partnership" in Asia and beyond'.

83 Ekman, 'China's "new type of security partnership" in Asia and beyond'.

84 Formerly known as 16+1, or China and the Central and Eastern European Countries, it was joined by Greece in 2019. The summit has been described as 'a network of bilateral relations more than anything else'. Richard Q. Turcsanyi, 'Growing tensions between China and the EU over 16+1 platform', *The Diplomat*, 29 November 2017.

85 See for example 9th Business Forum of CEEC & China, <https://croatia-forum2019-ceec-china.hgk.hr/>.

86 Piccone, 'China's long game on human rights at the UN', p. 18.

87 Ravid Prasad, 'EU ambassadors condemn China's Belt and Road Initiative', *The Diplomat*, 21 April 2018.

88 Information Office of the State Council of the People's Republic of China, 'Human rights in China', Beijing, November 1991, <http://www.china.org.cn/e-white/7/index.htm>.

89 'China Society for Human Rights Studies', Chinahumanrights.org, 1 August 2014, <http://www.chinahumanrights.org/html/2014/BRIEFINGS_0801/126.html>.

90 'Zhongguo renquan yanjiuhui jianjie' 中国人权研究会简介 [Introduction to the China Society for Human Rights Studies], Zhongguo renquan, 17 June 2014, <http://www.humanrights.cn/html/2014/1_0617/675.html>. For Cui Yuying, see 'Cui Yuying chuxi "goujian renlei mingyun gongtongti yu quanqiu renquan zhili" lilun yantaohui bing zhi ci' 崔玉英出席"构建人类命运共同体与全球人权治理"理论研讨会并致辞, humanrights.cn,

8 June 2017, <https://tinyurl.com/yzpgw2d3>. Since January 2018 she has been serving as the head of the Fujian PPCC.

91 'Zhongguo renquan yanjiuhui jianjie'.

92 'Human rights record of the United States', website of the Chinese embassy to the US, put online 23 October 2003, <http://www.china-embassy.org/eng/zt/zgrq/t36633.htm>.

93 'China Society for Human Rights Studies', Chinahumanrights.org, 1 August 2014, <http://www.chinahumanrights.org/html/2014/BRIEFINGS_0801/126.html>.

94 Sonya Sceats with Shaun Breslin, 'China and the international human rights system', Chatham House, October 2012, <https://www.chathamhouse.org/sites/default/files/public/Research/International%20Law/r1012_sceatsbreslin.pdf>, p. 10–11, 18–19.

95 UN Human Rights Council, 'Report of the Working Group on the Universal Periodic Review—China', pp. 8, 10, 13.

96 Danny Mok, 'Canto-pop singer Denise Ho calls on UN Human Rights Council to remove China over "abuses" in Hong Kong', *South China Morning Post*, 9 July 2019.

97 Anon., 'Internet regulations can protect human rights: experts', China Human Rights, 24 July 2014, <https://web.archive.org/web/20191206020516/http://www.chinahumanrights.org/html/2014/IE_0724/34.html>.

98 'EU: suspend China human rights dialogue', Human Rights Watch, 19 July 2017, <https://www.hrw.org/news/2017/06/19/eu-suspend-china-human-rights-dialogue>.

99 Hinnerk Feldwisch-Drentrup, 'Peking sagt Dialog mit Berlin ab', TAZ, 6 December 2019.

100 Piccone, 'China's long game on human rights at the UN', p. 4.

101 Piccone, 'China's long game on human rights at the UN', p. 4.

102 'Full text of Beijing Declaration adopted by the First South-South Human Rights Forum', South-South Human Rights Forum portal, 10 December 2017, <http://p.china.org.cn/2017-12/10/content_50095729.htm>.

103 'Chinese human rights delegation visits UK', *China Daily*, 5 July 2018, <http://www.chinadaily.com.cn/cndy/2018-07/05/content_36514008.htm>. The CSHRS has also been holding an annual Europe-China Seminar on Human Rights in different European cities since at least 2015. The 2019 invitation and program description is on file with the authors.

104 See for example State Council Information Office, 'The fight against terrorism and extremism and human rights protection in Xinjiang', White paper, March 2019; Jun Mai, 'Chinese state media "terrorism" documentaries seek to justify Xinjiang crackdown after US vote on human rights bill', *South China Morning Post*, 8 December 2019.

105 Anon., 'Human rights improve in Xinjiang, experts say', *China Daily*, 27 June 2018, <http://www.chinadaily.com.cn/kindle/2018-06/27/content_36464925.htm>.

106 Cate Cadell, 'China think tank calls for "democratic" internet governance', *Reuters*, 4 December 2017.

107 Josh Horwitz, 'Tim Cook and Sundar Pichai's surprise remarks at China's "open internet" conference', *Quartz*, 4 December 2017.

108 Horwitz, 'Tim Cook and Sundar Pichai's surprise remarks at China's "open internet" conference'.

109 Adrian Shahbaz, 'Freedom on the net 2018: the rise of digital authoritarianism', Freedom House, p. 8, <https://freedomhouse.org/sites/default/files/FOTN_2018_Final%20Booklet_11_1_2018.pdf>.

110 Trinh Huu Long, 'Vietnam's cybersecurity draft law: made in China?', *The Vietnamese*, 8 November 2017, <https://www.thevietnamese.org/2017/11/vietnams-cyber-security-draft-law-made-in-china/>.

111 Zak Doffman, 'Putin signs "Russian Internet Law" to disconnect Russia from the World Wide Web', *Forbes*, 1 May 2019.

112 Yao Tsz Yan, 'Smart cities or surveillance? Huawei in Central Asia', *The Diplomat*, 7 August 2019. For another example of the global expansion of the CCP's 'tech-enhanced authoritarianism', see Samantha Hoffman, 'Engineering global consent: the Chinese Communist Party's data-driven power expansion', *ASPI Policy Brief*, no. 21, 2019.

113 Joe Parkinson, Nicholas Bariyo and Josh Chin, 'Huawei technicians helped African governments spy on political opponents', *The Wall Street Journal*, 15 August 2019.

114 Kristin Shi-Kupfer and Mareike Ohlberg, 'China's digital rise: challenges for Europe', MERICS papers on China, no. 7, April 2019, p. 21.

115 Shi-Kupfer and Ohlberg, 'China's digital rise'.

116 Anna Gross, Madhumita Murgia and Yuan Yang, 'Chinese tech groups shaping UN facial recognition standards', *Financial Times*, 1 December 2019.

117 Gross, Murgia and Yang, 'Chinese tech groups shaping UN facial recognition standards'.

Index

Note: Chinese names are shown with surname first and personal name second. Where the owner of the name reverses the order, a comma appears after the surname. Most Chinese names are also given in Chinese characters to avoid ambiguities.

Also published by Hardie Grant Books